GENETICS

and the Races of Man

GENETICS
and the Races of Man

*An Introduction to Modern
Physical Anthropology*

by

WILLIAM C. BOYD, Ph.D.

PROFESSOR OF IMMUNOCHEMISTRY, BOSTON UNIVERSITY,
SCHOOL OF MEDICINE; FELLOW, AMERICAN ANTHROPOLOGICAL
ASSOCIATION; ASSOCIATE EDITOR, *American Journal of
Physical Anthropology*

With Illustrations

Little, Brown and Company · *Boston*

1952

Grateful acknowledgment is made of permission to quote from the following books:

Elementary Principles of Chemistry, by Brownlee, Fuller, Hancock, Sohon and Whitsit. Allyn and Bacon, 1947. *Elements of Genetics* by E. C. Colin. Blakiston Company, 1946. *The Races of Europe*, by C. S. Coon. The Macmillan Company, 1936. *Animal Ecology*, by C. Elton. The Macmillan Company and Sidgwick & Jackson, Ltd., 1939. *The Arabs of Central Iraq*, by Henry Field. Introduction by Sir Arthur Keith. Field Museum of Natural History, 1935. *The Genetical Theory of Natural Selection*, by R. A. Fisher. The Clarendon Press, 1930. *Up from the Ape*, by E. A. Hooton. The Macmillan Company, 1931. *Up from the Ape*, by E. A. Hooton. The Macmillan Company, 1946. *The Place of Prejudice in Modern Civilization*, by Sir Arthur Keith. John Day Company, 1931. *Distinguishing Races by Skull Characters*, by W. W. Krogman. FBI Law Enforcement Bulletin, 1939. *Race, Sex and Environment*, by J. R. Marett. Hutchinson & Company, Publishers of Scientific & Technical Data, 1936. *Twins*, by Newman, Freeman and Holzinger. University of Chicago Press, 1937. *Tempo and Mode in Evolution*, by G. G. Simpson. Columbia University Press, 1944. *Aspects of Science*, by J. W. N. Sullivan. The Bodley Head, Ltd., London, 1923.

To Concetta Blanciforti for her drawings in the text.

Publisher's Note

The publisher considered at one time publishing this book in two versions: (1) an edition for specialists in the field and (2) a simplified edition for the general reader. Considering, however, that we live in a modern world in which the consequences of new scientific theories are often very immediate or even revolutionary, it seemed that many a reader, even though not a specialist, would prefer the opportunity of reading a book of this importance in its original form — the same form in which it will be used by the specialists themselves. The lay reader should be warned, however, that he may not be able to follow the mathematics in the Appendices, and may not care to read certain chapters, such as Chapter II, in full detail.

Contents

	Preface	xiii
I	Possible Approaches to a Study of Man	3
II	Genetics	30
III	Heredity and Environment	82
IV	Gene Equilibrium Without Evolution	108
V	Factors Modifying Gene Frequencies (Evolution)	131
VI	The Influence of Geography on Racial Distribution	162
VII	The Concept of Race	184
VIII	Blood Groups	210
IX	Use of Blood Groups in Human Classification	252
X	Other Human Genes	276
XI	Incompletely Analyzed Genetic Characteristics	295
XII	Man's Past	323
XIII	Man's Future	349
	Appendix A: Statistical Methods	369
	Other Appendices: Mathematical Treatments of Problems	409
	Index	443

List of Illustrations

FIGURE

1 Mendelian segregation observed in offspring of hybrids — 34

2 Quantitative effects of a gene — 43

3 Chromosomes in *Drosophila* — 45

4 Three theories of the origin of dominance — 51

5 Different thresholds of response to various genes — 52

6 Hereditary absence of hands and feet — 65

7 The human X and Y chromosomes — 68

8 Inheritance of color blindness — 69

9 Interchange of genetic material between chromosomes — 72

10a Diagrammatic representation of crossing over — 73

10b Breakage of chromosomes followed by reattachment of parts — 73

11 Estimation of distance from cross-over frequencies — 74

12 Chromosome map of *Drosophila* — 75

13 Giant salivary chromosomes in *Drosophila* — 76

14 Siamese cat — 92

15 Temperature effect on development of eye facets — 93

16 "Intelligence quotient" of White-Indian mixtures — 105

17 Blood group frequencies of various mixtures — 112

18a Blood group gene B in Asiatics and Europeans — 117

18b Blood group gene B in various Europeans — 117

19 Production of homozygotes by inbreeding — 122

20   Equilibrium between selection and mutation   140

21   Action of slow selection on a gene   145

22   Results of deliberate selection in *Drosophila*   149

23   Blood group gene B in Australia and islands to the north   168

24   Crossing of a barrier by a gene   170

25   Independent geographical variations   172

26   Pigmentation and ultraviolet radiation in Europe   176

27   Skin pigmentation and ultraviolet radiation in Africa   177

28   Brown skin pigment in Eurasia and Africa   178

29   Yellow skin pigment in eastern Asia and Africa   179

30   Blood agglutinogens and agglutinins   214

31   Blood grouping in test tubes   215

32   Blood grouping on slides   216

33a "Isogenes" for blood group gene A   228

33b "Isogenes" for blood group gene B   229

34   Distribution of blood group A in Japan   231

35   Blood group gene M in Australia and regions to the north   233

36   Hypothetical human races   258

37   World distribution of six genetically defined races   271

38   Frequencies of various taste thresholds for PTC   278

39   Drawing of a Pygmy   296

40   Stature of Pygmies, Japanese, and Dinkas   297

41   Cranial index in Eurasia and Africa   301

42   Recent shift in cranial index in Europe   302

43   Photospectrometric analysis of skin color   309

44   Davenport's hypothesis of skin color inheritance   310

45   Skin color in a Negro family   310

46a, b, c, d   Hypothetical migrations of early man   338, 339, 340, 341

47 Hypothetical scheme of nose classification   354
48 Various grades of skin color in a population   372
49 Bimodal curve   376
50 Normal frequency curve   379
51 Scatter diagram   393
52 Random fluctuations in blood group frequencies   396

Preface

Whether or not it be true that the proper study of mankind is man, it is certain that he finds great difficulty in studying anything else.

— J. W. N. SULLIVAN: *Aspects of Science*

EVEN IF the human element were not so difficult to eliminate, there would be good reason to recommend the study of man because of its usefulness, actual and potential, in the interpretation, prediction, and guidance of human behavior. The present world crisis has made it very clear that unless mankind acquires deeper and more intimate information about the nature of man and the human societies he forms and their mechanisms of action, civilization as we know it may come to an end in the only too foreseeable future. This is still not realized as fully as would be desirable, but nevertheless some results of thought and investigations along such lines are beginning to appear.

The observations of the men of antiquity on their fellow men were largely restricted to aphorisms as to the motives underlying human behavior and to some scattered observations on differences in skin color and certain other aspects of human physique. It was not until the year 1775 that anything which one may regard as a really scientific study of mankind was published. I refer to the book by Johann Friedrich Blumenbach called *De Generis Humani Varietate,* or in other words, *On the Natural Varieties of Mankind.* This author set out to show what significance was to be attached to the differences, physical and mental, which were supposed to exist between men. He realized at the outset that no absolutely sharp distinction could be expected between different peoples and stated that the varieties of mankind, as accepted by various eminent thinkers, seemed to have been arbitrarily chosen as to both number and definition.

Once a movement to study mankind systematically had begun, many who became interested in this subject applied themselves to it, often with amazing energy and industry. Numerous observations on human physical varieties, and new techniques for detecting and measuring new characters, were published, so that an imposing mass of data was accumulated. However, this effort began before the science of genetics was founded, or in other words, before there was any knowledge of the mechanism of heredity, and consequently the mode of inheritance of differences between different varieties of man was for a long time uninvestigated. Therefore, it is not surprising that the chief methods of approach to a physical study of man were along other lines.

One of the most promising lines at first appeared to be a study of human physique, as revealed by a study of skin, hair and eye color, and by stature and various other physical measurements which were from time to time introduced. At one time it seemed that a clue to racial differences of very great value had been found when Retzius suggested that the ratio of the breadth of the head to its length was characteristically different among various peoples. Classical physical anthropology developed from this and similar suggestions.

Once the science of physical anthropology had been properly launched a great many investigations into human physique in various parts of the world were carried out. Various measurements of the head and other parts of the body were made and tabulated and the differences between the peoples in different parts of the world were analyzed. Until fairly recently these data and their interpretation constituted the science of physical anthropology.

But in the meantime one of the greatest of all scientific investigators, Gregor Mendel, had carried out experiments which revealed the true mechanism of inheritance. He was before his time, however, and his work passed almost unnoticed for nearly forty years. About the beginning of this century Mendel's principles were rediscovered and the whole scientific world became aware of them. It has thus been only about fifty years since this rediscovery occurred.

Once rediscovered, however, the science of genetics was developed with great enthusiasm and insight by numerous investigators in various countries of the world, and it was realized by a great many workers that the laws which were found to apply to plants and animals would doubtless hold true, perhaps with some variation, for human beings also.

As the new science of heredity became better known a gradual revolution began in the ranks of physical anthropologists. It was slowly realized that the proper study of mankind involved as one of its parts a study of the mechanism by which his various physical traits were inherited, and indeed that characteristics which were not inherited would be of small use to the would-be student of physical anthropology. This revolution, however, did not take place overnight, and was for years unperceived by many. It is the purpose of the present book to explain this revolution in anthropological thinking, the scientific basis on which it rests, and the way in which genetic knowledge can be applied to a study of mankind.

Even after the acceptance of Mendelism by geneticists, many of those who wrote on anthropology seem to have known little, if anything, of the new science of genetics. Others gradually discovered the subject as their researches progressed, and modified their points of view accordingly. In the chapters which follow it has sometimes seemed desirable to quote the opinions of certain individuals because they serve to illustrate the ignorance of, or a lack of appreciation of, the science of genetics. But in doing so it is not meant to imply that none of the authors quoted ever learned to understand the role of genetic principles and their application to physical anthropology. Also, it must be remembered that publication always lags behind research, so that in many cases at the time of the publication of a certain book, memoir, or pamphlet, the author of it was already painfully aware that his views, as therein expressed, were out of date.

It does not seem that any single volume has adequately summarized the new point of view towards physical anthropology which developed after the revolution initiated by a study of genetics had taken place. Some aspects of the new views were occasionally summarized in papers in various scientific journals, and the new doctrines were implicit in several remarkable books, none of which, however, were books on anthropology. We should mention partic-

ularly *Inbreeding and Outbreeding* by East and Jones, Fisher's
The Genetical Theory of Natural Selection, Hogben's *Genetic
Principles in Medicine and Social Science,* Dobzhansky's *Genetics
and the Origin of Species,* Mayr's *Systematics and the Origin of
Species,* Simpson's *Tempo and Mode in Evolution,* and Glass's
Genes and the Man. The debt which I owe to these books is
immense, and will be obvious to any reader of the present text.
Nevertheless, there still remained a gap to be filled by a book
which would attempt to summarize the results of a thoroughgoing
application of the new doctrines to the study of man.

In all humility, and conscious of its many imperfections, the
author offers the present volume to his readers as the missing
book. No claim is made to any great originality of thought, and if
any specialist fancies he recognizes his own thoughts and conclusions in one or more paragraphs, he is probably right, and this
seems as good a place as any to apologize for not making a more
specific acknowledgment of each such debt. The fallibility of
human memory, and the limitations which space imposes on
bibliographies, may serve as partial excuses. The chief effort in the
present writing has been to acquaint the reader with the important
results of the newer work, especially as they might apply to man,
and to summarize and synthesize the views of those who, often
working in very diverse fields, have contributed to our understanding of the problems considered here. If nothing but a clearer and
more complete exposition of the new point of view regarding
physical anthropology has been achieved, the author will feel more
than satisfied.

In scope, however, this book is somewhat more ambitious than
a mere summary of the applications of the newer methods of
physical anthropology, for it attempts also to provide the reader
who is willing to learn with the basic genetic (and to some extent
the mathematical) background which might make it possible for
him to make new applications of these very important principles.
For this reason Chapter II, for instance, is much longer than the
usual chapter on genetics in books on anthropology.

Although the present volume is limited to a consideration of
the genetic approach to physical anthropology, it is not implied
that other approaches do not have their own value. The various
morphological and metrical features of the human body are of

interest in themselves, for the setting up and description of anatomical races are of importance in medicine and criminology, and
their study will doubtless be continued. This work, however, is
already so well founded that it does not need encouragement by
writers working in fields outside of human morphology. It is
possible that the need is, rather, for an exposition of the newer
points of view, which have been accepted by many but have as yet
been expounded in detail by comparatively few, and which have
made possible a completely new approach to the problem of the
descent of man and the origin of human races. The present
approach, therefore, is only one of the many possible ones and
there is no encyclopedic thoroughness and no attempt to include the
kinds of treatment for which the author has neither the training
nor the inclination. As the subject of physical anthropology expands it will doubtless be more and more necessary to specialize
in the various branches of the study of the physical aspects of man,
and this book may be regarded as one dealing with a particular
aspect of this developing subject.

The production of this book was in large part made possible by
a grant from the Viking Fund, which helped defray expenses of
typing and preparing illustrations.

The author is enormously indebted to various colleagues, some
of whom are practicing anthropologists, and others who are
specialists in other fields, who have read and criticized the manuscript while it was in the process of preparation. Without their
advice it is doubtful if the book could ever have reached com-
pletion. None of these friends and colleagues should be blamed,
of course, for any errors in the present work, nor should they be
held responsible for any unorthodox points of view which may be
peculiar to the writer. Among those whose help deserves special
mention should be listed C. Blanciforti and J. Holbrook, who
drew many of the illustrations, and my wife, who read through
the entire manuscript several times, and made suggestions so valuable that without them the book would be much more imperfect
than it is.

WILLIAM C. BOYD

GENETICS
and the Races of Man

CHAPTER I # Possible Approaches to
a Study of Man

It is manifest that man is . . . subject to much variability.
— DARWIN: *The Descent of Man*

Introduction

ANTHROPOLOGY means the comparative study of man, and in this
broad sense there is no aspect of man or his works which should
be excluded from our inquiries. In practice it has proved convenient to break up this broad subject into a number of more
restricted fields, including, for example, physiology, psychology,
and the more narrowly delimited fields which we designate as
anthropology.

Anthropology in turn is divided into two main branches: *cultural*
anthropology (4, 35) and *physical* anthropology. Cultural anthropology is the study of man's works and social patterns; physical
anthropology is the study of the origin, development, and distribution of man's physical characteristics. In this book we shall be
concerned with the study of physical anthropology.

In any book written in the present epoch of world history, some
apology is required for writing on such an apparently academic
subject. But it should be evident even to the most elementary
student that what is desperately needed at the present time is
information about how man behaves and what makes him behave
as he does. We shall need to know this in order that we may help
prevent the human race from acting in completely unreasonable
ways, and help point out the more rational types of behavior
which alone will be compatible with its continued existence (40).
It is the writer's belief, and a main thesis of this book, that a study

of the physical man, and of the genes which determine his physical structure, will eventually lead to some knowledge of the genes which probably determine, at least in part, his behavior.

Such a basic inquiry must of course be conducted in a completely objective manner. I assume that readers of this book are willing and able to attempt to study mankind disinterestedly and scientifically, with as much detachment as they would use in dissecting a worm, or following the orbit of a comet. Persons not willing to make the *attempt,* at least, to do this may as well put the book down without reading further.

It is clear that one of the most important questions to be settled is this very vital one: do there exist, or do there not exist, important innate differences between different human racial stocks? If such differences exist, then perhaps some stocks are more suitable than others for "civilization," whatever this means exactly; if they do not exist, we obviously face a more simplified problem, even though we are still confronted with the undoubted existence of cultural and race prejudice. Before we start a study of the purely *physical* aspects of man, we must therefore first explain why we do not start by investigating cultural patterns and moral codes as they exist in different groups of mankind. The answer is that this problem belongs to the study of cultural, not physical, anthropology. It is the conviction of the present writer that genetically determined differences have little, if anything, to do with culture. But this conviction is evidently not shared by everyone, and is clearly a problem which we ought to examine a little further before we dismiss cultural problems from consideration here.

If we examine the doctrines of individuals who have preached the superiority or inferiority of certain races, such as Adolf Hitler's declaration in *Mein Kampf* (19) that the Jews are inferior as culture creators, and that the "Aryans" (Germans) are superior to other races, we find that all of these doctrinaires (see below) held the belief that there are inherited differences in ability or moral fiber or something of the sort between the different races. They believed that these differences are not merely cultural differences, but are based on real, fundamental, and *hereditary* factors. If such differences in racial ability did, in fact, exist, they would fall within the scope of our study. Whether such apparent differences are really innate, however, is certainly open to question (36, 2, 5), and the problem is certainly far more difficult to solve than the more restricted question we propose to examine here, namely, how great are the inherited *physical* differences between races? If a physical study of various groups of men does not reveal the existence of significant differences which in turn suggest the possibility that there may also exist differences in innate ability, then one of the fundamental assumptions of such "racist" doctrines is removed. Unless the psychologists make discoveries in the future which we cannot as yet even guess at, the extent and nature of the physical differences between the various human races are, and will remain, about the only guide we have towards solving the much debated question of the existence of mental and other intangible differences between races. We may, therefore, justifiably regard our present study as a kind of fundamental preparation for the study of the more important but more difficult questions of innate mental and cultural differences between different ethnic groups, a study which must be largely postponed to the future. Furthermore, a study of man's physical characteristics may enable us to make a guess, at least, as to the evolutionary history of mankind, a subject to which, since we are human ourselves, we can hardly be indifferent.

Cultural and Physical Traits

To begin with, we must distinguish clearly between cultural and physical traits. It might be supposed that the two things could never be confused, but actually observation makes it clear that many people, both specialists and laymen, do often mistake one for the other. Human actions which are fundamentally due to differences in culture are often very categorically stated to be due to inherited (and therefore physical) differences in different human stocks. The great traveler and linguist, Sir Richard Francis Burton, who fancied himself something of an anthropologist in his time, often refers to certain peoples as treacherous by nature, or lazy, or proud (6, 7). It was in fact once common for most travelers to speak of certain peoples as cruel, or as brave, or cowardly. Even distinguished anthropologists of our own time, such as the late Aleš Hrdlička, could list such behavioral traits as characteristic of different races (26). The common people have always spoken as though these qualities descended inevitably from one generation to the next, and as though they were permanent characteristics of certain racial groups. But even the most careless, or most prejudiced, observers could see in the recent Second World War the spectacle of the Germans, who genetically are not fundamentally very different from ourselves, equaling the genetically different Japanese in cruelty and fanatical bravery, and should have been able to deduce that neither cruelty nor bravery is determined exclusively by our genetic make-up. The purely "American" behavior of the American-born Nisei was also illuminating.

An important distinction between the cultural and physical characteristics of man is that physical characteristics are by far the more permanent, and are determined by heredity, by the environment, or by both. The color of the skin or the blood group may be given as an example of a physical trait. Cultural characteristics, on the other hand, since they are the result of the individual's social environment, often change, sometimes with great rapidity, as when a new invention like the bow and arrow is introduced into a cultural area. The rapid spread, after the discovery of America, of the custom of smoking tobacco could be given as an interesting example of the spread of a cultural habit. It is of course somewhat extreme, in that it has spread so completely into practically every corner of the earth.

Having decided that physical traits are the characters we want to study, and having examined some differences between physical and cultural traits, we may now approach the problem of identifying and describing physical differences between different races (the term "race" is discussed and defined on page 201). It will soon appear that a cursory visual examination is not sufficient, although certain earlier workers seemed to believe that it was adequate.

That not a few anthropologists as well as laymen were once convinced that they could identify race by a mere inspection of the individual is rather well shown by Sir Arthur Keith's remarks (33): "A Negro or a Chinese, a Hindu or an American Indian meets us in the street, and, before he has passed, we have assessed his racial characters and made our diagnosis. We can never hope to obtain, by the use of instruments, indices, and angles, the delicacy and precision of racial diagnosis reached by the tutored and experienced eye. Travelers and explorers may become so skilled that in a cosmopolitan crowd in an eastern bazar they will recognize the most delicate shades of race."

How well Sir Arthur could have sorted his individuals into races if they had filed past him clean-shaven and naked, we do not know. Certain it is that many of the factors on which these minute racial diagnoses are based are really cultural characteristics such as mode of dress, gestures used in speaking, expressions of the face, and so forth. Many of my readers will recall the experience of being recognized as Americans in foreign countries by dragomans or peddlers of "filthy postcards," even though their genealogies might be "racially" quite mixed. This sufficiently illustrates the superficiality of this sort of identification of race. Nevertheless, it cannot be doubted that many anthropologists and travelers do become very astute at guessing the racial origin of persons they meet. Although some of this is done on the basis of cultural traits, probably some morphological components play a role. Of course we are totally unable to estimate what genes, and how many, are acting to produce the "racial" appearance which the expert detects.

The "Noble Aryans"

At one time one heard a good deal of talk, particularly from certain Europeans and Americans, about "racial superiority" and "the white man's burden." A good deal of the responsibility for this philosophy goes back to the nineteenth-century French writer Gobineau (18, 44). The idea of an original, clear-cut, and permanent inequality is perhaps one of the oldest and most widely held opinions in the world. Nearly every people, great or small, has started off by making inequality one of its chief mottoes. In some cases, when a group has become powerful and civilized, and when it is clear that the majority of its people have "mixed blood" flowing in their veins, a certain number of them assert that all men are equal.

Count Gobineau maintained that all men are not equal. He asked, "If it is true that the brain of the Huron Indian contains in an undeveloped form an intellect as great as that of an Englishman or a Frenchman, why has he not in the course of the ages invented printing or steam power?" Gobineau asserted that the character of nations, whether they were progressing or stagnating, was independent of the conditions under which they lived. He says that nowhere is the soil more fertile and the climate milder than in certain parts of America, yet the greater part of this land is occupied by peoples who have not succeeded, to the slightest extent, in exploiting their resources. But other, unfavorably situated peoples have, according to Gobineau, become great.

Gobineau thought that our present civilization had been created through the mingling of the Germanic tribes with the races of the ancient world. He considered that he had established that contemporary savage tribes have always been and always will be savage, however high the civilization with which they are brought into contact.

The Count also maintained that the different languages are unequal and that they always correspond in relative merit to the races that use them. Considering the respective characteristics of the "three great races," he thought he detected a superiority of the white race, and within this type the Aryan family in particular. According to him, as civilizations derived from the white race and none could exist without its help, "A society is great and brilliant only so far as it preserves the blood of the noble groups that created it, provided that this group itself belongs to the most illustrious branch of our species." "There is no true civilization, among the European peoples, where the Aryan branch is not prominent." European peoples degenerate only in consequence of the various admixtures of blood which they undergo; their degeneration corresponds exactly to the quantity and quality of the new blood.

An Englishman, Houston Stewart Chamberlain, who went to Germany to live, wrote one of the silliest books ever written on this subject (8), but one which unfortunately had much subsequent influence (cf. 19), the dreadful consequences of which are too recent to demand retelling here.

Contrary to the claims of writers like Gobineau and Chamberlain, the civilization of various Eastern countries was for centuries superior to that of England or any other European country, and citizens of the East long felt quite superior to the barbarian peoples of the West. For example, at one time the English sent an embassy to the Chinese, proposing commercial relations between the two countries. The Chinese Emperor, Chien Lung, addressed in 1793 an epistle to King George III of England in response. We may quote some passages from it which display the same arrogance with which many Europeans later treated the Orientals (1):

> You, O King, live beyond the confines of many seas; nevertheless, impelled by your humble desire to partake of the benefits of our civilization, you have dispatched a mission respectfully bearing your memorial. . . . If you assert that your reverence for Our Celestial Dynasty fills you with a desire to acquire our civilization, our ceremonies and code of laws differ so completely from your own that, even if your Envoy were able to acquire the rudiments of our civilization, you could not possibly transplant our manners and customs to your alien soil. . . . If I have commanded that the tribute offerings sent by you, O King, are to be accepted, this was solely in consideration for the spirit which prompted you to dispatch them from afar. Our Dynasty's majestic virtue has penetrated into every country under Heaven, and kings of all nations have offered their costly tribute by land and sea. As your Ambassador can see for himself, we possess all things. I set no value on objects strange or ingenious, and have no use for your country's manufactures.

But neither the Chinese nor the English have ever had any monopoly of the tendency to consider themselves and their nation as superior to all others. Americans have done it all too frequently themselves, and Mark Twain aptly satirized the tendency in his "Extract from Captain Stormfield's Visit to Heaven" (9).

Some years ago writers on such subjects often candidly admitted views which today we can only characterize as prejudiced, but today most trained people are more cautious, and naked prejudice is less often displayed. Certain writers, however, still express and even defend prejudice. Although it might be claimed that Sir Arthur Keith is purely a morphologist, and Professor R. R. Gates chiefly a botanist, both men have published much on the subject of race, and evidently influenced the thoughts of many, so we can hardly refuse to take cognizance of their views. It is fortunate that their opinions do not represent those of the majority of workers in our science.

Race Prejudice

It is common to designate a person who believes in the inherent superiority or inferiority of one or more human races as a "racist." Convinced that the *important* (mental, moral, etc.) differences between races are great, some writers, especially white Europeans who believe in the superiority of the "white race," or "Nordic race," often seem to try to find as many physical differences as possible between races, apparently believing — a proposition which has not as yet been demonstrated — that great physical differences imply the existence of great differences in mental and other abilities. This tendency in its extremest form has been developed by a writer who takes the further step of dividing mankind, not into races, but into five separate *species*.

Gates (14, 15, 16, 17) states that the convention of assigning all living races to just one species, *Homo sapiens,* lacks scientific justification. Speaking of the great French writer, A. Dumas, who had one quarter Negro ancestry, he remarks that Dumas's genius must have been inherited from his grandfather, who was white and was a French Marquis, implying that a man of 100 per cent Negro ancestry could never become a great novelist, even if brought up in an environment with adequate cultural and educational advantages. Ignoring the possible effects of climate and disease, he contrasts the African tribes who never rose above the lower grades* of culture, despite contacts with Egypt and Arabia, with the Japanese who in one generation were able to absorb and begin making contributions to the advancement of Western science. He goes on to state that it appears probable that all colored people who show ability in Western civilization have derived it from their

---

* A brief investigation of African history suggests that this is not true, and that the art of ironworking may have originated in Africa, and that at least one great empire (cf. the Chakkas and Zulus) may have flourished there in the past.

white ancestry, thus making clear his assumption that the abilities of Booker T. Washington and George Washington Carver, for example, were due to their white ancestry and not to their Negro forebears. There is actually no evidence as to whether racial differences in ability to create or maintain cultures exist or do not exist. The question has really never been examined.

One of the outstanding students of human morphology in our time (32) has stated in an address to the students of Aberdeen University that he believes that prejudices are inborn, a part of the birthright of every child.

In the introduction he says, "I examine our local, national, and racial prejudices and trace them to the prehistoric stage of man's evolution. I demonstrate that in the prehistoric world these prejudices served a useful purpose. . . . I maintain that, for the ultimate good of mankind, we should nurse and preserve them."

He creeps up to his thesis very carefully, first playing on the emotions of *patriotism* which he thinks any Scotsman, or in general anybody, must experience, the feeling that your own university is the very best university in the world, etc. . . . He gradually introduces the term "prejudice" for such feelings, and finally expands the term to include dislike for what is foreign.

Keith then cites various writers (Carlyle, Adam Smith, Thomas Reid) as supporting his contention that prejudices are inborn. His only actual argument to support his idea that they were and are useful is based on the idea that evolution is impossible without isolation. He says: "A modern breeder, if he entered this prehistoric world, would at once perceive the object which Nature had in view ["Creative evolution"?] * If he were called upon to evolve a new human breed he would do just what Nature has done, separate mankind into herds and tribes and keep them isolated and pure for an endless period. Each tribe in our prehistoric world represented an evolutionary experiment. Without isolation Nature could have done nothing. How did she keep tribes apart? The answer to this question yields a clue to the object of our search — the origin of our prejudices. We are apt to think of seas, rivers, mountain-chains, deserts, and impenetrable jungles as the barriers

---

* The passages in brackets in this quotation are due to the present author, not to Keith.

which kept evolving tribes and races apart [see Ch. VI]. No doubt they have assisted to secure this object, but Nature did not trust to them. She established her real and most effective barriers in the human heart. These instinctive likes and dislikes of ours, which I speak of as prejudices, have come down to us from the prehistoric world. They are essential parts of the evolutionary machinery which Nature employed throughout eons of time to secure the separation of man into permanent groups and thus to obtain production of new and improved races of mankind." [This is most certainly not true; different human races have always interbred when they had the chance, and it is almost certainly geographic barriers which have allowed the creation of the present human races, whether we use the term race in the old or the new (genetic) sense.]

Sir Arthur continues: " . . . To obtain universal and perennial peace we must also reckon the price we will have to pay for it. The price is the racial birthright that Nature has bestowed on us. To attain such an ideal world, peoples of all countries and continents must pool their looks. Black, brown, yellows, and white must give and take in marriage and distribute in a common progeny the inheritance which each has come by in their uphill struggle through the leagues of prehistoric time towards the present. If this scheme of universal deracialization ever comes before us as a matter of practical politics — as the sole way of establishing peace and good will in all parts of our world, I feel certain both head and heart will rise against it. There will well up within us an overmastering antipathy to securing peace at such a price. This antipathy or race prejudice Nature has implanted within us for her own ends — the improvement of mankind through racial differentiation."

It is likely that Keith and others who have voiced such sentiments have been influenced by examples from domestic breeds of animals, where man, sometimes to increase their usefulness, sometimes apparently simply to gratify his whims, has produced specialized breeds. There is no doubt that crossing a high milk-producing breed of cattle with a breed designed for meat often gives progeny intermediate for both characteristics. From the point of view of the husbandman, something would perhaps thus be lost. But from the point of view of the cattle, this might not be true. The chances of survival of the hybrids in a "wild" environment might be increased. Since thinkers who are objective in their attitude towards the external world do not see in nature the purposefulness and special concern with man's destiny which Sir Arthur seemed to discern, we have to judge of success in evolution by survival. It has been pointed out by more than one writer that our specialized domesticated breeds of animals and plants could not compete successfully in a complete state of nature with their wild ancestral stocks, or even with the mongrel stock which would result from indiscriminate crossing. Therefore the mongrel, from his own point of view, and even from the point of view of evolution, is better. There is no evidence that the same would not hold true for human crossing; and thus the terrible loss of the "racial birthright" which so distressed Sir Arthur in prospect would prove no loss at all. And even if some slight deterioration of some particular human ability did result (which there is no reason to expect), it would be a justifiable price to pay for freedom from the all-destroying scourge which modern warfare has already become. And one wonders if even Sir Arthur Keith could have expressed quite the point of view above quoted had he known of the coming possibilities of atomic and bacteriological warfare. Would he have been quite so sure that "Nature keeps her human orchard healthy by pruning; war is her pruning hook?" Would he have said: "Without competition Mankind can never progress; the price of progress is competition."

A less rash, and a wiser man, Franz Boas, took issue (4) with Keith's statement about race antipathy and race prejudice, and challenged Keith to prove that race antipathy is implanted by nature and is not rather the effect of social causes. Also, it has still to be proved that achieving and maintaining a "pure" racial stock is necessarily going to result in physical or moral improvement. We shall show later in this book that racial differentiation can result from causes which almost certainly do *not* improve the stock.

Inherited Mental Differences

Klineberg (34), Dobzhansky (10) and Montagu (37) have stated that there is no clear evidence for the inheritance of mental traits in man, or for their being correlated with physical characteristics. With the second part of this statement we can agree without much more ado. The first part of the statement should probably be made somewhat less broad, for there is persuasive evidence that certain kinds of mental defects are inherited, and one is tempted to believe that genius, and perhaps other types of outstanding ability, are sometimes inherited, although this question is complicated by our ignorance of the extent to which environment plays a role. At any rate, there can be no doubt that great differences in mental ability do exist between different individuals, although an adequate scale of measurement has not yet been devised (p. 104), and it does not seem impossible that they are at least partly determined by hereditary factors. But we cannot assert that heredity does play any important role here without better data than those now available (p. 100). We really do not know.

Environment (including particularly the attitude of one's contemporaries) doubtless often leads certain individuals to behave *as if* one of their physical characteristics were the cause of a behavioral difference. Thus Topsy in *Uncle Tom's Cabin* (46) refused to behave properly because she was black, saying, "Couldn't never be nothin' but a nigger, if I was ever so good. If I could be skinned, and come white, I'd try then." Topsy seems to have appreciated also the difficulty of being accepted on equal terms by the majority, even if her behavior were up to their standards. No doubt many a person in real life is similarly deterred from attempts to live up to a different cultural ideal.

If any racial differences in mental ability *do* exist — and of this we have as yet no proof — they should of course be studied (22) when suitable methods are devised. Such methods do not seem available at the present time (see p. 100). Many present-day thinkers (36, 10) are inclined to doubt if such racial differences will ever be found. Thus Toynbee (47) in his *Study of History* specifically examines, and completely rejects, the old doctrine, revived in our time by the Nazis (19), that certain races are more fitted than others to give rise to civilizations.

We do not wish to deny that racial mental differences may someday be demonstrated, but we do not care to start our studies with *postulated* differences.

Classification and Physical Anthropology

We now face the question: which physical aspects of man do we wish to study? The complete ensemble of the various physical features of all human races is far too vast a subject to discuss in a volume of this size; probably it could never be mastered even in the entire lifetime of any one person. There are some physical characteristics, however, which we are going to consider as more important than others for our purposes. The primary reason for selecting certain characteristics and rejecting others is the wish to produce a classification which is meaningful in terms of modern biology; in other words, a kind of human taxonomy. We shall, therefore, choose physical traits which enable us to classify mankind into groups.

If we are confronted with a collection of objects which are more or less alike, and we wish to classify them into groups, the standards on which we shall base our classification will depend upon our purpose. If we have no underlying purpose except some basic human impulse to arrange things into categories, it will not matter what criteria we use. We could classify human beings according to the number of freckles on their noses, or the length of their fingers, or their speed in the hundred-yard dash, or however we liked. Even if arrangement into categories were our only motive, however, it is possible that we might eventually be led to look for categories which seem to mean something, using criteria which are relatively unaffected by the environment, and particularly those which do not change much with the age of the individual.

But the purpose of anthropological classification is more serious than the gratification of idle curiosity. If the anthropologist is not content with the current popular classification of men into "races" and nations, it is partly because he hopes to find something more fundamental, such as a classification which will tell him something of the history of the human race. Morant said in 1939 (39) that "the main aim of physical anthropology is to unravel the course of human evolution and it may be taken for granted today that the proper study of the natural history of man is concerned essentially with the mode and path of his descent." While it is doubtful whether all physical anthropologists restrict their studies solely to data bearing on the course of human evolution, nevertheless Morant is probably right in implying that such information seems of high importance to most workers in the field.

The prominent place which the subject of human evolution occupies in the thinking of physical anthropologists is pretty well shown by the amount of attention devoted to the study of anthropoids and other nonhuman primates. Taking a journal at random, we find that in volumes 1–5 (N.S.) of the *American Journal of Physical Anthropology* there were published no less than nine papers dealing with this subject. These papers constituted 9.3 per cent of the total appearing in those volumes, and their appearance in a journal devoted to anthropology would be hard to explain except on the assumption that such studies are expected to throw some light on the problems of human evolution.

We have to decide, then, which physical characteristics to use in classifying man, and particularly which can serve as the basis of a classification which will be meaningful in terms of the racial history of man. Certain characteristics which on first thought seem to be suitable may prove useless on further examination. To take an example from another species, every bird lover will recall that one of the characteristics of different birds is the call. Although bird calls of different species may sound more or less the same to some people, they exhibit distinct characteristics to those who are interested in birds (and presumably to birds). Nevertheless, there is good evidence to show that the calls of some species of birds are learned by imitation of examples which they hear, and in such cases are presumably not inherited (28). Any classification of birds based on their calls, therefore, is open to the objection that a species in a new environment may possibly, and sometimes does, change its characteristic call. A classification based on such a characteristic would therefore be of only temporary and limited value.

In man we find that there are two different ways in which an individual may clasp his hands and fold his arms. In clasping the hands, for instance, the right thumb may be uppermost, or the left thumb may be uppermost. A certain manner of clasping the hands and folding the arms is usually constant for each individual, and the habit he automatically follows in these actions persists throughout his life. It might be suggested that hand or arm folding would afford a reliable character for our purpose, and that we could classify people into "right thumbers" and "left thumbers," according to their method of clasping hands. On further investigation, however, we learn that the manner of clasping hands or folding the arms is not hereditary (49), and that the characteristic manner in which an individual performs either of those acts is generally due to a chance habit which he acquired early in life. We would, therefore, be very foolish to differentiate people into two human groups on the grounds that all (or most) of the people in the first group clasped their hands with the right thumb uppermost, while those in the second group clasped their hands with the left thumb uppermost. Since the difference is not hereditary, it could be changed very simply by cultural influence, although in the hypothetical populations where all (or nearly all) individuals performed the act in the same way, if some social significance were attached to the act one manner or the other might persist for generations, and thus *seem* to be genetically determined. In most existing human groups there are probably individuals of both types, as well as a few people who seem to have no fixed habit, and "racial" variations in the frequencies of the two modes of hand-clasping could probably be discovered. Clearly, however, this characteristic, since it is known not to be hereditary, is not suitable for our purpose, if we wish a classification which will tell us something about the physical history of the human race.

From the foregoing discussion, the fact begins to emerge that we are going to want to base our classification on hereditary characteristics, for otherwise our categories will be too ephemeral, and our "races" too susceptible to possible modification by environmental and cultural influences. However, among the many characteristics which are undoubtedly inherited, not all are going to be equally suitable. If we are interested merely in human taxonomy, we shall want characters varying from one geographical locality to another, but expressed, as nearly as may be, in the same way in each individual possessing them, and which are controlled by known genes. On the other hand, if we are primarily interested in human prehistory, we shall want characteristics which can be identified in ancient human remains. It is not immediately obvious that many characters will be found which satisfy simultaneously both of these requirements. We shall discuss this dilemma somewhat later on this page.

Our situation is not so very different from that of the taxonomist who is interested in classifying different species and subspecies of animals. He is interested in giving different names to the species which are really different and can be identified as being different in the *museum*. He wishes this difference to be something which will *endure;* that is, he does not wish to base his system of classification on a character which is at the moment especially prevalent as the result of an abnormally cold winter, or on a character which may merely differentiate the young and the old or the two sexes of the same species. The easiest characters to use are of course the morphological ones (differences in the shape of bones, organs, etc.), and external characters, since the skeleton or intact preserved organism is the specimen most often found in the museum. The number of genes required to determine a morphological character which may be considered decisive of species difference probably varies greatly in different cases. But in any case classification based on ephemeral characters is excluded.

Continuing the examination of characters which we might actually use in classifying human beings, we may consider left-handedness, for whether you are right- or left-handed is apparently determined by heredity (31, 50, 42, 16). Ignorance of the exact mechanism of inheritance, and the (relative) infrequency of left-handedness, however, combine to make this character unpromising for use in classification.

There can be no doubt that some characters are modified relatively rapidly by the action of selection (Chapter II). Such characters are called "adaptive." Since their frequency in populations can, and probably does, change relatively rapidly at times, they are not too reliable as a basis for speculations about the distant past, although they may nevertheless be useful for classification. At one time physical anthropologists preferred to base their classifications on "non-adaptive" characters (in order to get a long-range picture), and assumed that they knew what characters of man were non-adaptive. We shall see later that it is doubtful if any hereditary characters are completely non-adaptive, and that probably we can deal only with different degrees of adaptive value. We shall find that both sorts of characters are useful in their way, although taxonomists and systematists usually try to use the less adaptive characters.

In classifying plants, botanists have found that if a "natural" classification is desired, that is, one which gives information as to the degree of relationship of the various species, it is best not to use the vegetative* characteristics, which are fairly easily modified in the course of evolution because of the action of natural selection. It is preferable instead to utilize features of the relatively more stable reproductive organs (flowers, seeds, etc.). This principle may also apply in some cases to the attempt to recognize races within a species. Physical anthropologists,† like botanists, have long recognized the desirability of utilizing relatively stable (non-adaptive) characters, although some, surprisingly enough, were

* As an example of the failure of vegetative characteristics to distinguish quite unrelated plants sharply, we may mention the striking similarities in external appearance of *Trichocereus bridgesii* (a cactus native to America), *Euphorbia fimbrata* (a member of the spurge family, native to Africa), and *Trichocaulon flavum* (a member of the milkweed family, native to Africa) (21).

† Professor Hooton stated in 1931 (23): "If race implies the common possession of certain variations as a result of the same ancestry, significant racial criteria should be based principally upon non-adaptive bodily characters. No bodily characters are absolutely unmodifiable, but certain organs are more or less stabilized in their functions and the less important these functions are, the greater is the probability of hereditary variations manifesting themselves unimpeded and unmodified in such organs. . . . The very insignificance of certain features, such as the form of the hair or the thickness of the lips, insures their hereditary transmission in the absence of adaptive modifications that have survival value." In other words, Professor Hooton at that time (he has since modified his attitude) believed that racial classification should be based on characters which are not modified, not rapidly at any rate, by natural selection. Hooton went on to say, "I regard the following bodily characters as mainly non-adaptive variations: the form, color, and quantity of the hair, and its distribution in tracts; the color of the eyes and the form of the eyelid skin-folds; the form of the nasal cartilages, the form of the lips and of the external ear, the prominence of the chin; the breadth of the head relative to its length; the length of the face; the sutural patterns, the presence or absence of a postglenoid tubercle and pharyngeal fossa or tubercle, prognathism, the form of the incisor teeth; the form of the vertebral border of the scapula, the presence or absence of a supracondyloid process or foramen of the humerus, the length of the forearm relative to the arm; the degree of bowing of the radius and ulna; the length of the leg relative to the thigh." This is quite an impressive list, but scientific opinion changes, and in the second edition of his book Professor Hooton says, after quoting part of the above paragraph, "This insistence upon the use of 'non-adaptive' characters in human taxonomy now seems to me impractical and erroneous." Other students of anthropology would on the whole agree (11).

satisfied to study the more obvious and easily measured characters such as stature, and were rather too hastily convinced that such characters were not environmental and were truly non-adaptive, or else did not ask themselves this question at all. Actually, in the present state of our knowledge (4, 3, 43, 24), it can hardly be doubted that in addition to hereditary influences, environment, as in the form of mineral, vitamin, and calorific intake, may and does affect the stature of the individual. And the comparative ease with which true-breeding dwarf species of lower animals are established when the environment is unfavorable to the continued existence of normal-sized forms (as may happen on islands or in small isolated land areas) shows pretty clearly that size can be modified rapidly — in a geological sense at least — by evolutionary forces. Stature is, therefore, suspect as a basis for race classification.

Skin color, likewise, seems to be susceptible to alteration by natural selection, for it can hardly be doubted that the considerable degree of correlation which is observed to exist between tropical and semitropical climates and dark pigmentation has been brought about by natural selection. (See p. 176.)

We then face the question of what are the most conservative features of man, in the evolutionary sense. In animals, unlike plants, the reproductive organs may not be suitable for basic classification (although the question has been little studied); even if they were, anthropologists might find it difficult to make use of them, human customs and prejudices being what they are. Nevertheless the general principle of using conservative characters remains.

In many cases the only source of information about the cultural groups and races which formerly existed in various parts of the earth has been artifacts and skeletons. Having skeletons to study, the paleontologists very naturally attempted to base a classification chiefly on skeletal features. Measurements on bones showed that in skeletons of people who were considered to be different races there were morphological differences, and that even within the group designated as the "white" or Caucasian race, for example, fairly marked morphological differences could also be found between groups considered racially different. The bone method has the advantage of being applicable to the study of skeletons of early and prehistoric man, and allows the anthropologist and archaeologist to attempt to trace, through skeletal material, the ancestry of the various ethnic groups which exist today.

Morant (38) recognized the importance of using conservative characters, but his arguments that the characters of the skeleton are the most likely to be stable in evolution seem to be based upon nothing more than a feeling that bones, because they are *hard,* will therefore be more resistant to the action of evolutionary forces. It is to be feared that no such rule really exists in nature, and Morant expresses merely the hope that it is so, without offering any scientific evidence that it is. His assumption therefore seems hardly more than a pious wish:

> It is reasonable to assume that in a general way the skeleton is more stable than the soft tissues which clothe it, — more resistant to environmental conditions and conditions of life and hence of more fundamental importance in regard to relationships. Assuredly the anthropologist must hope that this is so, for if skeletal characters are unstable there can be little hope of finding solutions to those problems of human ancestry which can only be approached directly by using skeletal material.

Bones

Useful though it may have been in the infancy of physical anthropology, the bone method of morphological classification has grave defects which we must now consider.

First, it is rather difficult to determine accurately some of the morphological characters of the skeleton in living human beings; and peculiarities of religion, burial customs, and taboos make it difficult to examine much modern European skeletal material, leaving us with a scarcity of modern material, and a real gap between what we know of living and fossil men; to some extent, of course, this gap can be closed by more intense utilization of cadavers in dissecting rooms, etc.

Second, there is some evidence that adaptation, that is, the alteration of physical characteristics in response to the environment, has been relatively rapid in the case of skeletal characteristics (43, 41, 3).

It has been shown experimentally that the form of the skull depends partly on the muscles attached to it (48a).

Third, the characters of the skeleton or parts of the skeleton seem to be determined by the action of a number of genes simultaneously. It is difficult to know whether a certain morphological character in race X, for example, is determined by the same gene constellation as an apparently identical morphological character in race Y in some other part of the world, and we might falsely assume similarity of descent when as a matter of fact it did not exist. This will be illustrated in later chapters.

Fourth, the exclusive use of skeletal material for purposes of human classification is open to suspicion because, as Toynbee (47) phrases it in another connection, "it is a manifest example of the tendency of a student to become the slave of the particular materials for study which chance has placed in his hands."* He points out that it is a mere accident that the material tools which primitive man made should have survived, while the more important psychic artifacts, such as his institutions and ideas, are completely lost. It is the tools which leave a tangible detritus, and since the archaeologist deals with human detritus with the hope of extracting from it a knowledge of human history, "the archaeological mind tends to picture *Homo sapiens* only in his subordinate role of *Homo faber.*"* Similarly, it is to be feared that many anthropologists of the past have tended to confuse *Homo sapiens* with *Homo osseus.*

Fifth, although it is now agreed by many anthropological workers that anthropometry and craniometry are virtually *passé,* the reason for this is not solely that genetic studies in so many cases offer more information. One of the main reasons is that the metrical studies were themselves never very logical or well conceived. If we really believed that bones were the most important thing about a man, then we ought to measure such bones and such dimensions of the bones as would provide the most information about the development of the bony structure. Actually, however, the conventional measurements were, and to a large extent still are, taken with little if any regard for what is known of embryology, centers of ossification, etc. Thus the whole elaborate structure of anthropometry was never really consistent with its own basic

---

* From *A Study of History* by Arnold J. Toynbee, abridged by D. C. Somervell. Copyright 1946 by Oxford University Press, Inc. Published under the auspices of the Royal Institute of International Affairs.

assumptions, and was destined ultimately to collapse of its own weight, even if cracks in its edifice had not gradually been penetrated by the knowledge of genetics which had begun to diffuse, as Hogben (20) puts it, from the laboratories to the museums.

In spite of the zeal which the morphological school of anthropologists have exhibited in their search for criteria which would enable races to be distinguished, it is surprising to note how little can really be asserted positively if their criteria are the only ones used. For example, in 1936 Dr. A. E. Jenks (29) published a report in which he described a skeleton found in Minnesota which he ascribed to the Pleistocene age. On the basis of his measurements, Dr. Jenks concluded that this Minnesota skull represented quite a different physical type from any of the modern American Indians, and he concluded that this fitted well with the other evidence of its age. However, Dr. Aleš Hrdlička, who was one of the leaders of physical anthropology in America at that time, published a paper in the following year (27), in which he compared the measurements of this skull with the measurements of a group of about forty Indian skulls of recent origin, and concluded that the characteristics of this skull were those of the modern Sioux Indian type, and that the remains simply represented a recent Sioux burial. Dr. Jenks made a reply to this criticism of his work in 1938 (30), but it is not our purpose to inquire at the present time whose viewpoint may prove to be correct. The important thing is that two qualified authorities could have differed so widely in their interpretation of the significance of the usual measurements of skeletal remains. And this case is far from being an isolated example.

Snow (43a) in an analysis of early Indian skeletons from Kentucky, found some "white" skulls "which could easily be lost among many White European series." He also found "Negroid" types in this indisputably pure Indian series.

A contemporary physical anthropologist, Dr. William Howells, implies in his recent book, *Mankind So Far* (25), that apart from making a judicious guess, he cannot always identify race by measurements of any single skull, and the rest of the skeleton gives almost no indication at all. The trained eye, Dr. Howells thinks, can generally distinguish the skull of an Australian aboriginal from that of an Eskimo or of a European. But the skulls of Negroes and American Indians and Mongoloids in general are harder to distinguish from one another. However, certain other contemporary physical anthropologists seem somewhat more optimistic than this. Dr. T. D. Stewart (45), who is probably our outstanding expert today on skeletal remains, and whose opinion is often sought by the Federal Bureau of Investigation, was once able to identify a skull as being a white-Indian mixture. He does not, however, explain how he did it.

In spite of the somewhat limited usefulness of skeletal characteristics and morphological characteristics of the living, we should not conclude that morphological criteria are entirely devoid of value. As Dobzhansky and Epling point out (12), "a system of morphological averages may well serve as an exploratory device" (in taxonomy) but these workers go on to warn us that a basic understanding of principles of racial variation can come only from knowledge of the distribution and relative frequencies of variable genes and chromosome structures in a population. The difficulties in the above instances are due partly to the underlying assumption that any *individual* of one race should be distinguishable from any individual of any other race. This is not in general true, and we shall see (Ch. VII) that a more modern concept of race does not assume it.

Attempts to establish "racial" differences and similarities from a statistical study of measurements made on bones, particularly on skulls, have been frequent in the past.

The "coefficient of racial likeness" is a statistical concept (see App. A) which depends upon a comparison of the averages of various measurements made on two or more series of skulls. As a rigorous methodological concept, it has many weaknesses.

In the first place, the coefficient of racial likeness does not take any account of exactly which features are different in the two series, and if the series being compared differ considerably in any one measurable feature, whatever this may be, and however unimportant it may be racially, they are likely to be considered quite different. In any actual case we should want to know *what* the differences are and what other differences, if any, also exist. Fisher (13) points out that by using the coefficient of racial likeness one could be led to suppose two series very similar, simply because the measurements which we happened to have made were few or unimportant.

But perhaps the most serious defect in the thinking behind the use of the coefficient of racial likeness is the fact that it takes no account of the correlations or covariations of different measurements of the same skull, but treats them as though they were statistically independent. The effect of this, as pointed out by Fisher, is to cause very high or low values of the coefficient to occur more frequently than they should by chance. This effect increases rapidly as the number of different correlated measurements used is increased. The question of correlation between measurements on the skull has been discussed in a paper by Wallis (48) from which the reader may obtain further details.

Fisher (13) concludes that if craniometry is still concerned with clarifying its fundamental notions, at such an elementary stage of reasoning as this, it must be in a very primitive condition. And he asserts that the theoretical concepts developed in the subject have lagged far behind the mass of observational material which has been accumulated. He thinks this may be partly due to the sheer magnitude of the program which the energy of its founders sketched out, and partly to an "intuitive" confidence, which is widely held in other fields too, but which is very difficult to justify, that by amassing sufficient statistical material all difficulties may ultimately be overcome. He ends with the most devastating criticism of all: if we could establish statistically reliable differences between series of skulls from different parts of the world and from different periods, and succeed in evaluating with precision the magnitude of the measurable differences, we would still be no nearer than we were before to the stage of recognizing which, if any, among our measurements are of the greatest, and which are of the least, value as indicators of racial affinity. He points out that if we knew, for each of these measurements, whether it is largely or very little affected by purely environmental circumstances, and whether it is often and rapidly or seldom and slowly modified by evolutionary forces without racial intermixture, then it might be that some of these measurements, or more probably some particular aspect of the aggregate of these measurements, would prove of taxonomic value and could be used to provide quantitative indication of the extent to which primary race stocks (which are at present largely hypothetical) have been mingled in any particular observed population. But these necessary and preliminary inquiries seem largely to have been ignored. The reason seems to have been largely that the concentration of attention on skeletal remains resulted in a comparative neglect of measurements and genetic studies on living populations, which should be our proper object of study.

The durability of skulls has led to their being collected and stored in large numbers in museums, and students beginning the study of physical anthropology find this mass of material, standing as a challenge as it were, when they first begin their work. It is to be feared that some, without much consideration of the probable usefulness of the work, have plunged too enthusiastically and too hastily into the task of making a large series of measurements on skulls.

It seems clear that the ideal basis for human classification would be a group of characters which not only were hereditary but of which the exact mechanism of inheritance was understood. Neither of these desiderata, unfortunately, seems to apply to any of the morphological or metrical characters of the skeleton known at present. Therefore the lack of information about the genetics of skeletal characters to a large extent cancels out the advantages which the durability and ease of metrical study of skeletons offers as a basis of classification, even when fairly large series are compared.

Genes

Without more knowledge of the evolutionary behavior of human traits we cannot decide offhand which are the most stable. We can only guess. The sort of character we shall be led to choose as being relatively non-adaptive will probably be the characters for which we cannot imagine any survival value. (Of course the fact that we cannot imagine any usefulness in evolution of a character does not prove that such usefulness does not exist, but such characters are at any rate to be preferred to those which obviously have high survival value.) The bony structures obviously have high survival value, and we shall hardly select the more important features of them. Among the racial characters which we would be tempted to pick out at the present time as non-adaptive, there are certain serological features of the blood, such as the genes *O, A, B, M, N,* etc.; many other characters, such as the direction of hair whorls, general body hairiness (probably), tooth cusp patterns, fingerprint patterns, etc., might be considered.

The task of modern anthropology, just as of modern taxonomy, is to consider characters which are found to be determined by one or a definite number of genes, acting in a known manner. It is for this reason, among others, that a classification based on skin color in the human species is not satisfactory. The exact method of inheritance of skin color is far from being understood, and there is hardly any doubt that various combinations of quite a number of different genes may result in skin colors which to the eye seem virtually identical. To use the language of our next chapter, a classification based on phenotypes is not satisfactory when several different genotypes (that is, combinations of genes) may produce the same phenotypes, and we have no direct means of distinguishing these phenotypes.

The most compelling reason for the examination of genetically determined traits, rather than anthropometric measurements, should now be restated. Once we begin to acquire a fairly thorough knowledge of human genetics, we can begin to attempt to trace the inheritance and distribution of genes which actually influence human behavior. As examples of such genes, which may be very numerous, we may mention the genes which undoubtedly exist which influence endocrine development and endocrine balance in the individual. This future study will eventually provide us with information of enormous importance, not only for the anthropologist, but for the sociologist and political scientist as well. There is no prospect that similar information can ever be obtained by following anthropometric technics alone.

REFERENCES FOR CHAPTER I

1. Backhouse, E. T., and J. O. P. Bland, *Annals and Memoirs of the Court of Peking.* Houghton Mifflin Co., New York, 1914.
2. Benedict, R., *Patterns of Culture.* Penguin, New York, 1946.
3. Boas, F., *Changes in the Bodily Form of Descendants of Immigrants.* Columbia Univ. Press, New York, 1912.
4. Boas, F., *Race, Language and Culture.* Macmillan Co., New York, 1940.
5. Boas, F., *Race and Democratic Society.* J. J. Augustin, New York, 1945.
6. Burton, R. F., *Personal Narrative of a Pilgrimage to Al-Madinah and Meccah.* Tylston and Edwards, London, 1893.
7. Burton, R. F., *First Footsteps in East Africa.* Tylston and Edwards, London, 1894.
8. Chamberlain, H. S., *The Foundations of the Nineteenth Century.* J. Lane Co., New York, 1912.
9. Clemens, S. L., *Extract from Captain Stormfield's Visit to Heaven.* Harper & Bros., New York and London, 1909.
10. Dobzhansky, Th., *Teaching Biologist, 12,* 97–106 (1943).
11. Dobzhansky, Th., *A. J. P. A., 2,* 251–265 (1944).
12. Dobzhansky, Th., and C. Epling, Carnegie Institution of Washington Publication *554* (1944).
13. Fisher, R. A., *J. Roy. Anthrop. Inst., 66,* 57–63 (1936).
14. Gates, R. R., *Population, 1,* 25–36 (1934).
15. Gates, R. R., *A. J. P. A., 2* (N. S.), 279–292 (1944).
16. Gates, R. R., *Human Genetics.* Macmillan Co., New York, 1946.
17. Gates, R. R., *Human Ancestry.* Harvard Univ. Press, Cambridge, 1948.
18. Gobineau, A. de, *Essai sur l'inégalité des races humaines.* Firmin-Didot et Cie, Paris, 1854.
19. Hitler, A., *Mein Kampf.* Reynal & Hitchcock, New York, 1940.
20. Hogben, L., *Genetic Principles in Medicine and Social Science.* Williams & Norgate, Ltd., London, 1931.
21. Holman, R. M., and W. W. Robbins, *A Textbook of General Botany for Colleges and Universities.* John Wiley & Sons, New York, 1946.
22. Hooton, E. A., *Town Meeting of the Air, 5,* No. 6 (1939).
23. Hooton, E. A., *Up from the Ape.* Macmillan Co., New York, 1931.
24. Hooton, E. A., *Up from the Ape.* Macmillan Co., New York, 2nd Edition, 1946.
25. Howells, W. W., *Mankind So Far.* Doubleday, Doran & Co., Garden City, New York, 1944.
26. Hrdlička, A., *Human Biology and Racial Welfare.* Ed. E. V. Cowdry, New York, 1930.
27. Hrdlička, A., *A. J. P. A., 22,* 175–199 (1937).
28. Huxley, J., *Evolution, the Modern Synthesis.* Harper & Bros., New York and London, 1942.

29. Jenks, A. E., *Pleistocene Man in Minnesota, a Fossil Homo Sapiens*. Minneapolis, 1936.

30. Jenks, A. E., *Am. Anthrop.*, 40, 328–336 (1938).

31. Jordan, H. E., *J. Genetics*, 4, 67–81 (1914).

32. Keith, A., *The Place of Prejudice in Modern Civilization*. J. Day Co., New York, 1931.

33. Keith, A., Introduction to *Arabs of Central Iraq* by Henry Field, Field Museum of Natural History, Chicago, 1935.

34. Klineberg, O., "Racial Psychology," in *The Science of Man in the World Crisis*. Ed. Ralph Linton, Columbia University Press, 1945.

35. Linton, R., *The Study of Man*. D. Appleton-Century Co., Inc., New York, 1936.

36. Montagu, M. F. A., *Town Meeting of the Air*, 5, No. 6 (1939).

37. Montagu, M. F. A., *A. J. P. A.*, 26, 41–61 (1940).

38. Morant, G. M., *J. Roy. Anthrop. Inst.*, 66, 43 (1936).

39. Morant, G. M., *Biometrika*, 31, 72 (1939).

40. *One World or None*. Ed. D. Masters and K. Way, 1946.

41. Schwidetzky, J., *Verband Deutsche Gesell. für Rassen.*, 10, 65–74 (1940).

42. Schott, A., *Zeit. f. d. ges. Neurologie und Psychiatrie*, 135, 305–313 (1931).

43. Shapiro, H. L., *Migration and Environment*. Oxford Univ. Press, London, New York, and Toronto, 1939.

43a. Snow, C. E., *Reports in Anthropology*, Univ. of Kentucky, 4, no. 3, pt. II, 1948.

44. Snyder, L. L., *Race, A History of Modern Ethnic Theories*. Longmans, Green & Co., New York and Toronto, 1939.

45. Stewart, T. D., *A. J. P. A.*, 6, 315–322 (1948).

46. Stowe, H. B., *Uncle Tom's Cabin*. John P. Jewett & Co., Boston, 1852.

47. Toynbee, A. J., *A Study of History*. Oxford Univ. Press, New York and London, 1947.

48. Wallis, R. S., *Human Biol.*, 6, 308–323 (1934).

48a. Washburn, S. L., *Anat. Rec.*, 99, 239–248.

49. Wiener, A. S., *Am. Nat.*, 66, 365–370 (1932).

50. Wilson, D., *The Right Hand: Left Handedness*. New York, 1891.

CHAPTER 11 Genetics

And Ahaz begat Jarah; and Jarah begat Alemeth, and Az-
maveth, and Zimri; and Zimri begat Moza; and Moza begat
Binea. . . .

— I CHRONICLES ix. 42, 43

WE HAVE SEEN that for our purposes only inherited characteristics
are suitable for classifying human beings, and even then only on
condition that the mechanism of their inheritance is understood.
We must now inquire into the mechanism of inheritance in general, and in particular into the ways it operates in man. Certain
general laws are known and we may as well begin with a summary of them. They grew out of studies carried out by Mendel on
inheritance in the common garden pea, but it is now known that
they apply to all other complex organisms, including man.

We may devote a few pages to Mendel's actual experiments and
their results, and then pass to more general considerations.

Mendelian Inheritance

Gregor Johann Mendel was born in Austrian Silesia in 1822 (44),
the son of well-to-do peasants. He became a priest in 1847, and
studied physics and natural science at Vienna from 1851 to 1853.
From Vienna he returned to his cloister and became a teacher in
the *Realschule* at Brünn. As a sort of hobby he made hybridization
experiments with peas and other plants in the garden of the mon-
astery. He eventually became abbot, and his scientific work ceased.

Before this time, however, after years of patient experimenting
with hybridization, he reached important conclusions in regard to
heredity, which we refer to as "Mendel's Laws." His publication of
them in 1866 was in the *Proceedings of the Natural History Society*

*of Brunn** and passed practically unnoticed, even though copies of this journal reached various parts of the world, including the U.S.A. Those who knew of his work at the time all failed to realize its importance. About the beginning of our century Mendel's laws, and Mendel's previous work on them, were rediscovered by Correns, De Vries, and von Tschermak.

What Mendel tried to discover, and did discover, was the law of inheritance in hybrid varieties, and he selected for experiments the edible pea (*Pisum sativum*). He apparently (48) decided in advance that: the plants to be used for his experiments must possess constant characters differentiating them, and they must be easy to pollinate artificially; the hybrids of the plants must be readily fertile; and they must be easy to protect from the influence of foreign pollen which the experimenter does not deliberately introduce. These conditions were met by peas, and Mendel selected twenty-two varieties, which remained constant during the eight years of his experiments. Whether they should be called different species, or subspecies, or varieties, was a matter of little moment. In any case, they were groups of similar individuals which bred true among themselves. Peas had the particular advantage, for experimental purposes, that they are habitually self-fertilized, making the pollination question a simple one.

In studying the different varieties of peas, Mendel found seven differentiating characters which could be relied on: 1) The form of the ripe seeds, which could be roundish, with shallow wrinkles or with none, or angular and deeply wrinkled. 2) The color of the reserve material in the cotyledons, which could be pale yellow, bright yellow, orange, or green. 3) The color of the seed coats, which could be white, as in most peas with white flowers, or gray, gray-brown, leather brown, with or without violet spots, and so forth. 4) The form of the ripe pods, which could be simply inflated, or constricted or wrinkled. 5) The color of the unripe pods, which could be light or dark green, or vividly yellow, this color being correlated with that of stalk, leaf veins, and blossoms. 6) The position of the flowers, which could be axial or terminal. 7) The

---

* A translation into English of Mendel's paper has been made by the Royal Horticultural Society of London, and is available at the Harvard University Press under the title *Experiments in Plant Hybridization* by Gregor Mendel.

length of the stem of the plant, which could be tall or dwarfish.

Having found differentiating characteristics between the varieties, Mendel proceeded to make crosses between these, investigating *one character at a time*. Thus, he might apply pollen from a pea of the round-seeded variety to the stigma of a pea of the angular-seeded variety, the stamens of the latter being, of course, removed before they were ripe so that they could not pollinate the stigma themselves. Crosses of the other differentiating characters were performed in the same manner.

Mendel's Laws

1. INHERITANCE IS PARTICULATE IN NATURE

a. *Dominance.* Among the hybrid or cross-bred offspring, it was found in nearly every case that they showed just one of the pair of contrasted characters, to the total (or almost total) exclusion of the other. Intermediate forms did not appear.

Mendel called the character that prevailed *dominant,* and the character that was suppressed (or apparently suppressed) *recessive.* Thus the first important result was the discovery that, *dealing with pure lines,* crosses between a plant with the dominant character and a plant with the recessive character yielded offspring which, as regards the character in question, all resembled the dominant parent. If we designate the appearance of the parents as D (dominant), and R (recessive), Mendel's first result may therefore be expressed thus: The cross, Dominant by Recessive, produces Dominant appearing offspring. Or in symbols:

$$D \times R = D.$$

Later work has shown that *complete dominance* is much less common than was originally thought. In fact, some effects of each gene of the pair are generally discernible in the hybrids.

b. *Unit Characters Segregate* in Hereditary Transmission*
In the next generation the cross-bred plants which had been produced by crossing D and R (or R and D), and which were all apparently like D, were allowed to fertilize themselves; and it was

* Segregation means the separation, in offspring, of genetic factors not visibly distinct in the parents.

then found that *their* offspring exhibited *both* of the two original forms, showing on the average three dominants to one recessive. We may take as an example the tall × dwarf cross: 1064 second generation plants were produced; 787 were tall (D) and 277 were dwarfs (R).

When any of these "recovered" dwarfs (i.e. recessive descendants of a group of plants all "D" in appearance) were allowed to fertilize themselves, they gave rise to dwarfs (R) only, a process which could be continued for any number of generations. In other words, the *recessive* (R) character bred true. The hereditary unit tending to produce it (we call such units *genes*) had not been altered by its association in the hybrid with the "dominant" (D) gene for tallness.

On the other hand, when the dominant descendants, D, were allowed to fertilize themselves, one third of them produced "pure" dominants which in subsequent generations, when allowed to fertilize themselves, gave rise to dominant descendants only; two thirds of them, however, were an "impure" group which produced once again the characteristic mixture of dominants and recessives in the proportion of 3:1.

These results are shown in the following scheme. The result of the initial hybridization is a first generation (F_1) which resembles the dominant parent. They may be represented by the symbol (D), for though looking like the dominant, some of them carry within them the possibility of producing offspring characterized by the recessive character; that is to say, the recessive character has remained latent in the inheritance.

The genetic formulas of the various individuals are evidently as follows, where D represents the dominant gene and R the recessive:

Type as identified by inspection	Genetic type as identified by breeding experiments
D	DD
(D)	DR
R	RR

From this it will readily be understood that the pure dominant-D individual, which possesses only D genes, can produce only D offspring when it fertilizes itself and R can produce only R. The dominant-appearing (D) individuals, however, being genetically mixed, can produce D, (D) and R offspring, in the ratio 1:2:1.

Perhaps we can make the above scheme clearer by citing another example from Mendel's work. Peas with rounded seeds were

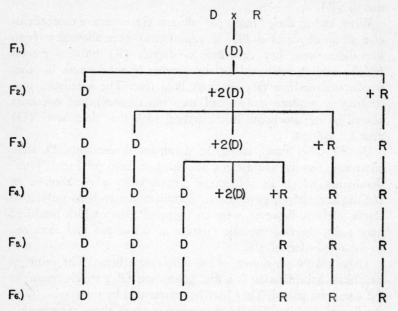

FIGURE 1. *Diagram illustrating "Mendelian splitting" or segregation which occurs when hybrids mate. The homozygous dominants and recessives breed true, but the heterozygotes (which, in the present case, resemble the dominant parent) continue to produce, in addition to heterozygotes, homozygous recessives and homozygous dominants.*

crossed with peas having angular wrinkled seeds. In the offspring the character of roundness was "dominant"; the angular wrinkled physical character had disappeared for the time being. It was not lost, or even permanently altered, however, as the next generation showed. For, when the hybrid offspring, all with rounded seeds, were allowed to self-fertilize themselves, among their progeny roundish seeds and angular wrinkled seeds occurred in the proportions of 3:1. The wrinkled characteristic of the seeds, the recessive, had turned up again, and when plants from such seeds were allowed to self-fertilize they produced pure recessives only — that is, the resulting plants all had angular wrinkled seeds.

The "dominants," however, were not all pure, for when they were allowed to self-fertilize they produced one third "pure" dominants and two thirds "impure" dominants, the latter being distinguished by the fact that among their offspring recessives reappeared in the proportion of one recessive to three dominants.

2. UNIT CHARACTERS ASSORT INDEPENDENTLY

Mendel's second law stated that each pair of hereditary factors showing this dominant-recessive relationship behaved quite independently from every other pair. This is called the law of independent assortment. This second law is not without exceptions, for reasons which will presently appear. However, it does hold for many factors, and unless the genes were connected together in some way in the organism, it would be expected to hold for all factors influencing inheritance. Reproductive cells (gametes) having all possible combinations of genes would be expected. The fact that the law does not always operate suggests then that there may be some physical connection between certain genes or, in other words, the genes may be transmitted in groups during the process of reproduction.

To take an actual instance of independent assortment: Mendel found that the character pair yellow-green (of which yellow is dominant) and the pair round-wrinkled (of which round is dominant) assorted independently. Crossing round yellow with wrinkled green peas, Mendel got a first generation of descendants (F_1) of all round yellows. Either gene pair, considered alone, in the F_2 generation produced dominants and recessives in the expected 3:1 ratio.

If the F_1 plants were next crossed with plants which were genetically pure (homozygous) for both of the recessive genes in question (i.e. wrinkled green peas), there were four possible types of offspring, namely, round-yellow, round-green, wrinkled-yellow, and wrinkled-green; the genes, assorting independently, produced the four possible types of offspring in equal numbers.

Mendel represented the dominant gene for round as *A*, and the recessive gene for wrinkled as *a,* the dominant for yellow as *B,* and the recessive for green as *b.* This would give us, for his hybrid (heterozygous) peas, the formula *AaBb.* The pure recessives would be *aabb.* They could produce only one kind of gamete, namely, *ab.* The heterozygotes could produce four kinds of gamete, in equal numbers, *AB, Ab, aB,* and *ab.* Combining these with the gametes of the wrinkled green peas, we get four possible combinations, and therefore four possible offspring, in equal numbers, namely, *AaBb, Aabb, aaBb,* and *aabb.* (See Table 1.) This was confirmed by experiment.

TABLE 1

Results of Crossing *AaBb* with *aabb* (Mendel)

Female gametes	Male gametes			
	AB	*Ab*	*aB*	*ab*
ab	*AaBb*	*Aabb*	*aaBb*	*aabb*

If the reader has followed this reasoning, he should have no difficulty in predicting the outcome of a cross of two plants heterozygous for both genes (or, what amounts to the same thing, the results of allowing a doubly heterozygous plant to fertilize itself). Each plant produces the four possible gametes, *AB, Ab, aB,* and *ab,* in equal numbers. It is a matter of chance which ovum is fertilized by which pollen grain, so we get all the possible combinations, as shown in Table 2.

Since round (*A*) is dominant over wrinkled, and yellow (*B*) is dominant over green, not all these sixteen different genetic types will be distinguishable in the offspring. We find, in fact, that just four types can be distinguished, and they are classified as shown in Table 3.

It will be noted that not only are there just four distinguishable types of offspring, but, since each type of gamete is produced as frequently as any other, the four types of offspring will occur in the ratio shown, which is 9:3:3:1. The actual ratio observed by Mendel (48) was 315 round and yellow, 101 wrinkled and yellow,

TABLE 2

Combinations Resulting from the Cross of Individuals Heterozygous for Two Characters

Female gametes	Male gametes			
	AB	*Ab*	*aB*	*ab*
AB	*AABB*	*AABb*	*AaBB*	*AaBb*
Ab	*AABb*	*AAbb*	*AaBb*	*Aabb*
aB	*AaBB*	*AaBb*	*aaBB*	*aaBb*
ab	*AaBb*	*Aabb*	*aaBb*	*aabb*

TABLE 3

Phenotypically Different Offspring from the Mating Shown in Table 2

AB (round, yellow)	*Ab* (round, green)	*aB* (wrinkled, yellow)	*ab* (wrinkled, green)
AABB	*AAbb*	*aaBB*	*aabb*
AABb	*Aabb*	*aaBb*	
AaBB	*Aabb*	*aaBb*	
AaBB			
AABb			
AaBb			
AaBB			
AaBb			
AaBb			

108 round and green, and 32 wrinkled and green. These conformed as closely to prediction as could have been expected.

The use of capital letters for the dominant gene, and small letters for the recessive, was continued by Mendel's successors, but when it was found that sometimes there were more than two genes which could occur at a chromosome locus, the system ceased to be so satisfactory. Also complete dominance is not quite as common as

was at first supposed (70). See p. 42. Modern practice inclines
to the use of a "carrier symbol" for the locus, with superscripts
indicating which gene is meant. Workers in human genetics, however, have sometimes followed neither of these systems.

One of the most important lessons for us to learn from Mendel's
work is this: we must not choose certain characteristics of an
organism and casually make assumptions about the way they are
inherited (even if we are sure that they are mainly controlled by
heredity); we must select characters easy to identify and to differentiate from each other, and patiently find out by experiment — not
by merely making a plausible guess — how they are actually inherited in the organism being investigated. Later work has shown
that sometimes enormous differences, such as an absence of hands
or feet (49), may be caused by genetic unit characters; in other
cases a unit character does no more than put a hydroxyl or methyl
group on a benzene ring in some chemical substance occurring in
the organism. But in all cases experiment is the only way of finding
such things out. We cannot simply *look* at two different forms of
an organism, such as two distinct fossils, or two distinct living
forms, such as an Englishman and an Ubangi Negro, and say:
"The difference which we see is doubtless due to a single gene (or
to *n* genes)." Questions of this sort are not to be solved by intuition.

Modern Genetics

Genetics, according to Babcock and Clausen (3), is the science
which seeks to account for the resemblances and the differences
which are exhibited among organisms related by descent.
Dobzhansky (15, 16) states that its task is to describe the mechanism which makes the offspring resemble their parents, which
makes individuals of the same and different species resemble each
other in certain respects and differ in others, and which causes some
organisms to undergo changes in the course of time, during the
process of evolution (75).

Every organism is begun either from sex cells or from other
vestiges received from its parent or parents. This vestige contains
the basic stuff of life, that is, the hereditary materials of the germ
plasm. Germ plasm possesses one highly remarkable property, that

of self-duplication. It has the ability to react with its environment and to draw out of that environment a collection of substances suitable for its nutrition and to transform these substances into its own likeness. This ability is something which no non-living chemical substance possesses, and the chemical mechanism of the process is still an unsolved problem. Simply by definition, any self-reproducing substance is a living substance.

"Blood" as Inheritance

Before we continue an examination of the subject of genetics we may mention briefly that the term "blood" was often confused with heredity by laymen, and even by the older anthropologists, and it was not uncommon even during the Second World War to hear uneducated people object to the idea that wounded American soldiers might receive blood or blood plasma from Negroes or from Japanese. Some of these people admitted that their objections were purely emotional, but others obviously confused "blood," in the sense of a circulating vital tissue, with "blood," in the sense of inheritance. Blood itself does not actually carry the units of heredity. These are carried by the genes, and transmitted to human beings by ova and sperm. Biologists are all agreed that no number of transfusions of Negro or Chinese blood into a white European would alter to any extent whatever the color of his skin or any of his other hereditary characteristics. Except for certain nonessential, although interesting, differences which will be noted below, the blood of all human beings seems to be the same. The hemoglobin of a Hottentot would bring oxygen from your lungs to your tissues with the same efficiency as the hemoglobin of a white member of the British nobility, and acquiring some foreign hemoglobin of either kind would not add anything to, or change in any way, the genes you already possess, and which you are capable of transmitting to your offspring.

No Blending Inheritance

Inheritance is particulate in nature, as we have seen in reviewing Mendel's work. That is, the germ plasm is passed from parent to offspring in the form of discrete particles, and not as a portion of a more or less uniform mixture of the germ plasm of mother and father. These units of heredity or of germ plasm are known as genes. Each inherited characteristic of every organism is the result of the interaction of all its genes. Usually one or two gene pairs are found to be chiefly responsible for the observed variations in any particular characteristic. Aside from a very few special instances (such as *plastids* in plants) there are no known examples of inheritance in sexually reproducing organisms which do not depend on genes.

It has not been proved, however, and probably can never be proved, that *all* the characteristics of a given organism are determined by genes. As has been pointed out by certain writers, for example Russell (62) and Glass (34), there is a reason why we shall never completely prove the genic nature of some of the really major characteristics of any form of life. Since these major characteristics, such as having lungs, eyes, blood, etc., are absolutely vital to the life of the organism, a change in the genes which control them is almost certain to lead to a condition which will interfere with normal development, or in other words will produce what geneticists call a *lethal*. A lethal gene is a gene which kills the organism which inherits it. It usually requires a double dose (i.e., lethals are usually recessive), but extremely undesirable genes might kill when present in a single dose (heterozygous). It can be seen that dominant lethals could not persist beyond one generation. Changes or mutations altering (for the worse) the absolutely essential features of an organism will be eliminated almost immediately by the action of natural selection, and each species will be homozygous for the normal (non-lethal) aspect of genes of such major importance.

The only kinds of genes we are able to trace in human or other heredity are those in which the members of the gene pair can produce different effects and which do not kill the organism, at least not when present in only a single dose, or at least not during the very early stages of development of the organism. Any other genes would never have survived the rigorous action of natural selection.

The importance to biology of the concept of particulate inheritance can hardly be overestimated, but until the discoveries of Mendel and those who confirmed his work became known, it was assumed by practically all laymen, and by biologists too, even by Darwin, that inheritance was of a blending character. For example, it was supposed that a parent with a black skin and a parent with a white skin would always produce children with intermediate brown type skins and that these brown children, mated with similar brown children, would of course have brown offspring, for it was thought that the two characters, or types of "blood," were forever mixed, just as ink and milk poured together into the same container can never again be separated.

When considerable numbers of genes are involved, as in skin color,* heredity does at first sight appear to be of a blending character. Genetic analysis of such characters is difficult. The genius of Mendel consisted in selecting for study varieties which differed from each other in only a few characters, genetically as well as apparently, so that he readily recovered the parental types from crosses among the offspring. All inherited characters which have been fully analyzed have always been found to depend on particulate genes which retain their individuality even in hybrids of mixed ancestry. This applies even to the apparent cases of blending inheritance which have been adequately investigated.

We may discuss briefly an example which, without careful investigation, might seem to be an example of the blending type of inheritance. Among chickens there are a number of genetically pure types, including the types *black* and *splashed-white,* each of which breeds true. When these two are crossed, however, they produce offspring having an intermediate character; the so-called *Blue Andalusians* (5). It seems almost self-evident to the uninstructed observer that the genetic material of the two parents has been blended in the offspring, to produce an intermediate and novel type, but this is not true. Breeding experiments reveal that "blending" is not the correct explanation. Crosses of Blue Andalusians among themselves produce both black and splashed-white offspring as well as the Blue Andalusian, and it is absolutely impossible to obtain a stock of Blue Andalusians which will breed true. The two types of hereditary material have not blended, but

* Davenport (see p. 310) proposed a theory involving only two pairs of genes for skin color; more are probably involved, however.

during a period of coexistence in a certain individual they combine their effects to produce a new type of appearance. The genetic materials, however, have remained unchanged, and when they again emerge by themselves in the offspring, they produce the same effects they produced in the original parents. A cross of Blue Andalusians gives the expected 1:2:1 ratio (see above).

Since the Blue Andalusians do not look exactly like either the black or the splashed-white parent, we miss in this case the complete dominance which Mendel observed in his peas. There are many other examples. Thus a cross between a "Chinese" primula which has wavy crenated petals and a "Star" primula with simply notched petals gives progeny intermediate between the two parents; and yet, as the next generation shows, the case is one of Mendelian inheritance, that is, the two characteristics have stayed distinct in the germ plasm, and both parental types, as well as the mixed variety, appear among the offspring.

In many cases the hybrid, while exhibiting on the whole the character of the dominant, may show also some influence of the recessive character, but not enough to warrant our speaking of the result as a "blend." Thus, when white (dominant) Leghorn poultry are crossed with brown (recessive) Leghorn, most of the offspring have some "ticks" of color. When these are inbred they produce a quarter brown ("expected recessives") and three quarters pure white or white with a few "ticks." Thus dominance here is not quite perfect, but in this case we may use the word if we like.

When dealing with characters which can only be present or absent, it is often not possible to measure degrees of "dominance," although in situations which at first seem to belong to this category (as in the case of the blood groups of man) some information as to degrees of dominance has been obtained. Such data are to be found in books on blood groups.

If we are dealing with quantitative characters, however (that is, characters which may be counted, measured, or in some other way expressed in numerical terms), it is possible to express the degree of dominance more exactly. The eye of the fruit fly *Drosophila* is made up of a number of separate elements or facets. The number of these elements in any individual eye can be counted and the effect of various genes on them can be determined. The accompanying illustration shows the effect of a gene which is called *Bar,* when it is present in the homozygous (see p. 40) and heterozygous (single dose) condition, and also shows the results of facet counts on the "wild" type, that is the type without the mutant gene. In this figure, the vertical axis represents the percentage frequencies of each of the three types, and the horizontal axis the facet numbers.

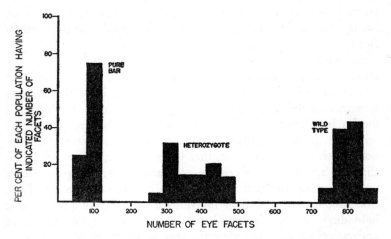

FIGURE 2. *Quantitative effects of a gene. Actual example of the way the number of facets in the eye of* Drosophila *is influenced by the gene, "Bar Eye."*

The three genotypes* are sharply distinguished although there is a certain normal variability within each type. Dominance is clearly incomplete in this case, since the heterozygote is decidedly different from either of the homozygotes. It has been suggested (70) that early in development a facet-forming substance is produced in the young fly and that the Bar gene starts up a new chemical reaction that breaks down this substance. In a later stage, a third set of processes, the actual process of facet formation, occurs, but the

---

*The genotype of an individual is a summary of his genetic constitution; the phenotype is a statement of his outward appearance (or what you can determine by direct tests).

number of facets formed is determined by the amount of facet substance which still remains. This interpretation is supported by studies on the effect of temperature on the manifestation of this gene (see Fig. 15).

Blending inheritance seems superficially so logical that it was accepted almost without question even by such pioneers in anthropology as Galton and Boas, although the latter abandoned it in his later papers. But it is totally wrong, and as Fisher (29) has pointed out, almost the whole of the revolutionary effects of Mendelism can be seen to result from a knowledge of the particulate character of the hereditary elements.

Although Darwin accepted the fusion or blending theory of inheritance, just as other men of his time did, and although he almost certainly never heard of Mendel's work, it is interesting to note that he did at certain times feel the need for a non-blending theory. In a letter to Huxley which was probably dated 1857 these sentences occurred (29): "Approaching the subject from the side which attracts me most, that is, inheritance, I have lately inclined to speculate, very crudely and indistinctly, that propagation by true fertilization will turn out to be a sort of mixture, and not true fusion, of two distinct individuals, or rather of innumerable individuals, as each parent has its parents and ancestors. I can understand on no other view the way in which crossed forms go back to so large an extent to ancestral forms. But all of this, of course, is infinitely crude." Fisher points out that this idea was never developed by Darwin, probably because of the rush of work preceding and following the publication of his great book, *The Origin of Species*.

Chetverikov (14) and Fisher (29) have also pointed out that on the assumption of blending inheritance, that is, if the genetic materials in the two parents were to be truly fused, then the heritable variability of the species is halved each generation. It was realized even by Darwin that domesticated species displayed far too much variability for this to be true, and modern studies have shown that wild organisms exhibit about the same degree of variability as the domesticated. The hypothesis of blending inheritance, which at first sight seems so reasonable, must be completely rejected.

Chromosomes

Mendel supposed that his hereditary factors were present in pairs in a mature organism, but single in the reproductive cells (or gametes). Soon after Mendel's work was rediscovered, it was noticed that there was a close parallel between this hypothetical

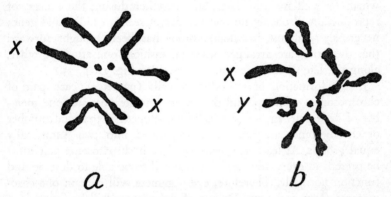

FIGURE 3. *Drawing of the chromosomes in* Drosophila. (*a*) *Female;* (*b*) *Male.*

situation and the actual position of certain rodlike structures which have been observed at certain times in the nuclei of reproductive cells. These rodlike structures have been called *chromosomes* because of their peculiar stain reaction in stained preparations. The chromosomes are normally visible only during cell division, and their visibility varies in different species. In stained preparations they appear as dark bodies in the nucleus. (See Fig. 3.) In living cells they can sometimes be photographed under suitable conditions by the use of ultraviolet light.

It has been observed that these chromosomes, present in pairs in the cells of the mature organism, separate themselves during the formation of gametes. The chromosomes cannot be identical with the hypothetical units of heredity of Mendel, however, because there are not nearly enough of them in any organism to account for the great variety of the known genetic factors. Furthermore, it is now known that the individual genes of any organism are transmitted in groups during the reproductive process, and it is generally believed that *the number of these groups is equal to the number of chromosome pairs*. Each group of genes which are present in a particular chromosome then assorts independently of other groups, according to Mendel's second law, during reproduction. Members of any given group, subject to certain exceptions which we will mention later, stay together during the process of reproduction. Probably no one has as yet *seen* an individual gene; nevertheless, almost irrefutable proof has been brought forward that the genes are arranged in serial fashion, one after the other, along the length of the chromosomes. (See Fig. 12, p. 75.)

In the formation of reproductive cells (gametes), each pair of chromosomes splits up, and thus every gamete possesses one member of each pair. In the process of gametogenesis the total number of chromosomes are not simply separated into two numerically equal groups. At least *one member* of each chromosome pair must be present in every adult cell for that cell to be able to develop and function normally. Therefore, every gamete will contain one chromosome from each pair. Details of the process will be found in a number of excellent books (64, 68, 70).

From the chromosomes of the gametes, combined after fertilization of the ovum by the sperm, appear new combinations of the various chromosomes. Since genetic experiments have shown it to be purely a matter of chance which chromosome of each pair enters into any given gamete, we are justified in stating, as Glass does (34), that the chromosomes are shuffled and redealt in single sets. The members of the different pairs recombine at random and all possible combinations will occur with equal frequency. Knowing the number of pairs of chromosomes in any given organism, we may compute the number of possible different combinations. For two pairs we have 2^2 which means four possible combinations. For three pairs we have $2^3 = 8$ combinations, and for four pairs $2^4 = 16$ combinations. For n pairs 2^n gives the number of combinations.

In man there are 48 chromosomes per adult cell, or 24 pairs, so the number of combinations is therefore 2^{24}. This gives the staggering total of 16,777,216 possible combinations, of which only two are exactly the same as either original parental combination. Therefore, the chances that a human being will repeat either of the parental combinations exactly is only one in 8,388,608 (assuming no crossing-over in this generation).

Dominants and Alleles

From the foregoing, it should be clear that each organism inherits two genes affecting its various characteristics, one from the mother and one from the father, and that in respect to the more vital characteristics of the organism, in all probability these two genes are substantially identical. Genes which affect minor external or less important characteristics may sometimes be different in the two parents. For example, one parent may have had a particular shade of brown eyes and the other blue eyes, and the eye color in each case was determined by the presence of a gene or combination of genes, capable of occupying a certain place ("locus") in the serial arrangement of genes on one particular chromosome.

When the two genes occupying corresponding loci in a chromosome pair are different, a number of different results are possible. One possibility is that the two genes may both exert their respective effects without much mutual interference. This is observed, for example, in the M, N blood types where either gene, if present, will produce its characteristic response in the red blood cells, whether or not the other gene of the pair is present.

In some cases we may find that the effect of the two genes together is more or less intermediate between the effect of either gene occurring in double dose, as in the Blue Andalusian fowl. In a common flower, the four-o'clock, offspring which possess one gene for red flowers and one for white flowers produce pink flowers. In this case, blending of characters appears to occur in individuals having two different genes, but genetic experiments prove that the genes remain different and distinct, although their combined manifestation has for the time being produced a blend in one of the visible characteristics of the flower.

In still other cases, we may find that the presence of one gene almost completely obscures the effect of the other and some particular feature of the organism is determined almost entirely by the one gene. This is the phenomenon observed by Mendel which he called dominance. Other genes, in different loci, may sometimes alter the expression of a certain gene. Such genes are called "modifiers."

Dominance was at one time supposed to be almost universal, but it has already been pointed out that in a great many cases organisms possessing two genes, one dominant and one recessive (such organisms are referred to as heterozygotes), may differ in some respect both from the homozygous organism possessing two of the dominant genes, and from the one possessing two of the recessive genes. The more careful and painstaking the examination, the more likely it is that the heterozygote will be found to be distinguishable from both of the homozygotes. However, substantially complete dominance is so common that Sewall Wright (73) has made the following rough generalization:

(1) Dominance of one allele of a pair is the rule. (Genes capable of occupying the same locus in members of a chromosome pair, both acting together in the process of development, are referred to as *allelomorphs* or *alleles*.) (2) The recessive allele is usually less advantageous to the species than is the dominant. (3) Organisms possessing only the recessive genes are generally found to lack something which the dominant gene would have caused to be produced. At least this is true in most of the cases where we have some knowledge of what the primary effects (the chemical reactions involved, for instance) of the gene really are. (4) The recessive genes are usually less abundant in natural wild populations than their dominant allelomorphs. (5) In cases in which new genes are known to have occurred suddenly (that is, by mutation) they are usually recessive. As will be seen from the examples already discussed, and as Professor Wright points out, all of these principles are subject to much qualification, depending on the particular case being studied.

Stability of Genes

Since we are going to be speaking from time to time about the changes in genes (which we refer to as mutations), it will be well to emphasize here and now the very great constancy of genes, as a rule and under ordinary circumstances. The recessive gene suffers no modification even if it is carried unexpressed for many successive generations in heterozygous individuals which show only the dominant phenotype. (Definition on p. 43.) Raymond Pearl (58) observed the transmission of a single gene in the fruit fly, Drosophila, through 300 generations. He arranged his experiment so that in each generation the gene was always associated with a degenerated allelomorph of itself. If we translate this experiment into terms of human generations, such an experiment would require a period of time beginning long before the Bronze Age, say about 7000 B.C. and extending up to the present time. Pearl observed no changes in this particular Drosophila gene in any phase of the experiment.

Origin of Dominance

A natural question to ask, of course, is what causes dominant genes to be dominant. It would not be easy to give a complete or specific answer to this question. We can, however, say that in many cases a gene is dominant because it is capable of starting some process in the development of the organism which makes impossible the simultaneous or later development of a process which would be caused by the recessive gene, or because it acts to cover up the effect which will be produced by the recessive gene. In the case which has been most thoroughly analyzed in this respect, the inheritance of flower pigment (40), it has been found generally that dominant genes which bring about a specific change in the pigment molecule all *add* something to it. In this case one might say that the dominant gene adds a new feature to, rather than covers up, the action of the recessive.

In spite of the relative constancy of genes it has been found, by patient study of millions of organisms, that certain genes do occasionally change. These changes (as well as certain other types of abrupt changes in the genetic mechanism) are referred to as mutation. We shall discuss only gene mutations here. Some genes are more subject to mutation than are others. It is generally found that a new mutation is recessive to the gene ordinarily occupying that locus, or, as geneticists say, to the wild-type gene. This fact brings up the question of why new mutations are usually recessive and the whole question of the *origin* of dominance in genes.

Fisher (29) proposed a theory of the origin of dominance which has much plausibility and which is supported by some experimental results. Fisher points out that as a result of natural selection, each organism is a delicately adjusted system of genes analogous in some ways to a microscope focused exactly on a given object. Any random change in this arrangement is likely to be a change for the worse, just as even a slight random turn of the adjusting screw of the microscope is likely to make the focus worse instead of better. Thus we should expect that mutations on the whole would be deleterious. Now the mutation and its normal gene capable of occupying the same locus on the chromosome are not the only genes which can alter characteristics which they affect. Fisher suggested that by the action of natural selection, genes ("modifiers") which operate to cover up the effects of new deleterious genes would be favored. This would mean that eventually the new gene would no longer exert its characteristic effect when present, while the normal ("wild") gene would still be able to act as usual, even when paired with one of the mutant genes. The net result of this would be to transform the new gene into a recessive.

It is true that natural selection and other agencies will probably sooner or later eliminate the new gene. We know from experimental observation, however, that most mutations tend to occur repeatedly. But after the process of selection for modifiers as outlined above had gone on, the make-up of all or nearly all of the individuals of the species would be such that when the mutation occurred again later on, it would automatically be forced into being a recessive by genes previously selected to have this action on it. This might mean that for the majority of recurring mutations, the organism has its already prepared set of "modifiers" ready to keep the gene from doing any harm, especially as long as it is present only in the heterozygous condition.

There are a number of examples of how the presence of other genes may alter the degree of dominance of a certain gene. One of the earliest examples concerns the horns of domestic sheep. A certain gene present in single dose will produce horns in the males, but it must be present in double dose to produce horns in the female. Here sex evidently plays a role, perhaps endocrinologically, perhaps through the action of some of the other genes in the "female" X chromosome. Or again, it has been found in fowls that a certain gene which produces a type of plumage called frizzled, which is normally partially dominant, is converted into an almost complete recessive by the presence of a particular modifier gene if this latter gene occurs in double dose. Other examples of this effect will be found in the writings of Fisher (29) and of Huxley (43).

Objections to Fisher's Theory

Wright (72, 74) has criticized Fisher's theory of the origin of dominance, on the ground that the selection pressure found in nature would not be sufficient to achieve the required results in the

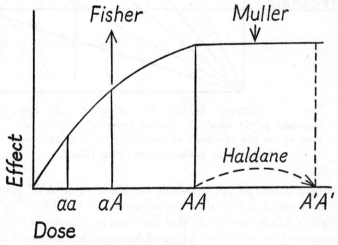

Figure 4. *Schematic representation of three theories of the origin of dominance (see text) (after Waddington).*

time available. Haldane (37) proposed rather similar criticisms of Fisher's theory, and suggested that the effect of natural selection on heterozygous harmful genes is to pick out, not a set of modifiers which act to suppress the action of the harmful gene, but a wild-type allele which has a considerable "margin of safety" in its action. This would give the same protective effect. In other words, Haldane supposed that if a wild-type gene A when homozygous (AA) produced the maximum "A" effect, but when heterozygous (i.e., Aa) did not, selection would favor the survival of another

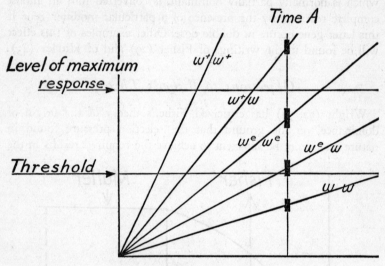

FIGURE 5. *Diagram showing how different gene combinations might result in various types of progeny, depending on the threshold of response of the organism to the action of various genes (after Glass).*

mutated allelomorph A′, in which the homozygote A′A′ reaches maximum effect, but so does the heterozygote A′a. (See Fig. 4.) Huxley (43), however, thinks that there can be little doubt that the dominance of the normal wild type allelomorphs has in general been achieved by such a mechanism as Fisher proposes. Plunkett and Muller independently (55) showed how the need for stability of gene-expression in development will secondarily result in the evolution of dominance (Fig. 5).

Experimentally, Ford (31) has been able to alter the dominance of a gene in the currant moth *Abraxas grossulariata*. This moth exists in two wild types. One of them (*lutea*) is due to a single gene difference which produces yellow instead of white ground color. Mated to the usual wild type, it normally produces an F_1 generation which is intermediate. By only four generations of plus and minus selection, Ford was able to make this gene either completely dominant, or completely recessive, whichever was desired.

The existence of dominant and recessive genes makes it possible for us to understand the phenomena referred to by breeders as sports, or throwbacks. In such cases an offspring displays a character found in ancestors more or less remote, but not exhibited by the immediate parents. If, for instance, skin color in man depended on a single pair of genes, with the gene for "black" skin dominant over that for "white" skin, it would be possible for two individuals with black skin to give birth to a white child, provided that each one of them carried one gene for black and one for white. In such a mating this "throwback" could happen on the average in 25 per cent of the cases. In studies on crosses between Negroes and whites in the United States, this is seldom if ever observed, so it seems obvious that more than two genes are involved in the determination of skin color. In fact, it is possible that a considerable number is involved. In the inheritance of fur color in rabbits, a number of genes, all capable of occupying the same chromosome locus, are thought to be involved (13). This leads to a brief discussion of such gene series, the members of which are called allelomorphs or alleles.

Multiple Alleles

In the case of the fruit fly, Drosophila, a series of genes has been observed, affecting eye color, which may produce colors ranging from the normal red of the Drosophila eye to coral, which is a very little lighter, to eosin, cherry, apricot, buff, tinged, and ivory, etc., to white. And even white is not quite equivalent of the entire absence of genes for eye color, for in the entire absence of eye color genes the eyes are even lighter in shade. Such a series of genes is called an allelomorphic series. Any adult organism, of course, possesses only two of these genes at a time, and any reproductive cell or gamete possesses only one of them at a time.

Where only two genes are available from any crossing, only three genetically different types of offspring are possible: an individual which is homozygous for the first gene, an individual homozygous for the second gene, and the individual which is heterozygous, that is, which has one gene of each kind. When a number of genes form the series of allelomorphs, the possible types are greater, and the number of different genotypes with n allelomorphs is equal to $\frac{n(n+1)}{2}$ (see 69). Thus the 8 allelic Rh genes now known in man (p. 243) make up 36 different genotypes.

Among the allelomorphic ("same locus") gene series which are known, most members of the series have some effect on the same characteristic of the organism. But this does not necessarily have to be so. In Drosophila, for instance, there is a gene which produces a disarrangement of the normal order of the rows of facets in the compound eye which this fly possesses. Another gene which can occupy the same locus in the chromosome seems to produce no effect on the eye but causes little scalloped incisions in the tips of the wings. The animal which is heterozygous for these two genes, that is, possesses one of each, is completely normal phenotypically and has neither the facet disarrangement nor the notches on the wings.

The knowledge that there may be a number of genes all having some effect on the same characteristic enables us to interpret the so-called continuous variability often observed in characters. Thus, although it is comparatively easy to classify men into four different blood groups which do not overlap, it is not possible to classify mankind into sharply different groups in regard to height (aside from perhaps the Pygmies), and we observe all sorts of gradations between tall men and short men, although stature is partly determined by heredity. To a certain extent skin color also furnishes an example of this type of continuous variability, and other examples, not relating to anthropology, have been observed in lower organisms, such as the rate of egg production in fowl, butter fat percentage in milk, and the yield of certain crop plants.

The existence of similar intergrading characters which cannot easily be classified into sharply distinct categories is partly responsible for the misunderstanding which for some time made many anthropologists reluctant to accept a genetic basis for *all* human physical traits. When cases of supposed continuous variability are thoroughly investigated genetically, however, they are found to be due to environment and/or to the effects of a considerable number of genes, acting generally two at a time, or in some cases acting several at a time, i.e. when more than one gene pair is involved ("multiple factors").

It would be possible to build up strains of Drosophila in which the eye color, even under identical environmental conditions, showed practically a continuous range from white to dark red, merely by making use of the allelomorphs which we have already mentioned above. No such artificial demonstration that apparently continuous variability can actually be due to the action of various combinations of discrete genes, which may be alleles or "multiple factors" (on different chromosomes), is necessary, however, for a situation identical in all essentials can be found in naturally occurring characteristics. Emerson and East (19), for example, in studying the inheritance of ear length in corn, found that by crossing a race of corn which produced short ears with one which produced long ears, it was possible in the second (F_2) generation to obtain plants which showed a variation of ear length covering the whole range found in the parents. The exact number of genes involved in this character has not been determined, but it has been pointed out (34) that it would be possible to explain the observed experimental results by assuming two pairs of genes acting without dominance, or by assuming a larger number of genes with partial or complete dominance.

Number and Size of Genes

While we are considering genes, it will be of interest to take up the question of how many genes are supposed to be contained in each gamete and what their approximate size may be. Considering the minuteness of the head of the spermatozoön, which we know must contain at least one out of every pair of genes which the adult organism is going to receive (ignoring cases where the Y chromosome has certain genes missing), we can see that a certain upper size limit can be set merely from considerations of space. To ascertain the size by discovering all the genes possessed by a given organism is obviously impossible, but an estimate of the number, plus the size of the sperm head, will give us at least the upper limit for the size of a given gene. In the chromosomes of the common fruit fly, Drosophila, more than 400 loci for recessive mutations have been recognized and others are constantly being discovered. It will, of course, be appreciated that the total number of genes possessed by this organism must be very much in excess of those which will come under laboratory observation as a result of mutation. The number of genes has been estimated by Muller and Prokofyeva (56), and by Gowan and Gay (35), by Gulick (36) and Huxley (43), as between a minimum of somewhat over 2000 and a maximum of something over 14,000, with a probable number of about 5000. The size of the gene in Drosophila must be between 10^{-8} and 10^{-5} cubic micra (μ^3) and probably between 10^{-7} and 10^{-6} μ^3. This is the equivalent of about 10 protein molecules of ordinary size. In some organisms the genes are apparently larger and in other organisms, as probably in man, they are considerably more numerous, say 4–5 times as many as in Drosophila. The size of the gene thus proves to be quite of the same order of magnitude as the size of certain virus particles, and it may be remarked that both of these are alike also in having the power of reproducing themselves very precisely.

The chromosomes of which we have already spoken are serial arrangements of a number of these genes. They may be looked upon, according to Huxley (43), as "super-molecules" built up out of genes and capable of breakage at points between the genes. Some non-genetic material is probably also present in the chromosomes. The number of chromosomes present in the organism tells us the number of groups of genes which are inherited independently of each other according to Mendel's second law.

Contributions from Remote Ancestors

In man there are 24 pairs of chromosomes in the nucleus of each cell, which means that 24 groups of genes will assort independently in inheritance. A little elementary arithmetic will enable us to draw some conclusions which are perfectly sound, but which will be rather startling to the more enthusiastic students of genealogy, some of whom are accustomed to tracing back their family lines to a single ancestor (such as William the Conqueror) who lived a considerable time ago. Any reader can readily supply examples of his own from knowledge of specific cases, from conversation, from popular books, and even, unfortunately, from some anthropological writings, in which it is supposed that the gene which determined traits of a remote ancestor accounts for the behavior of a present-day descendant.

It is obvious that the traditional genealogical methods entirely ignore the contribution of the females to the genetic material of the offspring, although we know that in any one mating, the female contributes exactly the same number of chromosomes as the male. Many genealogists have simply traced back successively through the male ancestors, ultimately arriving at some really or supposedly distinguished individual such as William the Conqueror. Even before we consider the specific number of chromosomes involved, it should be quite clear that scientifically this sort of thing is nonsense. Clearly a man's mother and her ancestors have the same chance as his father and his paternal ancestors to contribute to his heredity (33). We may say that the probability of her contribution is one half (see p. 377). The probability of a contribution from a grandparent is ¼, and from a great-grandparent ⅛, regardless of sex.

But, knowing that the various chromosomes can distribute themselves independently, we can discern a new, and what should be to the professional genealogists a more disturbing, possibility. You must receive one chromosome *of each pair* from each of your parents, but how about your grandparents? You had 4 grandparents each with 24 pairs of chromosomes to transmit, and you can have only 2 chromosomes in each pair. Looking at any particular pair of your chromosomes, therefore, it is clear that they represent only half of the genetic material which was potentially available to you from your grandparents. The half you happen to get is entirely a matter of chance. Thus, as Gulick (36) has pointed out, it is possible that either member of the pair of chromosomes we may be considering did not come from your grandfather, and more than that, there is a distinct though small *chance that not a single one* of your chromosomes came from that grandfather. The chance that you possess not even one chromosome from one grandparent (assuming no crossing-over in the interval) is 1 in 8,388,608. This is a small probability, but small though it is, it is a definite *possibility*. If we consider a more likely case, we find, for example, that there is about 1 chance in 300 that your grandfather did not contribute more than 5 chromosomes to the 48 with which you are equipped. No wonder you can be pretty different from your forebears, be they good or bad!

When more remote ancestors are considered, the likelihood that any particular one has made any considerable contribution to your heredity falls off very rapidly, and if we consider your 16 great-great-grandparents, there is somewhat better than an even chance that some of them will not have contributed a single chromosome to your inheritance. This has taken us back only four generations, or roughly 100 years; going back two generations more we reach a situation in which there are already more ancestors than chromosomes, so that it is literally impossible that you can have a whole chromosome from each of these 64 ancestors potentially represented in your genetic make-up.

Of course the number of *genes* is much more numerous than the number of chromosomes, and we shall see later that it is possible for genes to get transferred from one chromosome to another and thus to behave to a slight extent independently. Since we have seen that there is reason to believe that the genes are limited in number, and since we suppose that in man the number is something of the order of 20,000 to 42,000 (66), we find that if we go back *only 500 years,* we arrive at a time when there must have been many of our ancestors from whom we cannot have inherited even so much as a *single gene*. Of course, if there has been extensive inbreeding in the family line, the number of ancestors is somewhat less than the hypothetical 2^n at the nth generation. The degree of inbreeding which has existed in most countries known to us, however, is not sufficient to make any great difference in the calculations which we have been making. It seems abundantly clear, therefore, that even if you are able to trace your ancestry back to William the Conqueror, or Confucius or Saladin, the chances are pretty remote that your genetic constitution is any more similar to theirs than to that of any one of a large number of people who were alive at the same time. Gulick (36) and Glass (34) have suggested that this news should be kept quiet for fear that it might dishearten the many who are so enthusiastic about genealogies and pedigrees. Since, however, these conclusions will be found vitally to affect certain arguments which have been offered by early anthropological writers, I have felt obliged to violate the confidence of the geneticists and present the facts here to the public.

Gene Symbols

We said a few words about gene symbols at the beginning of this chapter. No attempt will be made to give a complete treatment of the subject, but an outline of present usage may be offered. For a long time it has been the custom in dealing with the genetics of the lower forms to give to all genes belonging to an allelomorphic series the same basic symbol, and to distinguish one member of the series from another by capitalizing it or by adding a superscript. For instance, the piebald alleles of the house mouse are designated as S and s, and the allelomorphic series of genes affecting the guinea pig coat color are designated as C, c^k, c^d, c^r, and c^a. However, these rules have generally not been applied to human alleles, perhaps because most of what little is known about human heredity has to a large extent been discovered by medical men and other scientists who were not geneticists, and did not follow genetic conventions. Geneticists and anthropologists, conversely, have on the whole concerned themselves surprisingly little with the very important question of *human* inheritance.

The best understood series of genes in man are the genes which determine the occurrence of various specific antigens in the blood, or, in other words, the genes which determine the blood groups and blood types. The mechanism of inheritance of the classical blood groups which is now known to be correct was proposed by a mathematician, Felix Bernstein, and the symbols suggested for the genes were R, A, and B. Bernstein later substituted O for R. These genes will be discussed in Chapter VIII. The mechanism of the inheritance of the M, N blood types was worked out by two immunologists, Karl Landsteiner and Philip Levine. The symbols proposed for the genes were M and N. Later on Strandskov, followed by certain other geneticists, proposed replacing these symbols by others which would be consistent with previous practice in the genetics of other species. The accompanying Table 4 will show the old and proposed new designations.

TABLE 4

Proposed Symbols for Blood Grouping Genes

	Original Symbols	Strandskov's Proposed New Symbols
Classical groups	O, A, B	i, I^A, I^B
M, N types	M, N	A^M, A^N

Unfortunately the symbols proposed by Strandskov are not entirely free from objection, because they might possibly cause some confusion, especially in the minds of students and medical men unfamiliar with genetic terminology. Since practically all of the extensive original research on blood groups was and is published in medical journals, and employs the older terminology, I have not thought it desirable to introduce the proposed new terminology into the text of this book, especially since geneticists and other authorities who work in the field have not yet agreed on any single proposed new set of symbols. In this book, therefore, I shall follow the traditional designation of human blood group genes, even though admitting that it is desirable that they should eventually be altered to conform with the practice of geneticists in general. We shall begin a study of the human blood-grouping genes and their anthropological significances in Chapter VIII.

Mechanism of Gene Action

Exactly how each gene produces its effects is not known. There is no general rule. A logical hypothesis for the mechanism of the formation of the blood group antigen A, for instance, would be that the gene for A was simply one molecule, or several molecules, of the group A substance and that in some way it could cause itself to be duplicated (as viruses can) in the cells of the body during development. There is no adequate way of testing such a hypothesis, since the hypothetical amount of A constituting a gene is far below the limits of detectability, but it is at any rate extremely unlikely that *every* single chemical substance present in the mature organism is determined by a special gene. There are simply too many substances present at the end. The role of genes is more likly to be found in some effect on chemical reactions and rates of reaction in the developing organism.

An illustration from a lower form of life will assist us to understand how the determining factor in the formation of the chemical substance is not necessarily that substance itself. The micro-organisms known as pneumococci can be separated into more than 40 groups, based on the presence of different carbohydrates in the capsule which surrounds them. It has recently been shown, however (2), that the substance which determines the production of a given carbohydrate in the capsule is itself a nucleoprotein which apparently contains none of the carbohydrate at all. The carbohydrate alone is unable to stimulate the pneumococcus to produce more of the carbohydrate, but the nucleoprotein, added to organisms which would normally develop without capsules, causes the production of a capsule containing the particular polysaccharide it sponsors. How it does this we are unable to say, and, of course, we do not know at all whether the action of genes in the higher forms is similar to this process. The general question of the physiology of the gene and the mechanism of gene action has been admirably discussed by Wright (74) and Beadle (6) in reviews to which the reader may turn for further information.

Glass (34) points out that, since the results of gene action are chemical, these reactions may have their rates controlled by (a) physical factors, such as temperature, light, dilution of reactants, etc., or (b) chemical factors, such as the hydrogen ion concentration (or pH) or (c) by catalysts. It has been found in the study of the genetics of flower pigmentation that genes do exist which control the pH (acidity) in localized portions of the plant. It is probable that genes in general exert their effects by processes (b) or (c), since the physical factors affecting the organism are generally beyond its control.

It should not be concluded, however, that environment has no effect on the manifestation of the gene. On the contrary, in a great many cases a particular environment is indispensable for the normal manifestation of the gene effect. This question will be discussed further in Chapter III. Here we will simply emphasize once more that we must sharply distinguish in our minds between the genotype, which is determined purely by the genetic constitution, and the phenotype, that is, the visible or detectable aspect of the organism, which is determined partly by the genetic constitution and partly by the environment.

General Physiological Effects of Genes

We have already pointed out that human genetic nomenclature is not quite in line with that used by most geneticists for the lower forms. Even in the lower forms, however, it is impossible to devise a nomenclature which will take into account all of the facts about a gene, and indeed, no attempt is made to do so.

The usual system of naming genes is based on the principle of naming them for whatever is the most prominent (or the first discovered) effect produced by them. Thus in speaking of a mutation in Drosophila which is called white, we mean the gene which changes the eye color from the normal red to white. The gene "vestigial" causes vestigial wings. The gene "stubbloid" produces a form with shorter bristles, etc. This system of naming is convenient and will certainly be retained, but it must not be supposed that these genes affect *only* the characteristics implied by their names. On the contrary, there is reason to believe that practically every gene which the organism possesses exerts some effect on almost all the other characteristics. Thus the gene "vestigial" not only reduces wing size, but it modifies the balancers, causes certain bristles to be erect instead of horizontal, changes the wing muscles, changes the shape of the spermatheca and alters the rate of growth, the fecundity, and the length of life.

As another illustration of the general physiological effect of genes, we may take the gene for albinism. This gene produces an absence of pigment in the superficial layers of the body, including the eyes. But this does not seem to be its only effect. In mice, rats, and rabbits, the albino gene has a pronounced effect also on the disposition. White rats, mice, and rabbits are much more tame than their fully pigmented relatives, even when they come from the same litter, and it is partly for this reason that they are generally preferred as pets.

A more general proof of the multiple effects of genes comes from the study of deficiencies in the chromosomes which result from the losses of small portions during the processes of cell division and gametogenesis. In some cases, these losses are so small that they probably involve not over a single gene or two. Relatively few such deficiencies have been studied which are not lethal to the organism when they are present in the homozygous condition. Most of them are lethal even to single cells if these cells are homozygous for the lethal, even when these cells are surrounded by heterozygous cells and the organism as a whole is capable of life and growth.

We may conclude from this that the function of the gene is far more vital than merely producing a change in the color of the eye, the shape of the wing, or characteristics of the hair. These are only superficial aspects of the action of the gene. Most genes which the organism possesses are evidently absolutely essential to the proper growth and development of each individual organism and each individual cell. We may discount in advance, therefore, any attempt to belittle an anthropological classification based on genetic differences which starts by stating that these differences are not important. Genes are the very stuff of life itself.

The Same Effect from Different Genes

Having seen that one gene may exert a multiplicity of effects on the organism, we must now consider a proposition which is practically the converse of this, namely, that the same effect, or what is to all appearances the same effect, may be produced sometimes by quite different combinations of genes. The genes which produce a lack of pigment in the fur and eyes of certain species (albinism) are generally recessive, and must be present in double dose to produce their characteristic effect. However, in certain species dominant genes for albinism have been discovered, and these, even when present only in a single dose, produce an appearance practically indistinguishable from that produced by a double dose of the recessive gene. Some genes are even known which, although they occur on different chromosomes, appear to be duplicates of one another and produce identical effects (70, 68). Traits which are determined by independent "duplicate" genes are represented by feathered shanks in poultry and the typical triangular, rather than ovoid, seed capsules of the weed called shepherd's-purse. In such cases only $\frac{1}{16}$ of the F_2 offspring will express the recessive trait. A somewhat similar instance occurs in hogs, where there are two dominant genes, each belonging to a different pair of chromosomes. Either gene when present alone produces a typical sandy color, but when they are present together the effect is additive and the characteristic red color of the Duroc-Jersey breed is obtained. The double recessive is white.

Action of Genes in Man

It is harder to give an example of this same situation in human heredity because so little is known of the subject, but it is stated by Baur, Fischer, and Lenz (4) that the same ratio of head breadth to head length can be the result of quite different bone formations in different human races. It is logical to suppose that such different bone formations are the result of different combinations of genes.

The basic genetic principles discussed above have been found to have an astonishingly general application to all living forms, whenever an attempt has been made to apply them; actual detailed knowledge of the genetic structure of an organism is available, however, only in the case of a few well-studied species. Of these, the classical example is the fruit fly, *Drosophila melanogaster*. It is with this organism that much of the classical work was done, beginning with the work of Morgan and his school (52).

Many of the genes which have been studied in Drosophila produce slight or relatively unimportant effects. At one time this fact led certain biologists to attack the gene theory, and to suggest that the really important features of organisms were not caused by genes but were determined in some other way. This point of view did not prevail, however, and today few biologists doubt that all our inherited characteristics are determined by genes, acting in the particular environment in which we develop.

Certain genes having very vital and important effects have been observed; for instance, in man a dominant mutation which results in the congenital absence of hands and feet has been studied (19). Few readers who have seen the pathetic picture of a family so afflicted would be willing to state that this is a gene having only a minor effect (see Fig. 6).

Another illustration of an important effect which a single gene can have is furnished by Fisher's discovery (30) that the gene which,

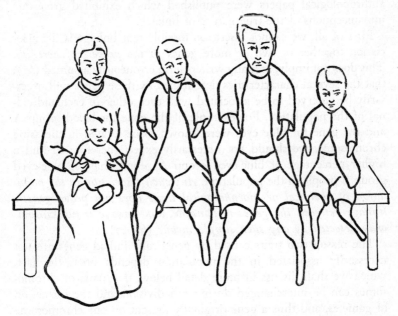

FIGURE 6. *Hereditary absence of hands and feet, presumably due to the action of a single gene (after Mohr).*

when heterozygous, produces the ornamental feature called crest in the common domestic fowl, when homozygous produces cerebral hernia, a condition which is very often fatal to the fowl.

Linkage

Since the genes are arranged in serial fashion in the structures called chromosomes, and since the chromosomes assort independently in inheritance, it is natural to predict that all the genes in a single chromosome will be found associated with each other in the offspring possessing that chromosome. This "sticking together" of the genes in inheritance, due to their being in the same chromosome, is called linkage, and we must now examine in somewhat more detail what linkage is and what it is not. It is especially important to know what linkage is *not,* for a number of early anthropological papers were published which exhibited grotesque misconceptions of the true nature of linkage.

First of all, we cannot assert too forcibly that linkage is the association together of two or more genes *in the process of heredity.* This does not imply, as many writers have erroneously assumed (67), that the several characteristics determined by these genes will necessarily be observed to be associated with each other in each individual of the population. For example, if the gene for blood group A and the gene for blue eyes were known to be located in the same chromosome, we should not necessarily expect therefore to find a higher percentage of blue-eyed group A people than of blue-eyed group B people in the population. *Any such association in the population of chemical or morphological traits does not prove genetic linkage between the genes responsible, and linkage is not customarily detected by any such simple means* (60, 67).

The reason two traits caused by genetically linked genes are not necessarily associated in the population depends upon the fact, which we shall discuss in more detail below, that parts of chromosomes can be interchanged during cell division and the formation of gametes, and thus a gene originally present on one chromosome of a pair may come to be on the opposite chromosome of the pair. This step is called "crossing-over" and it occurs frequently enough to destroy, within the space of relatively few generations, any original association of the characteristics in the population. To return to our hypothetical illustration, crossing-over will sooner or later produce chromosomes which will have the blood group gene A associated with genes for darker eye color and chromosomes for blood groups other than A will be formed which will have on them the gene for blue eyes. The result will eventually be a mixture of physical types such as blue eyes, group A; blue eyes, group B; blue eyes, group O, etc., in the same proportions which would be found if the genes responsible were on different chromosomes, so that a mere inspection of the population will not enable us to tell whether or not these two gene series are genetically linked.

In practice, genetic linkage is detected by observing that the two genes are always associated in inheritance. At first sight such observation may seem impossible, since crossing-over has usually resulted in the production of all the different combinations of the two gene series on various chromosomes of the pair which will be found in the population. However, an inspection of the accompanying illustration (Table 5) will show that, under ordinary circumstances,

TABLE 5

Backcross in Maize Demonstrating Linkage
(Contrast Table 1)

$$\frac{S\ su}{Lala}\ \textrm{♂} \times \frac{susu}{lala}\ \textrm{♀}$$

Sperms (pollen)

Eggs	$S\ La$	$sula$	$(S\ la)$	$(suLa)$
$\dfrac{su}{la}$	$\dfrac{S\ su}{Lala}$ 45.5%	$\dfrac{susu}{lala}$ 45.5%	$\dfrac{S\ su}{lala}$ 4.5%	$\dfrac{susu}{Lala}$ 4.5%

The symbol S stands for a dominant gene producing starchy kernels, su for a recessive producing sugary kernels; la stands for a recessive gene producing "lazy" sprawling type of growth of the stalks, La for its dominant normal allele. The types of sperm in parentheses are produced by crossing-over. In the absence of crossing-over, linkage would be complete and only two of the four possible types of offspring would be produced. The inequality in frequencies of the various types is a measure of the degree of linkage (p. 74).

linkage of the two genes will be demonstrated by the fact that from any given combination of parents only certain of the theoretically possible types of offspring will be produced, whereas if the genes were on different chromosome pairs and thus assorted independently, all the possible types would be produced with the theoretical frequencies.

The first known case of linkage was found in the sweet pea in 1906 (34). It was found that the gene for purple flowers and the gene for cylindrical pollen grains were inherited together, or, conversely, that the gene for red flowers and that for disk-shaped pollen were linked.

A type of genetic linkage which is particularly easy to detect is sex linkage. This occurs when a gene is carried in one of the so-called sex chromosomes. It will do no harm if we oversimplify the

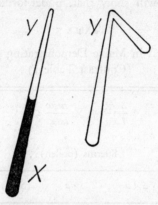

FIGURE 7. *Diagram of the human X and Y chromosomes, showing the homologous regions.*

real situation a bit and state that in man, as in a number of other organisms, sex is determined by a particular one of the 24 pairs of chromosomes, and that the female is produced from a fertilized ovum containing 2 such chromosomes, both of the same kind (they are called the X chromosomes), and the male is produced when the two members of the chromosome pair are not alike, one being the so-called Y chromosome (Fig. 7). From data compiled on organisms that have been rather thoroughly studied, such as the fruit fly, it has been concluded that the Y chromosome, the presence of which determines maleness (or we might perhaps better say that it takes two X chromosomes to determine femaleness), contains very few genes of any sort. In fact it seems to be practically inert, genetically.* This means that genes in the X chromosome, even when they are recessive, will not have their expression repressed in the male, since

---

* The homologous portion of the Y chromosome in mammals seems to have quite a few genes.

there exist no corresponding genes in the Y chromosome which is paired with the X chromosome and thus there is nothing to repress their effect. As an example of such genes, we may mention the deficiency in clotting power of the blood which is called hemophilia. Another example is the inheritance of "ordinary" red-green color blindness.

It seems clear that the gene for color blindness (of the sort to which we have referred) is in the X chromosome and that it is a

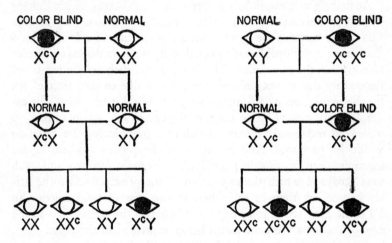

FIGURE 8. *Diagrammatic representation of the supposed mode of inheritance of ordinary (red-green) color blindness. The symbol X indicates a normal X chromosome; X^c indicates an X chromosome which carries the gene for color blindness.*

recessive. The female having only one such gene therefore will still have normal color vision, because of the dominant action of the normal gene in the other X chromosome, but the male having one such gene will be color-blind because of the absence in the Y chromosome of the dominant gene, which would otherwise suppress the action of the color-blind gene. A mating between a color-blind male and a homozygous normal woman would produce normal males and normal females. It will be seen from the diagram, however, that the female offspring will carry in one of their X chromosomes color-blind genes. Consequently, on the average, half of their sons will be color-blind. Color blindness is fairly common in men, running at least as high as 5 per cent in some populations, but it is quite rare in women. An inspection of the diagram will show that for a woman to be color-blind, it is necessary for her father to be color-blind and for her mother either to carry the color-blind gene in a single dose or, which is of course much less likely, to be herself color-blind.

At first sight it might be thought that the existence of sex linkage disproves the earlier statement that linkage is detected by association of two traits in the population, for in the case of color blindness there is unquestionably an association between maleness and color blindness in the population. The point is that such association is not necessarily due to sex linkage, but may be due to the effect of sex on the expression of an autosomal gene. If color blindness, for example, were caused by an autosomal gene which was dominant in males but recessive in females, much the same picture of association would be produced. And human traits have been studied, as, for example, taste reaction to phenyl-thio-carbamide (10, 20) and baldness (40a), in which the expression of the gene seemed to be better in one sex than in the other. In the case of taste reaction to PTC the gene seems to be expressed better in the female, but in the case of baldness the gene seems better expressed in the male.

Sex-linked inheritance can be distinguished from autosomal sex-limited or sex-influenced inheritance only by the study of descendants of affected males (61). To determine whether an apparently sex-linked character could reach full expression in females, homozygous individuals from matings between female carriers and affected males would have to be examined.

More than twenty examples are known of genes which are apparently carried in the X chromosome of man. It is clear that any two of these genes will be themselves genetically linked since they are carried on the same chromosome, and the study of human pedigrees supports this idea. In 1937, Dr. Julia Bell and Professor J. B. S. Haldane studied six pedigrees in which both hemophilia and color blindness occurred (7). They found a close degree of linkage between the two factors, which means that if a hemophiliac is color-blind, a majority of his hemophiliac relatives will also be color-blind. Conversely, if a person is not a hemophiliac, but is color-blind, then a majority of his hemophiliac relatives will not be color-blind. Further details on linkage and crossing-over in the human sex chromosome will be found in papers by White (71), Riddell (59), and Kloeppfer (45).

The existence of linkage means that unexpected results will sometimes be found to follow domestic selection even though the experimenter or breeder may be selecting for a gene which in itself does not seem to be very important. For example, the absence of horns in goats is inherited as a simple dominant. Hornlessness is considered a desirable cosmetic feature and selection for it has been practiced by pedigree goat breeders for some time. It has only recently been pointed out by Asdell (1) that there seems to be a close linkage between the gene for hornlessness and a gene which, acting as a simple recessive, causes some of the potential females to become intersexes and not usable in breeding. The latter characteristic of course is deleterious to the economic value of the stock.

Linkage in man, except between characteristics carried on the sex chromosomes, has only recently been demonstrated, for the M, N blood types and sickle cell anemia (65). A few doubtful examples were previously known (12a). Since the exact genetic mechanism of only a few human characteristics is known, this is perhaps not surprising. The best known characteristics of men, genetically speaking, are the various blood groups and blood types, and if linkage other than sex linkage is to be found in the near future, it is to be expected that it will be between blood groups and some other characteristic. A number of possibilities have been investigated without yielding certain evidence of linkage (11, 21–28, 8, 65, 45).

That genetic linkage between blood types and other features such as morphological characteristics is possible is shown by the recent detection of such a case of linkage in the rabbit by Sawin and others (63).

Crossing-Over

Crossing-over evidently occurs during the phase of cell division during which the homologous chromosomes of each pair are lying very close together and are twisted about each other. Later on, as they loosen up, they form a number of nodes and internodes. (See Fig. 9.) It is believed that these nodes indicate that the homologous chromosomes have broken at these points and equivalent segments have been interchanged between the two pairs. (Fig. 10a.) The way the breaking apart and reattachment of parts of chromo-

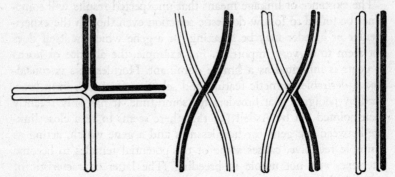

FIGURE 9. *Diagram showing how contact between chromosomes and formation of chiasmata results in interchange of genetic material (after Glass).*

somes may alter the arrangement of genes is shown in Figure 10b, taken from Dobzhansky. In Figure 10b, (A) shows normal chromosomes; (B) shows a deficiency resulting from the loss of part of a chromosome; (C) shows a duplication resulting from the attachment of part of the white chromosome to the black; (D) shows a "translocation" (transposition of parts of chromosomes); (E) a homozygous translocation; (F) a heterozygous inversion; (G) a homozygous inversion.

As pointed out by Sturtevant in 1913, if the genes are really arranged in a linear series in the chromosomes, then the farther apart two genes lie, the higher the chance of a cross-over between them. From this it follows that the frequency of cross-over enables us to estimate the distance apart, in terms of arbitrary units, of the different genes on the same chromosome. Suppose we are studying three genes which we may call *P, Q,* and *R.* Let us suppose that *P* and *Q* cross over 4 per cent of the time and *P* and *R* cross over 10 per cent of the time. We thus suppose that *Q* is 4 units from *P* and *R* is 10 units from *P.* The question now arises how far from

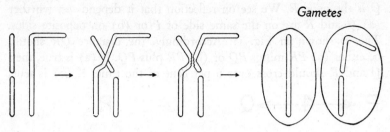

FIGURE 10a. *Diagrammatic representation of crossing over, showing interchange of genetic material.*

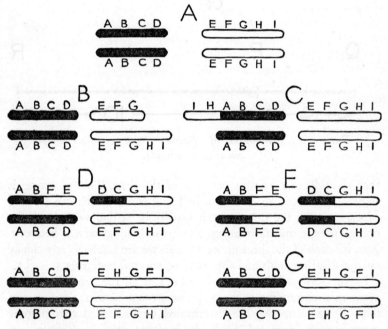

FIGURE 10b. *Diagrammatic representation of results of breakage and reattachment of parts of chromosomes. (a) Normal chromosomes; (b) Deficiency; (c) Duplication; (d) Heterozygous translocation; (e) Homozygous translocation; (f) Heterozygous inversion; (g) Homozygous inversion (after Dobzhansky).*

Q is the gene R. We see on reflection that it depends on whether (a) Q and R are on the same side of P or (b) on opposite sides. This is shown in Fig. 11. Accordingly, the distance QR should be either (a) PR minus PQ or (b) PR plus PQ. If (a) is true, then Q and R should cross over 6 per cent of the time. If (b) is true,

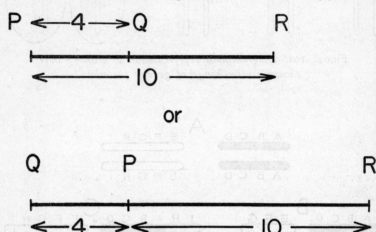

FIGURE 11. *Estimation of distance from cross-over frequencies (see text).*

they should cross over 14 per cent of the time. This of course is something which can be tested. In lower forms which can be bred experimentally, the question can usually be settled very simply by doing an experimental mating with an individual who is heterozygous for each of the three genes. In man we are forced to rely chiefly on statistical methods and the study of selected pedigrees.

By the study of the cross-over values of all the genes known to occur in a chromosome, the order of arrangement of the genes in that chromosome may be determined and so-called chromosome maps may be prepared. Such chromosome maps have been prepared for *Drosophila melanogaster* and are shown in Figure 12. The exact details of computation are irrelevant for our purpose here and will be found in any good textbook on genetics, such as those by Waddington (70), by Sturtevant and Beadle (68), and by Glass (34). It has been possible to test the accuracy of maps of

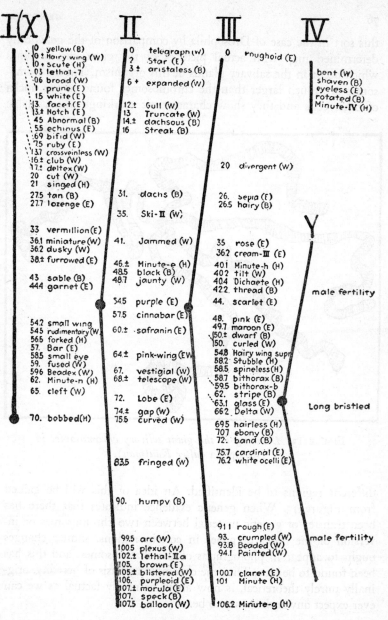

FIGURE 12. *Chromosome map of* Drosophila (*after Bridges*).

this sort in the case of Drosophila by comparison of the genetically determined map with actual pictures of the giant chromosomes which occur in the salivary glands of this organism. These chromosomes are much larger than the chromosomes found in the nuclei of other cells and they show characteristic markings which enable

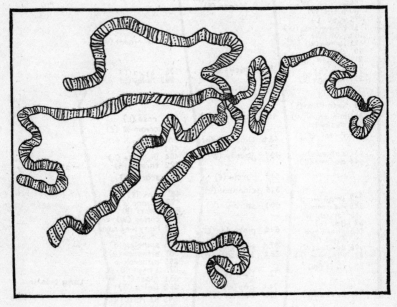

FIGURE 13. *Drawing of the giant salivary chromosomes in* Drosophila (*after Kaufman*).

different regions to be identified. An idea of this will be gained from Figure 13. When genetic evidence indicates that there has been transfer of genetic material between two chromosomes or inversion of the order of genes in certain regions, similar changes ought to appear in photographs of the chromosomes, and this has been found to be true. Thus the chromosome basis of heredity, originally purely theoretical, is now about as nearly factual as we can ever expect any such theory to be.

Differences Between Genes

There are two terms applying to the manifestation of genes which we will have some occasion to use. The first is called *expressivity* and is a measure of the amount or kind of effect shown in an individual possessing the gene. The second is called *penetrance* and is frequently measured as the percentage of individuals who, when they possess the gene, show any effect from it. Naturally, most of the genes which have been chosen for experimental work with the lower forms show a very high or complete penetrance; in other words, every organism homozygous for a recessive factor will show its effects. They have been chosen partly on account of this. But complete penetrance is not always found and incomplete penetrance is observed with a good many genes. The frequency with which the gene is effective in producing its effect depends both on the environment and on the genotype, the effectiveness in the heterozygous condition being often less. A good example of environmental influence is found in the gene "giant" (32) in *D. melanogaster*. Here lack of sufficient food for the larvae results in fewer giants. The *expressivity* of this gene is nearly uniform, all giants being nearly the same size relative to the normal. Such genes would seldom be used in experimental work with lower forms. In man, however, we cannot pick and choose our material to the same extent, but must take it as it comes, and we shall have to deal with some genes which do not show complete penetrance. Differences in the penetrance of the gene which determines a person's ability to taste the synthetic substance, phenyl-thio-carbamide, might be expressed to some extent by differences in the age at which this ability is manifested (39). In the case of deleterious genes, of course, natural selection would tend to postpone more and more the age of onset of the symptoms, possibly by the selection of suitable modifying genes.

Genetics and Anthropology

It is an unfortunate historical accident that Mendel's work was neglected by his contemporaries, and that the science of genetics was so late in developing. Genetic methods are now beginning to be employed by physical anthropologists (50, 18, 12, 9, 42), but the biometrical approach to anthropology was already well under way before modern quantitative genetics developed, and until recently anthropologists have on the whole not been influenced by modern genetics, and have not always utilized its concepts correctly. Thus Hogben was led to say in 1931 that "systematic biology in general and physical anthropology in particular have pursued their course with a serenity unimpaired by the results of experimental investigation. This is perhaps because geneticists have courteously refrained from commenting on the devastating consequences of their discoveries" (41).

It must be admitted that ignorance of the real nature of the genetic mechanism seems to have been at one time regrettably widespread among certain groups of anthropologists. The reader can still readily verify this fact by discussing with almost any of the older anthropologists practically any genetic phenomenon; for example, that of dominance. He will find that there are a good many who labor under the misconception that if a character is "dominant" genetically, it is bound to become more and more frequent in the population and will eventually replace the alternative "recessive" gene altogether.

As we shall point out below (p. 412), in the absence of mutation or selection, equilibrium between the frequencies of the two autosomal genes is reached after one generation of random mating. After this time no over-all decrease in recessives, or increase in dominants, will take place. Another illustration of the unfamiliarity with genetics on the part of anthropologists is provided by the quotation from Morant (51), already given in the first chapter, in which he supposes that characters of the skeleton must in general be more stable in an evolutionary sense than characters of the soft tissues. There seems to be not the slightest shred of evidence to justify this supposition.

Another illustration may be taken from a book (47) by J. de la H. Marett written in 1936. This author was perhaps not what is properly called a practicing anthropologist, and it is possible that if he had not lost his life during the Second World War his opinions might have changed later on. The chief reason for referring to his book now is that at the time of its appearance a number of persons working in anthropology and other persons with anthropological interests read and recommended the book, and apparently took the opinions expressed in it seriously. Some of these opinions were stimulating and perhaps not incorrect (p. 94), but throughout the book the author exhibited a regrettable and pathetic ignorance of the basic foundations of genetics, although he freely mentioned the subject. Few will fail to see that the author was poorly versed in genetic principles if they read Marett's statement made on page 38 of his book.

"It is reasonable to attribute to horns a value for the purpose of offense and defense. Males use them to fight each other for the possession of the females. It is thus legitimate to assume a linkage between the genes making for growth of horns and those which encourage a combative attitude to other males. Now the immature males do not fight with the adults, and there is no reason to believe that most of them even attempt to do so. I conclude, therefore, that the inhibition of horn growth and the inhibition of the combative instinct is likewise linked; and, seeing that the growth of horn in the female is repressed; and that she does not fight the male, it seems probable that they are both sex-linked." It seems just possible that the failure of the females to fight the males, in Marett's example, might be due to something other than a gene repressing the natural combative attitude of males to males, and it is hard to believe that a book containing such unfounded speculations and misconceptions was ever taken seriously. It is to be hoped that any person who has read the present chapter would at once detect the illogical nature of such a passage.

REFERENCES FOR CHAPTER II

1. Asdell, S. A., *Science, 99,* 124 (1944).
2. Avery, O. T., C. M. MacLeod, and M. McCarty, *J. E. M., 79,* 137-158 (1944).
3. Babcock, E. B., and R. E. Clausen, *Genetics in Relation to Agriculture.* McGraw-Hill, New York, 1918.
4. Bauer, E., E. Fischer, and F. Lenz, *Menschliche Erblichkeitslehre.* J. F. Lehmanns Verlag, München, 1927.
5. Bateson, W., and R. C. Punnett, *Proc. Roy. Soc. B, 84,* 3-8 (1911).
6. Beadle, G. W., *Chem. Rev., 37,* 15-96 (1945).
7. Bell, J., and J. B. S. Haldane, *Proc. Roy. Soc. B, 123,* 119 (1937).
8. Bernstein, F., H. L. Borison, and S. Finkel, *J. Imm., 46,* 245-248 (1943).

9. Birdsell, J. B., *Viking Yearbook of Physical Anthropology*, 1946.
10. Boyd, W. C., and L. G. Boyd, *Ann. Eug., 8*, 46–51 (1937).
11. Boyd, W. C., and L. G. Boyd, *Ann. Eug., 11*, 1–9 (1940).
12. Brues, A. M., *A. J. P. A., 4*, 1–36 (1946).
12a. Burks, B., *Proc. Nat. Acad. Sci., 24*, 512–519 (1938).
13. Castle, W. E., *Genetics and Eugenics*. Harvard Univ. Press, Cambridge, 1927.
14. Chetverikov, S. S., *J. Exper. Biol.* (Russian), *2*, 3–54 (1926).
15. Dobzhansky, Th., *Genetics and the Origin of Species*. Columbia Univ. Press, New York, 1941.
16. Dobzhansky, Th., *The Teaching Biologist, 12*, 97–106 (1943).
17. Dobzhansky, Th., and B. Spassky, *Genetics, 29*, 270–290 (1944).
18. Dunn, L. C., and Th. Dobzhansky, *Heredity, Race, and Society*. Penguin Books, New York, 1946.
19. Emerson, R. A., and E. M. East, *Bull. Agric. Exper. Stat. Neb., 2*, 1–120 (1913).
20. Falconer, D. S., *Ann. Eug., 13*, 211–222 (1947).
21. Finney, D. J., *Ann. Eug., 9*, 203–207 (1939).
22. Finney, D. J., *Ann. Eug., 10*, 171–214 (1940).
23. Finney, D. J., *Ann. Eug., 11*, 10–30 (1941).
24. Finney, D. J., *Ann. Eug., 11*, 115–135 (1941).
25. Finney, D. J., *Ann. Eug., 11*, 224–232 (1942).
26. Finney, D. J., *Ann. Eug., 11*, 233–244 (1942).
27. Finney, D. J., *J. Heredity, 33*, 157–160 (1942).
28. Finney, D. J., *Ann. Eug., 12*, 31–43 (1943).
29. Fisher, R. A., *The Genetical Theory of Natural Selection*. Clarendon Press, Oxford, 1930.
30. Fisher, R. A., *Science, 80*, 288–289 (1934).
31. Ford, E. B., *Ann. Eug., 10*, 227–252 (1940).
32. Gabritschevsky, E., and C. B. Bridges, *Z. I. A. V., 46*, 248–284 (1928).
33. Galton, F., cited in: Newman, H. H., *Evolution, Genetics and Eugenics*. Univ. of Chicago Press, Chicago, 1925.
34. Glass, B., *Genes and the Man*. N. Y. Bureau of Pub., Teachers College, Columbia University, 1943.
35. Gowen, J. W., and E. H. Gay, *Genetics, 18*, 1–31 (1933).
36. Gulick, A., *Quart. Rev. Biol., 13*, 1–18, 140–168 (1938).
37. Haldane, J. B. S., *Am. Nat., 64*, 87–90 (1930).
38. Haldane, J. B. S., *Ann. Eug., 7*, 28–57 (1936).
39. Haldane, J. B. S., *J. Genetics, 61*, 149–157 (1941).
40. Haldane, J. B. S., *New Paths in Genetics*. Harper & Bros., New York and London, 1942.
40a. Harris, H., *Ann. Eug., 13*, 172–181 (1946).
41. Hogben, L., *Genetic Principles in Medicine and Social Science*. G. Allen & Unwin, Ltd., London, 1931.
42. Hooton, E. A., *Up from the Ape*. Macmillan Co., New York, 2nd Edition, 1946.

43. Huxley, J., *Evolution, the Modern Synthesis.* Harper & Bros., New York and London, 1942.

44. Iltis, H., *Life of Mendel.* G. Allen & Unwin, Ltd., London, 1924.

45. Kloeppfer, H. W., *Ann. Eug., 13,* 35–71 (1946).

46. Landauer, W., *Arch. Int. Pharmacodynamie et de Thérap., 56,* 121–129 (1937).

47. Marett, J. R., de la H., *Race, Sex, and Environment.* London, 1936.

48. Mendel, G. J., *Experiments in Plant Hybridization.* Harvard Univ. Press (translated by Roy. Horticulture Soc., London), 1948.

49. Mohr, O. L., *Heredity and Disease.* W. W. Norton & Co., New York, 1934.

50. Montagu, M. F. A., *An Introduction to Physical Anthropology.* Charles C. Thomas, Springfield, 1945.

51. Morant, G. M., *J. Roy. Anthrop. Inst., 66,* 43 (1936).

52. Morgan, T. H., *The Theory of the Gene.* Yale Univ. Press, New Haven, 1926.

53. Muller, H. J., *Proc. Int. Cong. Plant Sci., 1,* 897–921 (1929).

54. Muller, H. J., *Proc. 6th Int. Cong. Genetics,* 213–255 (1932).

55. Muller, H. J., *J. Genetics, 30,* 407–414 (1935).

56. Muller, H. J., and H. A. Prokofyeva, *Proc. Nat. Acad. Sci., 21,* 16–26 (1935).

57. Painter, T. S., *J. Heredity, 25,* 465–476 (1934).

58. Pearl, R., *J. Wash. Acad. Sci., 25,* No. 6, 253–296 (1935).

59. Riddell, W. J. B., *Ann. Eug., 13,* 30–34 (1946).

60. Rife, D. C., *Human Biol., 11,* 546–548 (1939).

61. Rundales, R. W., and H. F. Falls, *A. J. M. Sci., 211,* 641–658 (1946).

62. Russell, E. S., *The Interpretation of Development and Heredity.* Clarendon Press, Oxford, 1930.

63. Sawin, P. B., M. A. Griffith, and C. A. Stuart, *Proc. Nat. Acad. Sci., 30,* 217–221 (1944).

64. Schrader, F., *Mitosis.* Columbia Univ. Press, New York, 1944.

65. Snyder, L. H., H. Russell, and E. B. Graham, *Science, 106,* 347–348 (1947).

66. Spuhler, J. N., *Science, 108,* 279–280 (1948).

67. Strandskov, H. H., *Science, 100,* 570–571 (1944).

68. Sturtevant, A. H., and G. W. Beadle, *An Introduction to Genetics.* W. B. Saunders Co., Philadelphia, 1939.

69. Taylor, G. L., and R. R. Race, *Brit. Med. Bull., 2,* 160–164 (1944).

70. Waddington, C. H., *An Introduction to Modern Genetics.* Macmillan Co., New York, 1939.

71. White, T., *J. Genetics, 40,* 403–437 (1940).

72. Wright, S., *Am. Nat., 63,* 274–279 (1929).

73. Wright, S., *Am. Nat., 68,* 24–53 (1934).

74. Wright, S., *Physiol. Rev., 21,* 487–527 (1941).

75. Wright, S., *Bull. Am. Math. Soc., 48,* 223–246 (1942).

76. Wright, S., *Biol. Symposia, 6,* 337–355 (1942).

CHAPTER III Heredity and Environment

Then it got down off the mushroom, and crawled away into the grass, merely remarking, as it went, "One side will make you grow taller, and the other side will make you grow shorter."
— LEWIS CARROLL: *Alice in Wonderland*

IN the preceding chapters we have learned that (ignoring for the moment the effects of evolutionary changes) the genes possessed by one generation of a species are identical in nature with those which were possessed by the preceding generation. Therefore, if there are no evolutionary factors operating which alter the gene frequencies in a population in a state of *panmixia* (p. 110), we should expect that any one generation would look much the same as its ancestors, unless there have occurred in the meantime changes in the environment which are able to cause the gene to be expressed somewhat differently.

In Chapter II we saw that the genes themselves are intrinsically very stable, and environment, even when it affects the manifestation of the gene, does not seem to affect the gene itself. We may offer a further example of this. In the early days of genetic research in America, Drs. W. E. Castle and J. C. Phillips (7) conceived the idea of removing the ovaries of an albino guinea pig and transplanting in their place the ovaries of a black guinea pig. This operation was successful. The new ovaries remained alive and became functional in their new owner. The experimenters then had at their disposal an albino female with the albino constitution, but possessing ovaries which contained the "black" gene. The blood supply was of course that of the albino. The question was: would the genes be altered by their new environment? Today the answer to such a question is almost a foregone conclusion, but in these earlier days of genetic science it was by no means clear which alternative was to be expected. When the experiment was carried out, and the female with the transplanted "black" ovaries was mated to an albino male, she had six offspring all of which were black. The altered environment of the transplanted ovaries had not significantly affected the characteristics of this one gene, at any rate, and there is no reason to suppose it had altered any of the others.

Effects of Environment on Expression of Genes

Although it seems quite certain that the environment (if we exclude the operation of certain chemicals, X-rays, cosmic rays, and so forth) has never been found to alter the characteristics of a gene, we may not say that the environment never alters the *expression* of the gene. The final expression of any gene depends upon the complex end result of chemical reactions started by the gene, combined with concurrent reactions started in other ways, and these reactions can be influenced by the internal and external environment of the organism and by the action of other genes present. It is, therefore, not at all unreasonable that differences in environment may, in many cases, without altering the genetic constitution of an organism, cause marked differences in the expression of certain genes. Such effects are in fact often observed. Some genetic traits are more readily altered by environment than others; in fact some *seem* not to be affected at all.

Hogben (22) illustrates this principle by pointing out the great difference which exists between genetic inheritance and legal inheritance. The layman tends to suppose that you inherit your physical characteristics — for example, your nose — from your ancestors, in much the same way you may inherit their bank balance. The geneticist knows, however, that what you really inherit from your parents are simply genes. If your environment (internal and external) corresponds exactly to that of the parent or parents from whom you inherited a given gene, then this gene will produce the same effect in you as it did in them, but if the environment is different then the gene may or may not produce the same effect as it did in your ancestors.

The effect of differences in environment on the manifestations of genes is so important that it will be worth while to consider a number of examples. To take a specific instance: there is a genetic difference between chickens which determines whether they have yellow shanks or colorless shanks. Crosses between such varieties give a numerical ratio of the two types corresponding to the usual Mendelian laws. This difference is found, however, only if the chickens are fed on yellow corn, or given green feed, for these seem to provide the yellow pigment which manifests itself in the yellow-shanked chickens. If all the chickens are fed on white corn, without any green feed, they will all have colorless shanks. If we take chickens all belonging genetically to the yellow-shank variety and feed some of them on yellow corn and some on white corn, the former group will have yellow shanks and the latter will have colorless shanks. Since the genetic composition of the two groups is the same, so far as this characteristic is concerned, the difference between them in this characteristic is due to a difference in environment. Hogben points out that with genes of this sort, differences in environment could very easily upset the predicted outcome of matings if the predictions are based solely upon the known genetic differences. For if we were to cross fowls of the "yellow" variety with fowls of other varieties and feed some of the offspring yellow corn and some of them white corn, thus depriving some of them of material vital to the proper manifestation of the "yellow" gene, we could not expect to obtain constant numerical ratios which would agree with Mendel's laws. The genetic differences which were present would be irregularly expressed or totally lacking in expression.

Sometimes, it is true, variations in environment of very great magnitude seem to make no difference in the expression of a gene, but if tests are deliberately devised to achieve extreme departures from the ordinary environment, environmental effects can often be observed. As Hogben (22) again mentions, genetic differences in chickens determining the color of the feathers may be constant over a very wide range of environment. The differences between the pure black plumage of the Langshan and the mottled plumage of the Light Sussex is not absolute, however, for by feeding thyroid to the Light Sussex breed, the extent of the black areas present can be considerably extended.

Similar examples may be found in human beings. In some areas of the world, such as certain parts of Switzerland and in the areas around the Great Lakes in the United States, a disease called goiter, which consisted in an enlargement of the thyroid gland because of a deficiency of iodine in the diet, used to be quite prevalent. (By putting iodine in the diet it has proved possible almost to eliminate the condition.) This disease, however, did not attack all the members of the populations of these areas. There also seems to have been some sex difference, so that more females (but not all females) than males exhibited the disorder: fewer males, but a significant number, were attacked. We may suppose that the differences in susceptibility, apart from the sex differences which may have been affected by endocrine factors, were largely genetically determined. This supposition is supported by the fact that certain lower organisms, such as the European newt, although they ordinarily complete their development from the larval to the adult form, may fail to do so if they are kept in water which has insufficient iodine or iodine compounds. There is, however, a certain local race of the American newt (*Amblystoma tigrinum*), found in the neighborhood of Mexico City, which will not grow up into the terrestrial form even if plenty of iodine is present in the water, although it will do so if it is fed on thyroid glands. In most other localities in America the newt will complete its development if adequate iodine is available. There is evidently a genetic difference between the European and Mexican newt. This was not at first realized, and the Mexican newt, never seen in the adult form, was considered an entirely different species, and called by its native Indian name of *axalotl*.

As another illustration we may mention a mutation which has been observed in the fruit fly Drosophila; one which causes a deformation on the hinder part of the body. Flies which are pure for this mutation regularly exhibit a deformation, which is referred to as "abnormal abdomen," if they are grown in moist cultures. They are, however, perfectly normal when grown in a dried culture. If the experiments are carried out in moist cultures, mating between the mutants and wild types produces numerical ratios which conform with the supposition that the differences between the mutant stock and the wild type are due to a single gene difference. However, if the cultures are allowed to dry while the flies are developing, naturally no consistent numerical results can be obtained since flies developing under drier conditions fail to show the full effect of the gene.

Examples of genes which do not exert their effects consistently unless the environment is suitable are also found in plants. Engeldow (11) found that when two varieties of wheat, known as the "Red Fife" and "Hybrid H," are grown under conditions such that plants are spaced at $2'' \times 2''$, the Red Fife yields the larger crop, but when spaced at $2'' \times 6''$, the yields are almost equal, and at greater distances Hybrid H yields a better crop than Red Fife. Again we have a clear example of the influence of the environment, which in this case is the degree of crowding of the individuals together.

Deliberate Alteration of Environment

One important conclusion which can be drawn from facts such as the above is this: if we understand the way in which a gene operates to exert its effects we may perhaps be able, by controlling the conditions, to limit the effect of the gene to some particular (or even no) effect. For example, there is a variety of the domestic fowl, known as "Frizzle," which has defective plumage. Fowls which are heterozygous for this characteristic are characterized by curling of their feathers upwards and outwards. The purebred Frizzle strain remains practically bare throughout its first year of life, and thus seems to be in a perpetual molting state. It is extremely delicate and difficult to bring up. When newly hatched, the Frizzle chick has a down feathering which is so fragile that it usually breaks off. The resulting exposure of the skin leads to a great loss of body heat from the surface, which evokes increased metabolism, increased heat production, increased heart rate, lack of fat deposit, and diminished hemoglobin in the blood. Landauer and other workers (3) have shown, however, that the pure Frizzle chick will develop a complete plumage over the whole body within three weeks if it is protected from heat loss by enclosure in a woolen jacket and confinement to a warm room. This is an example of how, if we know the way in which a single dominant gene produces a deleterious manifestation, we can artificially prevent the appearance of this manifestation, if we wish to do so.

As an analogous example from human genetics, we may consider the once very serious disease, diabetes mellitus, which according to Pincus and White (34) is probably inherited and is commonly due to a recessive gene. Until fairly recently, individuals who were homozygous for this gene were bound to become diabetic and in most cases their lives were considerably shortened as a consequence. The chief effect of the gene, however, is merely a failure of the pancreas to produce a certain hormone, namely insulin, which happens to be essential for proper metabolism. Diabetic individuals who are supplied artificially with this hormone, as can now be done as a result of the discovery of methods of isolating it by Banting and Best (1), are enabled to live a fairly normal existence and in the majority of cases to achieve a normal old age. Thus the great British writer, H. G. Wells, born in 1866, was for years a diabetic but lived to be nearly eighty.

Interaction of Genes and Environment

Dobzhansky (8) has stated that the relation between the genotype and the phenotype is a dynamic one. The genotype determines the reaction of the organism to its environment, but does not determine the external environment. The phenotype is always the resultant of the interaction between a certain genotype and a certain environment. The end result depends upon both factors. Different genotypes may react in some environments to produce similar phenotypes; therefore similarity of phenotypes under identical environment is not always proof of identity in the genotypes. On the other hand, the same genotype may react differently in different environments and produce dissimilar phenotypes. So dissimilarity of phenotypes is not necessarily proof of dissimilarity of the genotypes.

To realize more fully the possible effects of differences in environment on the manifestation of gene differences in populations, we need to take account of one further fact, which has been graphically stated by Dobzhansky and Spassky (10). This is, that natural populations in general contain a tremendous variety of genotypes, each of which may have its own "reaction norm." * For example, in one of the chromosomes of *Drosophila pseudoobscura,* there are certain

* Environment in which the genotype gives rise to a normal individual.

genes which produce a certain set of visible changes. These genes, acting in conjunction with a standard modifier system (see p. 50), produce changes which are extreme at a temperature of 25.5° Centigrade, mild at 21° and almost absent at 16.5°. By altering one modifier system the same changes may be either exaggerated or suppressed in flies grown at 21°. (More will be said about temperature effects below.) This observation provides some support for Fisher's theory (14, 15, 16) of the action of modifiers in determining the action of genes. Experiments by Eugen Fischer (12) on rats have also shown the same tendency for environment to affect the manifestation of genes.

It has been pointed out by Mayr (29) that differences in the environment of lower forms have frequently been found to affect characters which we use for taxonomic purposes. He mentions that water snails and mussels have certain forms in the upper parts of rivers, where there are lower temperatures and a more rapid flow of the water, and somewhat different forms in the lower parts of the stream where the waters are warmer and more stagnant.

Mayr (29) mentions that in limestone districts (where there is more calcium in solution in the water) the shells of mussels, etc., are heavier and have a different shape from those of relatives which grow in waters poor in lime.

These examples suffice to show, and Huxley (24) warns us to keep it in mind, that we must clearly distinguish between the intrinsic nature of a gene and the expression of a gene. The gene itself can alter only by mutation, but its expression in an individual can be affected in a number of ways.

About 1910 Franz Boas (4) called attention to possible effects of environment on the manifestation of hereditary characteristics in man. He reported important definite differences in bodily form between immigrants from Europe and their descendants in America. Boas studied hair color, height and weight, head length and breadth, and face breadth, in foreign-born Bohemians, Slovaks, Hungarians, Poles, Jews, Sicilians, Neapolitans and Scotsmen, and their foreign- and American-born children. He found important cephalic differences between the foreign born and their children. These differences tended to be greater the longer the parents had lived in the United States. Guthe (20) and Hirsch (21) obtained similar results. Morant and Samson (31) published objections to the conclusions of Boas, but Boas (5) showed that some of the countercharges of Morant and Samson were not justified.

Later, all doubt as to whether the environment *could* affect many of the physical characteristics of man which had formerly been used for anthropological characterization was removed by the work of Shapiro (38), who made a detailed comparison between a group of Japanese in Hawaii, their relatives who remained in Japan, and their offspring who were brought up in Hawaii. Shapiro found that growing up in the new environmental conditions in Hawaii had produced marked differences between the Hawaiian-reared Japanese offspring and their Japanese-born fathers and mothers. For instance, the mean sitting height of the Japanese born in Hawaii was significantly greater than the corresponding value for either the immigrants or the immediate ancestors in Japan. Even changes in the dimensions of the head and its proportions in the Japanese born in Hawaii were definitely significant. In the Hawaiian-born Japanese there was a great decrease in head length, and a compensatory increase in head width. The total male Hawaiian-born Japanese showed a difference in cephalic index from the total male immigrants of 2.60, a difference which was more than nine times its probable error.* The nasal dimensions of the Japanese born in Hawaii also changed, in the direction of longer and narrower noses. Both immigrants and Hawaiian-born yielded nasal indices much lower than those found for the Japanese remaining in Japan.

The work of Shapiro and Hulse, who aided him, provides a striking example of marked differences in human physical characteristics which are unquestionably due to environment, since their observations were carefully controlled by comparison with close relatives in Hawaii and in Japan, these relatives presumably having closely similar genetical constitutions. Of course relatives may sometimes differ considerably genetically; however, such genetic differences would vary in random fashion from family to family. The significant thing about Shapiro's work is that he found the trend to be operating on most families, quite apart from the chance variation in characteristics from family to family.

Shapiro also found a significant physical difference between the

* See App. A.

immigrants to Hawaii and the related Japanese who had remained at home, a difference which he thinks might be found in many other cases but which is not too easy to explain.

From all this it should be clear that, in general, no statement about a genetic difference has any scientific meaning unless it includes or implies a specification of the environment in which the gene difference is to manifest itself. (Some genes, it is true, are known which are either unaffected, or affected very slightly by environmental changes, and some changes in gene manifestation would not be consistent with the survival of the organism at all.) But our knowledge of human genetics is so meager that we seldom know which variations in the environments of human beings will alter the expression of a given gene. Our inability to make sure that the environment affecting different individuals is always the same is a further reason for preferring an anthropological classification based on differences in *gene frequencies,* rather than mere differences in external physical characteristics.

It has not always been appreciated how much environmental variation may affect the characteristics we ordinarily observe. The fact is, the changes in organisms which can be produced by certain changes in the environment may be so great that, compared to them, any changes due to ordinary gene variation would seem trivial. Thus the plant *Limnophila heterophylla* (8), when grown under water, is so different in appearance from the same plant grown on land that it at first seems almost inconceivable that the two should even belong to the same species. As another illustration, we may cite the fact that the males of the parasitic wasp *Trichogramma semblidis* may be with or without wings and may have different structures of the body and appendages, depending on the host in which they develop (36).

Plasticity of Gene Effects

There exist (24) all degrees of plasticity of the operation of genes in regard to environmental influence. The blood group genes produce the same characteristics in all known human environments.*

* The "Lewis" blood group gene manifests itself differently in infants and adults.

The effect of environment on the manifestation of the genes for eye color seems slightly doubtful. Stature, body weight and skin color are obviously definitely influenced by certain differences in environment; stature and body weight by diet (27), and skin color (at least over the exposed parts of the body) by the degree of exposure to sun. We have already mentioned the effect of insulin injections on the expression of at least the major effect of the gene for diabetes. Since genes manifest themselves and influence the development of the organism through changes in physiological and therefore chemical reactions, it is *theoretically* possible that the action of any gene could be controlled if we knew enough about the way it produced its effect.

Seibert and Steggerda (37) have made measurements which suggest that the shape of the cross section of the head hair of man tends to change with age, showing a certain lability of this character also.

Temperature Effects

Some of the most striking effects of environment on gene manifestation are produced by differences in temperature. There is in the barley plant a type of albinism which depends on the action of a single gene. If the plants are grown below 6.5° C., they entirely lack the green pigment chlorophyll, but if they are grown at about 18° C., they are quite normal. Grown at temperatures between these limits they produce graded amounts of chlorophyll. Another example is the Drosophila gene, "short wing," a sex-linked recessive which at 27.5° C. markedly reduces wing length and affects eye development. At lower temperatures the effects of the gene are less, and at 14° C. they are not found. The temperature of the environment also affects higher forms of life. In Himalayan rabbits and Siamese cats (see Fig. 14), the black pigment is produced only below a certain threshold temperature.

Another example of the effect of temperature on a characteristic in Drosophila is furnished by the gene "bar" (25) and its allele* "double bar." Bar reduces the number of facets in the eye and the

* "Double bar" is probably not strictly an allele, but a duplication (6).

gene double bar reduces them still more. The number of facets developed is lessened by any temperature increase in the period during which the eye is susceptible. But the two bar alleles do not act proportionately at different temperatures. A change in temperature of 9° makes a much greater difference in the effects of bar than it does in the effect of the double bar allele. If we investigate

FIGURE 14. *Siamese cat.*

the effects of genetic differences by comparing the size of the eyes in two different stocks at any one temperature, we shall generally find that the difference between the two is greater at 16° C. than at 25° C. (19). This is shown in the accompanying illustration (Fig. 15). If we wish to try to evaluate the effect of a difference of 9° in temperature (of course temperature is doubtless not the only environmental factor), it is obvious that the difference in environment is more important for the bar stock than for the double bar stock.

It is possible that this single example provides us with a slight clue to the answer to the question of the relative importance of nature and nurture. For it is clear that in this case (and, as experience proves, in many others) there can be no one single answer as to the question of the relative potency of the genes and the environment. In this case, if we conduct our experiments at 16° C., the important differences are due to the genes, but if we conduct our experiments at 25°, the important differences are due to environment (temperature).

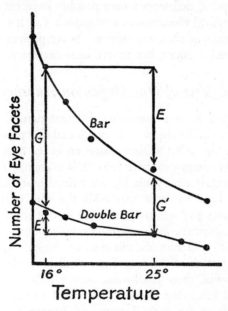

FIGURE 15. *The effect of temperature on the development of eye facets in fruit flies* (Drosophila) *possessing the genes "bar" and "double bar."*

Chemical Effects

Just as genes exert their effects by initiating or influencing chemical reactions, chemical factors have important influences on the action of various genes. There are numerous examples of this. For instance, the chemical substance phenyl-thio-carbamide, when fed to black rats in suitable concentration, caused the fur of 22 out of 23 experimental animals to show a definite tendency to become gray, thus providing an example of the influence of a chemical substance on a manifestation of the genes of pigmentation. Re-

moval of the phenyl-thio-carbamide from the diet allowed the rats
to return to their normal color (35).

The effect of vitamin deficiencies on constitutional traits is now
known to nearly everyone. The effect of lack of sufficient iodine in
the diet has already been referred to. Marett (28) has pointed out
that other mineral deficiencies may possibly have important effects
on human physical characteristics. Baudisch (2) has discussed the
possible influence of chemical elements never present in more than
very small concentrations, but nevertheless necessary.

Effects of One Organ on Another

Another example, of a somewhat different nature, of the effects
of environment on development is mentioned in a paper by Weidenreich (39) on the effect of brain size on other human characteristics. Here the change in environment is a change in part of the
body itself. In early embryonic life the animal brain has a relatively
high growth rate. In most mammals the rate of brain growth
slows down later and the growth of the rest of the face continues,
but in dwarf animals, as in some domestic breeds, and in some
species of small wild animals, this does not happen to the same extent and the growth of the rest of the skull is checked fairly early.
As a consequence, there results not only a relative orthognathism
(more vertical face), but also the absence of certain cranial super-
structures such as the sagittal crest and supraorbital ridges. One
finds persistent cranial sutures, rounded palate, smaller teeth, often
with a simplified pattern, a relatively wide cranial cavity (analogous to brachycephaly). Now, whether or not man is a dwarf
species, he shows the dwarf type of skull, which is due to the per-
sistence in his case of the higher relative growth rate of the brain
in the later stages of facial development. Effectively we may say
that the genetic "environment" in which man's facial characteristics have to develop is different from the environments they find
in other primates.

Thus the effects of environment and genes interact, and neither
factor can be neglected. For this reason, Dobzhansky (9) has stated
that heredity is not a status but a process. According to him, when
we speak of the inheritance of skin color or of intelligence or any

other character, we are merely using a figure of speech. What is inherited is not that character but the manner or "norm" of reaction of the organism to the environment. Due to differences in heredity, the reaction of different human individuals to exposure of their skin to sunlight may be quite different. Some may be easily sunburned to the point of blistering and find it difficult to acquire a tan, others who appear about equally white before exposure may be tanned, and as a result their skin becomes considerably darker, while others may develop considerable skin pigment even without exposure to the sun. The effect of environment on the manifestation of such genes is one of the factors which operate to make it difficult in many cases to determine the exact genetic mechanism of many important inherited characters in man. At the same time, environmental differences make it difficult to predict at all times what the form of the adult organism will be, even though we may know something about its genetic constitution, unless we know the precise environment in which it will be brought up.

For a long time there has been a debate as to the relative importance of heredity and environment in human lives. The examples we have just considered should be enough to show us that in many cases no precise answer to this question can ever be made, because in the case of many characteristics the question, as it is proposed, is meaningless, since the exact situation is not specified. However, we know that some characteristics are more readily influenced by environmental factors than are others. Glass (19) has pointed out that although there is no hard-and-fast boundary, we may roughly subdivide all characteristics of living organisms into genetic and environmental characteristics. Each of these classes can be further subdivided as is shown in the accompanying table (see Table 6).

Cases falling into classes 1) and 4) are clear-cut, and we have no hesitation in saying that heredity, or environment, respectively, predominates in such cases. But unhappily, most of the traits we wish to study seem to fall into class 2) or 3), in which it is difficult to decide which influence predominates.

It will be understood, of course, that there is no sharp break from one of these categories to the next. Also, sometimes the same or a very similar variation in phenotype can be produced by either a genetical change or an environmental change (19).

TABLE 6

Four Types of Behavior

(1) Heredity	(3) Environment and Heredity
Genetic differences manifested in practically all environments.	Differences due to environment manifested only in a restricted range of genotypes.
(2) Heredity and Environment	(4) Environment
Genetic differences manifested only in a restricted range of environment.	Differences due to environment manifested in practically all genotypes.

(Modified from Glass [19])

Attempts to Measure Effects of Environment and Heredity

Accurate knowledge of the effects of environment on the manifestation of genes in lower organisms usually results from our being able to place organisms known to be of identical genetical make-up in different environments and to observe the effects, using large enough numbers so the results will be statistically significant (see App. A). We are not permitted to do this with human beings, and as a result our knowledge of the relative role of genes and environment (or in other words, nature and nurture) in regard to man is still relatively scanty.

Possible Statistical Fallacies

Attention has been called to a possible fallacy involved in statistical attempts to estimate the degree of importance of heredity and environment by Hogben (22), who offers the following imaginary example.

Suppose that during a war a certain city has been under a prolonged siege or blockade, so that the food supplies which contain certain necessary vitamins have been more or less exhausted and as a result the average person is not obtaining enough vitamins. Young children who ought to be growing are stunted as a result, and will weigh less than the average weight of prewar children of the same age. Let us suppose further that there is in the city one biochemist who had realized in advance the importance of whatever vitamins the war was likely to cut down on, and, anticipating events, had laid up a sufficient stock of pure vitamins for his family during this period. His four children will grow up normally. However, there might be in the city a million starving children to counterbalance the four healthy ones. Let us suppose that a political party which believes that the environment is the important thing in determining human characteristics demands peace, on the grounds that wartime conditions are stunting the growth of the children. If they were influential, they might finally succeed in having the government appoint an official group to make an inquiry into the subject. This group, however, would report that very much *less than 1 per cent* of the variation which can be found in regard to body weight in the children of the city is due to differences in diet. Since only four children out of a million would be found to show normal growth, the difference would not be statistically significant. The committee might argue from this that the effect of any improvement in diet which would come from making peace would be negligible, and war would continue.

As Hogben points out, it is easy to see what is wrong with such a conclusion. For it would still be true that by adding the proper vitamins to the diet, the mean body weight of the young population would be increased by something like 30 per cent if all the children of the city were to receive the proper vitamins. The error consists in confusing the small effect of a measure poorly applied or applied only to a slight extent, with the effect which a proper application of it would produce. Such statistical errors and blunders in logic must of course be avoided if we wish to make any progress in evaluating the relative roles of heredity and environment. Even so, many difficulties still remain.

Relatives and Twins

Everybody has observed that the physical similarity between close relatives is in general greater than the similarity between strangers from the same locality, and especially greater than that between people from different parts of the world. If we are dealing with measurable characteristics, the degree of correlation which various degrees of relationship would be expected to produce can be calculated (13). But difficulty is experienced in trying to check these calculations by observations on human material, because close relatives are generally brought up in the same or very similar environments. The old question arises once more: are the similarities due to similarities in the environment, or to similarities in the genetic make-up? Even when, after great effort, we have assembled pairs of identical twins in which the two members of each pair were brought up in different environments, there still remains the fact that in spite of differences in rearing, their intra-uterine environment was nevertheless the same, or at least as nearly identical as environments can ever be. We do not know how big a role this common intra-uterine environment plays. But if we are willing to ignore the possible effects of similarities or differences in the environment of individuals before they were born, it is possible in some cases to devise means of measuring the relative effects of environment (meaning post-partum environment) and genetic differences.

Numerical Treatment

We compare the variability from each other of pairs of identical twins with the mutual variability of pairs of fraternal twins of like sex, when the two members of each pair are brought up in the same family. We are then comparing two variabilities: 1) the variability within the family when gene differences and differences within the family environment were both present, but eliminating those differences due to sex and birth rank, and 2) the variability within the family when such genetic differences as serve to distinguish one member of a family from another member of the same family do not enter into the results. Holzinger (23) has proposed two formulas to express the ratio of "nature" to "nurture," both based on various measures of variability. The first formula is as follows:

$$T = \frac{\Delta f - \Delta i}{\Delta i}$$

Here Δf is the mean difference between dizygotic (fraternal) twins of like sex and Δi is the mean difference between identical twins. T is the proposed mathematical measure of the relative effects of heredity and environment. The denominator measures the mean differences when there are no genetic differences within the family, the numerator measures the difference between the variability which exists when both sources of variability are present and the variability when gene differences have been eliminated in the sense just defined.

The second formula given by Holzinger is as follows:

$$t^2 = \frac{r_i - r_f}{1 - r_i}$$

Here r_i and r_f represent the correlation coefficients (App. A) for identical and fraternal twins respectively. This formula differs from the first chiefly in that the variance (mean square difference) has replaced the mean differences. The letter t symbolizes mathematically the ratio between hereditary and environmental effects.

Hogben (22) points out that Holzinger's first formula is misleading, if it is taken to signify that the numerator measures the average difference due to heredity alone, for variability due to the influence of diverse agencies is not additive when measured in mean differences. The second formula is open to another criticism, according to Hogben (22), who does not believe that the separate sources of variability can be treated as purely additive, even when we have eliminated differences between the environment of one family and another as we have done above, unless the significance of gene differences is interpreted in a very special way. For instance, Hogben (22) says that in dealing with intellectual and physical resemblances we must keep in mind that the greater physical similarity of twins may be partly due to their more restricted choice of environments. The fact that t^2 is greater than one might indicate that genetic differences are more important than differences in environment, at least in producing striking discrepancies between members of the same family and the same birth rank. However, striking differences of environment are more likely to occur between two nonidentical twins than between two identical twins, and this may contribute a considerable part of the effect.

There still remains a theoretically possible way of estimating the relative importance of nature and nurture. Muller (32) pointed out that if there were sufficient material available to enable us to determine the correlation ($_a r_i$) for identical twins reared separately, it would be possible to extend the conception of the nature-nurture ratio beyond the limits of the family unit. Assuming that the correlation of the pairs of other related individuals taken at random from the same population was zero, Holzinger's second formula, interpreted in this more general sense, would read as follows:

$$t^2 = \frac{_a r_i}{1 - {}_a r_i}$$

Perhaps some day enough data will be available to enable us to attempt to apply this formula. Hogben thinks that the values obtained might differ greatly according to the magnitude of the differences of environment in the population and the distribution of these differences.

In spite of these limitations, studies of twins have enabled certain important conclusions to be drawn.

Twins and Crime

The results obtained in studies of twins in relation to crime are shown in Table 7 (30). Newman has called attention to the greater similarities in environment, especially social activities, of monovular (identical) twins as compared to biovular (fraternal) twins, and of course this means that the differences shown in the table are only partly due to heredity.

Therefore, although the results are sufficient to convince most biologists, probably, of the reality of a genetic effect in this matter, they do not suffice to measure the relative importance of environment and heredity. For an accurate estimate of this we shall have to wait for the sort of information suggested as necessary by Professor Muller (referred to above). All we can say at present is that it seems perfectly certain that environment is more influential in regard to certain characteristics than in regard to others. We can state without much reservation, for example, that the blood group

TABLE 7

Criminal Behavior of Twins

| AUTHOR | MONOVULAR TWINS | | BIOVULAR TWINS | |
	Similar Behavior	Dissimilar Behavior	Similar Behavior	Dissimilar Behavior
Lange (1929)	10	3	2	15
Legras (1932)	4	0	0	5
Krauz (1936)	20	12	23	20
Stumpfl (1936)	11	7	7	12
Rosanoff (1934)	25	12	5	23
Total	70	34	37	75

$\chi^2 = 25.40$
$p = < 0.001$

of an individual will not be influenced to any appreciable degree by his environment. On the other hand, it is extremely probable that his attitude towards society may be importantly influenced.

Some Results of Family Studies

Although a comparative study of identical and fraternal twins does not enable us to arrive at a final conclusion regarding the general question of the relative roles of environment and heredity in human make-up, it does allow us to draw *some* conclusions as to the relative degree of influence which environment has on certain human characteristics. Thus Newman, Freeman and Holzinger (33) point out that, even if we accept the hypothesis that the monovular twins constitute a group in which the biological relation between pairs is such that their heredity is identical, the heredity of fraternal pairs overlaps genetically only in part. Thus the degree of contrast between the distribution of the differences in a given trait among the two groups of twins may be taken as an indication of the extent to which that trait is determined by inborn or inherited structures. Newman, Freeman and Holzinger did not report the blood groups of the twins they studied, but it is generally known that the monovular twins are always of exactly the same blood groups, depending on the groups of their parents (Table 8) and the genes which they

TABLE 8

Illustrations of a Few Possible Combinations of Blood
Groups of Twins

Mating	O × O	AB × AB
Possible Blood Groups of Fraternal Twins	O + O	A + A, B + B, A + B, A + AB, B + AB, or AB + AB
Possible Blood Groups of Identical Twins	O + O	A + A, B + B, or AB + AB

happen to inherit. The contrast between the two kinds of twins is thus in this case as sharp as it can well be. Newman, Freeman and Holzinger (33) reported that in the case of morphological characteristics, the contrast is sharpest in the number of finger ridges, less sharp in height and head width, and in respect to cephalic index it is less sharp still. This latter observation might be interpreted as meaning that environment exercises a great effect on cephalic index, but the authors point out that it could be partially due to the unreliability of the measurements of head width.

The book by Newman, Freeman and Holzinger also contains important information on the extent to which personality and social traits are influenced by environment, an influence so great that it could be inferred that such traits are not usually determined primarily by heredity.

These authors made detailed studies on nineteen pairs of identical twins, separated in infancy, and brought together in adult life; in a few cases the twins met for the first time in the laboratory where they were studied. In all cases the merely physical resemblances were as great as you might expect from monozygotic twins, and greater than for fraternal twins. In most cases also "intelligence" as measured was found to be more or less equal. But the twins were sometimes found to differ in state of health, in emotional reactions and social reactions. The authors also found evidence that the *expression* of undoubtedly identical genes has sometimes been altered by the environment. They express their belief in narrating their hypothetical case of twins, John Doe and Richard Doe.

"These twins were reared in the same general community but were separated by social barriers. The foster parents of the twins were quite different in their social attitudes. John's foster father brought him up to be industrious and respectable, while Richard's foster father was neither industrious nor respectable. The result was that John grew up to be a good, steady, respected citizen, while Richard early got into bad company, has lived a very irregular life, and has had several difficulties with the laws of the land, which he has had to expiate in appropriate ways." These environmentally determined differences are not without interest for anthropology but apply rather more on the cultural than on the physical level.

Newman, Freeman and Holzinger found that some of their identical twin pairs showed marked differences in "ability," which always correlated with marked differences in the educational opportunities given the twins. "In no case is there a large and consistent difference in ability without marked difference in the environment. On the whole, analysis of the cases studied adds convincing evidence to the statistical analysis of the marked effect of education on ability."

Handwriting was generally found not to be similar. The authors believed that the handwriting was unlike because "it expresses the individual's personality, if we mean not a fixed and unalterable innate personality, but the personality which has been formed by the interaction between the given organism and its environment."

A study of personality differences and likenesses was made on the twins. The authors conclude "that forms of behavior exist which are determined largely by the original character of the organism. None of these forms of behavior is impervious to influence, but some of them may actually not be greatly modified because they have not, as a matter of fact, been incorporated into an organized system of learned behavior. The forms of behavior which constitute the adjustment of the individual to his environment, on the other hand, are on a higher level of performance, which is the product of both the organism and the environment interacting. This product is affected both by the original nature of the individual and by his environment and is not the sole product of either."

"Physical characteristics are least affected by the environment, intelligence is affected more; educational achievement still more; and personality or temperament . . . the most."

It will be seen that some separation of the effects of heredity and environment has been achieved in certain special cases, subject to the possible errors mentioned above, and that the patterns of emotional reactions and social attitudes were most affected, as would have been anticipated, by environment. Basic intelligence, however, may be mostly influenced by genetic factors, although the analyses on which this statement rests are far from being free from the sort of objection we have already discussed. The subjects studied were far from being as different as could be found by taking the complete range of conditions under which human beings can exist.

"Intelligence"

A word may be said about measurements of "intelligence" which usually enter into any discussion of the relative roles of heredity and environment. Various methods have been proposed, and some of them give remarkably reproducible results when the same subject is repeatedly examined. Nevertheless it is very doubtful if any tests have been devised whose results do not depend to a considerable extent on the environment as well as the heredity of the individual. For instance, Garth (17) made an attempt to ascertain the correlation between "intelligence quotient (I.Q.)" and the amount of Indian blood in 1400 Indian school children. He obtained for the full-blooded Indians a relative I.Q. (referred to the "white" I.Q. as 100) of 72, for those with ¾ Indian blood an I.Q. of 74, for the half-breeds 75, and for the quarter-breeds 78. This looks pretty impressive, until we graph the results (Fig. 16) and note that if we extrapolate to zero Indian blood (i.e. pure whites) we obtain a predicted I.Q. of 80. But the white I.Q. is taken as 100 in computing

the data. Therefore the difference between 80 and 100 reflects a bias
in the determinations. By hypothesis it cannot be genetic, and must
therefore be due to environment. One might suppose that white
children, brought up under the social conditions of Indians on a
reservation, would show a relative I.Q. of about 80. Kroeber (26),

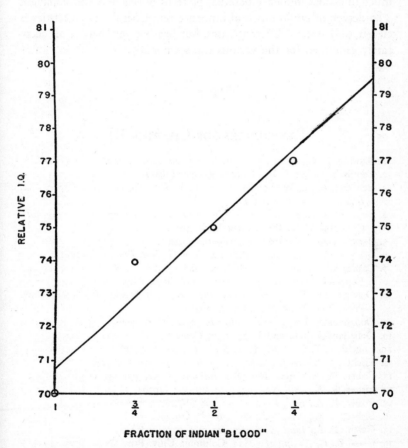

FIGURE 16. *"Intelligence quotient" of Indians with various
degrees of "white" ancestry (after Garth).*

who refers to Garth's work, supposes that one might infer about two thirds of the "inferiority" of the Indians is due to their environment. This is all very well, but it is interesting to note that Kroeber does not take the further step of concluding that one third of the inferiority is genetically caused. Our above discussion should have made it clear why such a conclusion would be quite unjustified.

We are thus left with suggestive evidence that environment probably does not influence "basic intelligence," whatever that is, very much, but does influence habitual patterns of reaction and behavior. The degree of environmental influence on physical characteristics is clearly different in different cases, but has not yet been at all accurately estimated for the various traits we study.

References for Chapter III

1. Banting, F. G., and C. H. Best, *J. Lab. Clin. Med., 7,* 251–266 (1922).
2. Baudisch, O., *J. A. M. A., 123,* 959–966 (1943).
3. Benedict, F. G., W. Landauer, and E. L. Fox, *Storrs Agric. Exper. Stat. Bull., 177,* 13–101 (1932).
4. Boas, F., *Changes in the Bodily Form of Descendants of Immigrants.* Columbia Univ. Press, New York, 1912.
5. Boas, F., *Am. Anthrop., 42,* 183–189 (1940).
6. Bridges, C. B., and K. S. Brehme, *Carnegie Inst. Pub., 552* (1944).
7. Castle, W. E., and J. C. Phillips, cited by: Castle, W. E., *Genetics and Eugenics.* Harvard Univ. Press, Cambridge, 1927.
8. Dobzhansky, Th., *Genetics and the Origin of Species.* Columbia Univ. Press, New York, 2nd Edition, 1941.
9. Dobzhansky, Th., *The Teaching Biologist, 12,* 97–106 (1943).
10. Dobzhansky, Th., and B. Spassky, *Genetics, 29,* 270–290 (1944).
11. Engeldow, F. L., *Jour. Agric. Sci., 15,* 125–146 (1925).
12. Fischer, E., *Zeits. f. Morph. u. Anthrop., 24,* 37–45 (1924).
13. Fisher, R. A., *Trans. Roy. Soc. Edinburgh, 52,* 399–433 (1918).
14. Fisher, R. A., *Am. Nat., 62,* 115; 571–574 (1928).
15. Fisher, R. A., *Biol. Rev., 6,* 345–368 (1931).
16. Fisher, R. A., *Am. Nat., 68,* 370–374 (1934).
17. Garth, T. R., *Jour. App. Psy., 11,* 268–275 (1927).
19. Glass, B., *Genes and the Man.* Columbia Univ. Press, New York, 1943.
20. Guthe, cited by: Gates, R. R., *Human Genetics.* Macmillan Co., New York, 1946.

21. Hirsch, N. D. M., *A. J. P. A., 10,* 79–90 (1927).
22. Hogben, L., *Nature and Nurture.* W. W. Norton & Co., Inc., New York, 1933.
23. Holzinger, K. J., *J. Educ. Psych., 20,* 241–248 (1929).
24. Huxley, J., *Evolution: The Modern Synthesis.* Harper & Bros., New York and London, 1942.
25. Krafka, J. F., *J. Gen. Physiol., 2,* 409–432; 433–444; 445–464 (1920).
26. Kroeber, A. L., *Anthropology.* Harcourt, Brace & Co., New York, 1948.
27. Lasker, G. W., *A. J. P. A., 5,* 323–341 (1947).
28. Marett, J. R. de la H., *Race, Sex, and Environment.* London, 1936.
29. Mayr, E., *Systematics and the Origin of Species.* Columbia University Press, New York, 1942.
30. Montagu, M. F. A., *Ann. Am. Acad. Pol. & Soc. Sci.,* September, 46–57 (1941).
31. Morant, G. M., and O. Samson, *Biometrika, 28,* 11 (1936).
32. Muller, H. J., *J. Heredity, 16,* 433–448 (1925).
33. Newman, H. H., F. N. Freeman, and K. J. Holzinger, *Twins: A Study of Heredity and Environment.* Univ. Chicago Press, Chicago, 1937.
34. Pincus, G., and P. White, *Am. J. Med. Sci., 186,* 1–14 (1933); *188,* 159–168 (1934); *188,* 782–790 (1934).
35. Richter, C. P., and K. H. Clisby, *Proc. Soc. Exp. Biol. & Med., 48,* 684–687 (1941).
36. Salt, G., *Parasitology, 29,* 539–553 (1937).
37. Seibert, H. C., and M. Steggerda, *J. Hered., 35,* 345–347 (1944).
38. Shapiro, H. L., *Migration and Environment.* Oxford Univ. Press, London, New York, and Toronto, 1939.
39. Weidenreich, F., *Trans. Am. Phil. Soc.* (N.S.), 31, 321–442 (1941).

CHAPTER IV Gene Equilibrium Without Evolution

> Consider again the action between iron and water. The two constituents are heated in a *sealed* glass tube. Under this condition no substance can escape. Consequently, after a little hydrogen and iron oxide have been formed, they immediately begin to act on each other, independently of the action which produced them, forming iron and water again. In the beginning the direct action proceeds with the greater speed; but the reverse action gradually gains, until finally they are going with equal speeds, thus balancing each other, so that the action *seems* to stop . . . the equilibrium reached is dynamic in character.
>
> —R. B. BROWNLEE, R. W. FULLER,
> W. J. HANCOCK, M. D. SOHON, and
> J. E. WHITSIT: *Elementary Principles of Chemistry*

Application of Genetic Principles

SOME genes are commoner in a given population than are others. Let us assume for the moment that we know accurately what is meant by a "population"; a definition will be offered later. If every individual in the population possesses the gene W in homozygous form, then we say that the gene frequency, which we may represent by w, is 1.00 (one hundred per cent). If the gene is not present at all in the population, we say its frequency is zero. Values between these two extremes are often observed, and methods of calculating them from observations on the phenotypes will be discussed below. Let us first consider only some of the simpler ideas involved.

The gene frequencies of natural populations are continually being changed by natural evolutionary forces such as selection and mutation. In the following chapter we shall discuss the nature of these forces and the way in which they operate. But before doing this, we might ask ourselves a preliminary question: what happens to gene frequencies in a population which is not being altered by the forces of evolution? We shall find that they quickly settle down to a steady state — in other words, an equilibrium is reached. What exactly is meant by the idea of an equilibrium of gene frequencies, or, as we shall call it for the sake of brevity, gene equilibrium? As already noted (p. 78) the concept has not always been understood, and even today geneticists are not infrequently asked questions which show that the questioners do not understand it. For instance: if dark eyes are dominant over blue eyes, why have they not completely replaced blue eyes? If blood group gene O is recessive to A and B, how does it happen that today's populations contain any group O? It is even possible that similar questions may have occurred to some of the readers of this book while reading the exposition of genetic principles in Chapter II.

Knowing the principles of genetics, however, it requires only an elementary knowledge of algebra to see why, with random (non-assortive) mating, the expected phenomenon, which Laughlin has christened "genophagy" (complete replacement of all the recessives by dominants), does not occur. Mathematical demonstrations that this replacement does not happen, but that instead an equilibrium is reached, were put forth independently by Weinberg (26) and by Hardy (8) so that the principle is now generally known as the Hardy-Weinberg law. Pearson (25) had previously treated a somewhat specialized case.

Before offering a mathematical proof, however, we may attempt in simple words to lay bare the fallacy underlying the common misapprehensions of genetic equilibrium. In brief, we may say this: recessives breed true always, so that offspring of R × R matings are always R, and the heterozygotes are always capable of producing offspring of the recessive type; therefore new recessives continually arise from matings of individuals not openly displaying the recessive trait. Heterozygotes are continually being produced from matings between heterozygotes, between heterozygotes and recessives, between heterozygotes and dominants, and between dominants and recessives. Therefore, it can be seen that recessive offspring will continue to be produced, at least for some time. It remains, however, to show that they will not be produced with gradually diminishing frequency. This can be understood if we can show that the frequency of the recessive genes will not, simply because they are recessives, diminish in the population with the lapse of time, apart from the action of selection, mutation, or other influences; for the frequency of the genes determines the frequency of the various types of offspring. And if the frequency of the genes does not change, we have the condition called gene equilibrium.

Gene Equilibrium

One of the clearest expositions of the elementary mathematics underlying the principle of gene equilibrium has been given by Dobzhansky (10, 11). He says: Suppose that two varieties of a sexually reproducing organism are brought into contact and allowed to interbreed at random. Let us suppose that one variety is homozygous for the dominant gene Y, while the other variety is homozygous for the recessive gene y. If the two varieties are originally present in equal numbers, one half of the original population will consist of YY and the other half of yy individuals. As a result of the mating between these two varieties, we can easily show by writing down the matings and their outcomes that the next generation will consist of 25 per cent of individuals homozygous for Y, 25 per cent homozygous for y, and 50 per cent which are hybrids, or heterozygotes, Yy. In other words, we have again the familiar Mendelian ratio: YY, 2Yy, yy.

Now if we assume that these different types of individuals exhibit no differences in viability or fertility, each one of them will produce, on the average, the same number of sex cells (gametes) which will be successful in giving rise to their proportional part of the next generation. Individuals of the constitution YY or yy each produce only one kind of sex cells in equal numbers, one kind with Y and the other with y. If we take the population as a whole, we shall find that there are $\frac{1}{4} + \frac{1}{4}$ ($= \frac{1}{2}$) sex cells with Y and $\frac{1}{4} + \frac{1}{4}$ ($= \frac{1}{2}$) sex cells with y. That is, the Y sex cells and the y sex cells will be equally numerous. Since the mating, by hypothesis, is again at random, the next generation will again consist of 25 per cent YY, 50 per cent Yy, and 25 per cent yy, and so will each subsequent generation. In other words, in spite of the dominance of Y over y, no over-all change in gene frequencies will result.

Of course it might be objected that we have taken a somewhat special example for the above illustration, because we have assumed that the two pure varieties were mixed in equal proportions. However, it is very easy to show that, no matter what the proportions in which the varieties are mixed, the phenotype frequencies will remain constant from generation to generation after equilibrium is reached. In the case of ordinary autosomal genes (that is, genes not carried on either of the sex chromosomes) the equilibrium is reached after one generation of random mating. A detailed mathematical proof of this is given in Appendix IV–1.

Mixtures of Populations

In general, if we knew the genetic composition and the numbers involved in a mixture of two populations we could predict the frequency of the various genetic types in the offspring, assuming that they are not modified by evolutionary influences such as selection or mutation. The arithmetic of such calculations is given in Appendix IV–2.

The following diagram (Fig. 17) will serve to illustrate the results which would result from the mixture in various proportions of a hypothetical "white" group, which we have chosen to possess blood group frequencies somewhat similar to those of the English explorers of North America (3), allowing for some possible French and Spanish mixture (Table 9), and another hypothetical group of North American Indians supposed to possess only blood group O. The computations were made as outlined in Appendix IV–2. It will be seen that the change is roughly proportional to the amount of new genes introduced.

Methods of computing the gene frequencies p, q, and r are given in Appendix A and Appendix IV–2.

If we consider a pair of *hypothetical* genes D and d, for instance, where d is recessive to D, and D is responsible for the production of individuals of short stature while d produces individuals who are tall, and the heterozygote Dd is of intermediate stature, assuming that equal numbers of the two parent stocks were involved, the result of the crossing of a pure short race DD with a pure tall race dd would be the production of a new type with 25 per cent tall, 25 per cent short, and 50 per cent intermediate in height. If we suppose that only 20 per cent of the original population belonged to the short stock DD, then the composition of the new population will be given as follows:

Let t represent the frequency of the gene D and $(1 - t)$ that of the gene d. Then $t = 0.2$ and $(1 - t) = 0.8$.

DD (short) $= t^2 = 0.04 = 4$ per cent
Dd (intermediate) $= 2t(1 - t) = 0.32 = 32$ per cent
dd (tall) $= (1 - t)^2 = 0.64 = 64$ per cent.

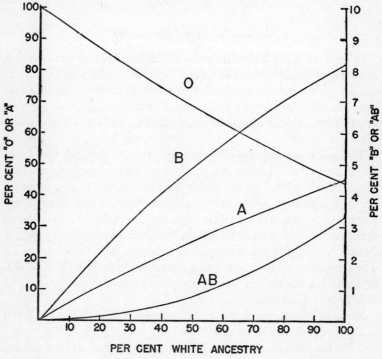

FIGURE 17. *Blood group frequencies resulting from mixture of Indians (supposed to be 100 per cent group O) with a representative "white" population in various amounts (Boyd).*

The new population would be predominantly tall or intermediate in stature with relatively few short individuals.

Shapiro, when he tested the blood groups of the mixed descendants of the mutineers of the *Bounty,* and the Polynesians they took

TABLE 9

Results of Four English, One French, and One Spanish Blood Group Studies

Author	*Number Tested*	*Per Cent of Group*				*Gene Frequencies*		
		O	A	B	AB	p	q	r
Taylor and Prior	422	47.9	42.4	8.3	1.4	0.250	0.050	0.692
Kirwan — Taylor	500	40.4	46.8	9.6	3.2	0.297	0.072	0.637
Hirszfeld and Hirszfeld	403	44.6	44.6	7.7	3.0	0.277	0.055	0.668
Penrose and Penrose	1000	43.2	47.7	6.4	2.7	0.295	0.048	0.658
Dujarric and Kossovitch	1265	39.8	42.3	11.8	6.1	0.276	0.088	0.632
Bote Garcia	296	44.3	46.6	5.4	3.7	0.288	0.040	0.666
Average	—	—	—	—	—	0.281	0.059	0.660

to Pitcairn's Island, obtained blood group frequencies intermediate between those of English and Polynesians.

This method is entirely general (in the mathematical sense) and if we knew the mechanism of inheritance of other human traits, such as hair pigmentation and skin pigmentation, exact numerical predictions could be made as to the composition and appearance of race mixtures of any sort we knew about or cared to imagine.

In general, the effects of mixture will depend on the gene frequencies of the component populations, and the relative numbers of individuals belonging to each component population. If the numbers of individuals of breeding age in the two populations are to each other as c is to d, and the gene frequencies are q_c and q_d, the

new gene frequency in the mixed population will be $\dfrac{cq_c + dq_d}{c + d}$.

Spread of a Gene

When a new gene is introduced into a population, it does not increase in frequency, even if it is a dominant, unless it is favored by some evolutionary agency.

Reference has already been made to the importance of knowing the numbers of a population which is supposed to introduce a new gene into some other population, as when a new characteristic in one human population is supposed to result from its being brought in from the outside, as by invaders. While it is true that one immigrant possessing the secret of making fire might be able to change the cultural habits of a whole population over a vast area, immigration of one man possessing the blood group B into a large population will not appreciably change the blood group frequencies of the population into which he migrates, unless we assume that there is some pronounced selective advantage for group B in this particular environment, or assume that the man is considered more attractive sexually than the local males, or has other special opportunities to breed with the local females.

Since we do not have any evidence of a selective advantage for B in any environment we know about, we may state that if one group B individual, heterozygous for the blood group B gene, enters a population of 999 individuals, none of whom belongs to blood group B or AB, there is no reason to suppose that at the end of 10 or 10,000 or 10,000,000 years the proportion of group B in the population descended from this mixture would be any greater than what it was originally, namely 0.1 per cent. This is a point worthy of noting, for some persons at one time evidently believed that a new gene, once it appeared in a population (whether it was brought there by migration or arose *de novo* as the result of mutation), would in the course of time spread through the population, becoming more and more frequent, especially if it were a dominant.

The reason for this misapprehension is fairly clear. The number of descendants of any individual in the fourth generation will, in the average case, be greater than the number in the first generation (his immediate children). If an individual rears four children, he may reasonably expect to have considerably more than four great-great-grandchildren. This will be especially true if the population as a whole is on the increase. Even in a strictly static population (one not increasing or decreasing in size) each mating yields, *on the average,* two children who reach the mating age, four grandchildren, eight great-grandchildren, etc. There is a *chance* that any of these descendants of a newly introduced or mutated B individual will inherit the factor B. So one can visualize, in a lazy sort of way, how the B factor might spread throughout the whole population, like the mycelium of a mold spreading through bread. But this lazy picture is wrong. For, if we analyze the process more carefully, we see that our B individual will probably have, in a static population, just two children who grow to maturity and have offspring of their own. The probability that one of these will have the gene B is $\frac{1}{2}$, the probability that both will have gene B is $\frac{1}{2} \times \frac{1}{2} = \frac{1}{4}$. If only one has it, the chances that his offspring belong to blood group B are computed in the same way. The probability that the four grandchildren of the original group B are also group B is $\frac{1}{16} \times \frac{1}{16} = \frac{1}{256}$. The further we go down the generations, the less likely it becomes that all the descendants of our group B individual will be also group B, until, in the end, the chances against it are overwhelming. Further analysis shows that the *proportional* representation of B in the gene population is therefore likely to stay the same as in the beginning if no other effects operate. After gene B has been introduced, there seem to be three factors which might affect the total number of B genes in the population: (a) increase in the total size of the population, (b) random genetic variation (the Sewall Wright effect), and (c) the action of selection, if gene B has any selective value. All of these will be discussed below.

When populations are mixed (mixture is probably now the main agency for modifying gene frequencies in human groups), it is very seldom, of course, that we have any adequate evidence as to the relative numbers of the invaders and of the invaded, or of the gene frequencies which prevailed in the two different groups before their combination. Also, "immigration pressure" in favor of one gene may persist for long times and act relatively slowly, so that the final effect is achieved only after generations or perhaps millennia.

Introduction of a New Gene

A concrete example of the introduction of a new gene into a population, by invaders from outside, is probably provided by the history of the blood group gene *B* in Europe. From the relative frequencies of this characteristic in Europe and Asia at the present time, we may estimate with some accuracy the probable amounts of "foreign" genes contributed by the invaders.

The progressive increase from west to east in the proportion of blood group B in Europe has frequently been commented on. In trying to solve the problem of when, and by whom, the B factor was introduced into Europe, Candela (8) assembled very convincing evidence that group B (and probably brachycephaly) were introduced into Europe by the Asiatic armies, the Huns and Tatars, about the fifth century, and continued to be imported during the ten centuries of their intermittent invasions, conquests, and occupations, and that before their arrival the B factor was almost or completely absent from European populations (5, 15). (We may remark in passing that the high B in Africa and India can hardly be accounted for as coming from Mongoloid peoples, and is thus presumably of earlier origin. Also, the only blood group series we have for Iceland (22) shows rather more B than one would expect from Candela's theory.)

Candela bases his conclusions essentially on the results of considering five different population groups. He finds 1) the modern descendants and representatives of the "pure" Mongoloid invaders have a higher proportion of group B than any of the other four ethnic groups considered; 2) the mixed (partly Mongoloid) population whose ancestors accompanied, and for long periods of time superseded, the Mongols along the path of invasion are possessed of smaller, but still quite high proportions of group B; 3) in the zone of contact, the third group, European populations which must have mixed with the invaders to some extent have smaller amounts of B than the Turks and Tatars who make up the second ethnic group, but larger amounts than the peoples of the next class; 4) the peoples who are geographically remote from the scene of the invasions have smaller amounts of B than peoples of any of the first three categories,

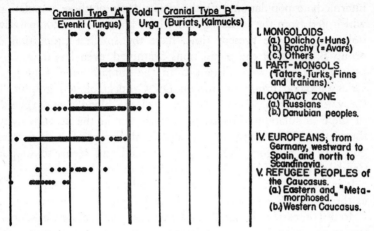

FIGURE 18a. *Gene frequencies (q) of blood group gene B in Asiatics and Europeans (after Candela).*

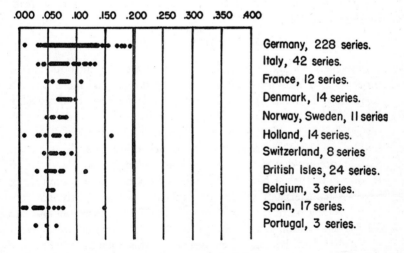

FIGURE 18b. *Blood group frequencies (q) of blood group B in various European peoples (after Candela).*

having acquired the B factor presumably by genetic contact with intermediate populations; 5) the descendants of those populations which fled from the invaders, and which have lived in comparative isolation until the present time, have the smallest proportion of group B of any of the populations examined, even less than those populations who were distant from the contact zone. Using 749 series of blood grouping studies, Dr. Candela plotted graphically the value of q, that is the frequency of the blood group gene B, in these populations. His results are shown in the accompanying illustration. The progressive decrease in the value of q, from category one to category five, is quite marked and seems to support Candela's theory. (Note the correlation with brachycephaly.)

It is especially notable that in the so-called refugee peoples, such as the eastern Caucasians (8) and the Basques (4), the amount of B found is extremely small, and there is good reason to suppose that what little B is present is the result of recent mixture with foreign elements. Candela's theory is supported by another consideration; if the introduction of B had happened a very long time ago, the close correlation which is still visible in the contact zone between the percentage of other Mongoloid characteristics in the population and the frequency of gene B would not be expected to be so readily demonstrable.

Separation of Genes

However, enough time has gone by since the introduction of group B into Western Europe so that we do not find there is much correlation between the blood group and the degree of possibly Mongoloid characteristics (dark eyes, skin, and hair, and brachycephaly) which exist in the population. The individual "Mongoloid" genes have got separated from each other to such an extent that in present-day Europe, individuals belonging to blood group B may nevertheless have blond hair, fair skin, blue eyes, and long heads. Characteristics which are inherited independently get separated as they are transmitted from generation to generation, and any original correlation which existed in the parent populations is eventually abolished. Because of crossing-over, this separation eventually occurs even in the case of linked genes (pp. 72 and 73).

It follows that we cannot usually reconstruct, from a study

of present-day populations, the particular constellation of physical (or mental) features characterizing the ancestral groups which mixed to produce our modern racial cocktails. (See p. 192.)

As has been pointed out by numerous workers (21), since race mixture is a mixture of genes, no mixed human population is likely ever to become genetically pure or even pure for a few of the genes involved. Certain writers have assumed that genetic purity, or at least substantial homogeneity of physical types, would arise after a certain number of generations, and that ethnic groups, even if originally of hybrid origin, could after the lapse of sufficient time be treated as "pure races." We shall see (p. 128) how even "inbreeding" will not bring this about. This conclusion, of course, bears importantly on the question of whether or not pure human races ever did exist.

These statements should, however, not be taken to conflict with the rule that as time goes on traits from the parent populations will become more uniformly distributed in the new ethnic group. This rule is in the main correct, and makes for a more homogeneous-appearing population, with fewer extreme types. If we start with a mixture of 800 individuals of blood type OM and 200 individuals of blood type AN, we shall have, when genetic equilibrium is attained, a population containing about 41 per cent of individuals of blood type O M, 20 per cent O MN, 3 per cent O N, 23 per cent A M, 12 per cent A MN, and 1 per cent A N, which provides quite a contrast to the frequencies with which we started. The inheritance of skin color furnishes an even better example, for the number of genes involved is greater, and the apparent blending greater, so that a black and a white race may produce, in the end, a roughly homogeneous brown hybrid group, as the various genes for pigmentation get uniformly distributed (Fig. 19). However, if inbreeding in local groups should be at all intense, some diversity in color would result because of the resulting diminution of the intermediate-looking heterozygotes. In such a case the pigmentation might vary considerably from individual to individual. Families are in fact seen in numerous populations in which pigmentation grades do vary quite perceptibly from one member to the next.

It has long been known to geneticists that the above calculations pertaining to race mixture can be reversed, and if we know that the frequency of a gene in a mixed population has been increased by mixture of a population without this gene with a population containing a known amount of it, we can compute the proportions in which the two original populations mixed. If our mixed population contains a gene frequency of 0.5 for the gene X, and is made up of a mixture of population A, which has no X, and population B, which has $X = 1.00$ (in other words all members of B possess the gene X), then we can see that the populations A and B mixed in equal numbers.

Even if our mixed population represents the end result of the mixture of two populations, both of which possessed the gene X, but in unequal amounts, we can still compute the proportions in which the two original populations mixed, if we know the frequencies of X which each originally possessed. In Appendix IV-2, it is shown how such calculations can be made. Using such formulas, we may compute that the Navaho Indians examined by Allen and Korber (1) possessed 17.4 per cent "white" blood (see App. IV-3).

Inbreeding

A factor which can modify the proportions of different phenotypes in man (and other organisms) is *inbreeding*. In its correct sense inbreeding means mating between close relatives. Unless this occurs, a population, though it may be cut off from all contact with the outside world, is not inbred; it is merely reproductively isolated.

The reason inbreeding modifies the proportion of genotypes and phenotypes is fairly easy to understand on genetic principles (Ch. II). Close relatives are more likely to be of the same genotype than are unrelated members of the population, and thus inbreeding will mean that matings of dominant with dominant, of recessive with recessive, and of heterozygote with heterozygote, will be relatively more frequent than the other matings (dominant with recessives, etc.).

The results of this are comparatively simple to deduce. The heterozygotes will continue to produce both dominants and recessives among their offspring, but a simple diagram will show that only half of their offspring are heterozygotes, the remainder being equally divided (on the average) between dominants and recessives.

Dominant × dominant matings produce only dominants, and recessive × recessive matings produce only recessives. The range of variability of the population is continually reduced, and the proportion of homozygotes is increased at the expense of the heterozygotes.

Let us take a simple hypothetical illustration. Suppose that we start with a population of 128 individuals, 25 per cent of whom belong to blood type M, 25 per cent to type N, and 50 per cent to MN. Such a population is in genetic equilibrium (p. 110). Now let us suppose that a law is promulgated that individuals of type N can mate only with other type N's, M's with M's, and MN's with MN's. This would constitute selective mating, the most intense form of inbreeding possible, more intense actually than continued brother-sister matings. The outcome is shown in Table 10. (We assume

TABLE 10

Showing Effects of Selective Mating on the Frequencies of the M, N Blood Types

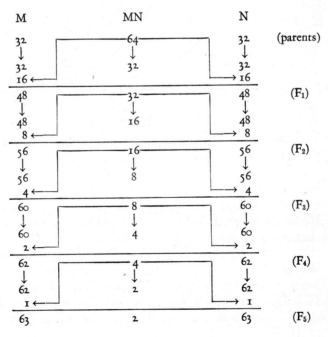

that chance does not upset the process just outlined; at the most it would only delay the attainment of the final result.)

If each individual in the population has on the average just one child who reaches the reproductive age, we find that each of our 32 M's has produced an M, and each of our 32 N's an N, in

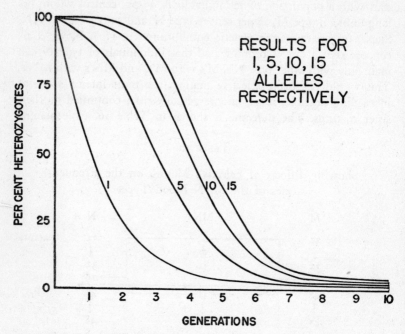

RESULTS FOR
1, 5, 10, 15
ALLELES
RESPECTIVELY

FIGURE 19. *The rate at which intensive inbreeding produces homozygosity when various numbers of alleles are involved (after East and Jones).*

the F_1 generation. But our 64 MN's have only produced 32 MN's, for they have produced also 16 M's and 16 N's. So the numbers in the new generation are: 48 M's, 48 N's, and 32 MN's. Continuing the process, we arrive, in the fifth filial generation, at the figures shown at the bottom of the table. In five generations our percentages have changed from M = 25, N = 25, MN = 50, to M = 98.22, N = 98.22, and MN = 1.56. It is clear that the heterozygote is on the way out. In spite of this change, however, the genes *M* and *N* are still present in the population in equal numbers, and in fact it can easily be shown that in general inbreeding does not change the gene frequencies. Such change is only brought about by other agencies such as mutation, selection, and genetic drift (Ch. V).

The general mathematical formula for the reduction of heterozygosis by inbreeding was given by Mendel in his original paper.

It has been seriously proposed that Rh-negative women should marry only Rh-negative men. It is unlikely that this recommendation will be followed by any large number of our population, but if it were, it would provide an actual illustration of the hypothetical case just discussed.

The rate at which homozygosity is approached depends on the number of allelomorphs which are involved. This is illustrated in the accompanying figure (Fig. 19) taken from East and Jones (12). The rate at which homozygosity is approached in successive generations of mating when just two alleles are involved, assuming, in the first instance, self-fertilization (which we might find in plants), and in the second instance, brother and sister mating, is shown in the accompanying Table 11. Wright (27), (28), and Hogben (17) have derived formulas which enable one to compute the effect of inbreeding of a given intensity, continued for a given time, on the distribution frequency of characteristics in a population.

In the case of self-fertilized organisms, each heterozygous pair forms in the next generation half homozygotes and half heterozygotes and the homozygotes remain constant and breed true; the number of heterozygotes is thus halved in each generation. At the end of about ten generations the incidence of heterozygosity is so small as to be practically undetectable. In organisms such as man it is not quite so obvious from first principles, but it can be shown by very simple mathematics that the reduction in heterozygosity is an inevitable consequence of inbreeding.

This increase in homozygotes and decrease in heterozygotes as a result of inbreeding has been shown by a number of experimental studies on lower forms. Among them there is the study of Sewall Wright (29) on guinea pigs. Wright's study illustrates what is one of the most important consequences of inbreeding, namely the bringing to light of unfavorable (see p. 40) recessive characters in a family. In the case of many genes of the guinea pig (and in other organisms which have been subjected to extensive experimental study as has, for example, Indian corn — maize) the mechanism of heredity is thoroughly understood, and the succession of phenotypes observed as inbreeding progresses can be seen to be a logical consequence of the above mechanism. Wright (29), and East

TABLE II

Effects of Inbreeding on Phenotypic Frequencies, Starting with Heterozygous Parents

(*Self-Fertilization*)

Parent Type	P	F_1	F_2	F_3		Limit
		Generation				
YY	0	1/4	3/8	7/16	....	1/2 YY
yy	0	1/4	3/8	7/16	....	1/2 yy
Yy	1	1/2	1/4	1/8	....	0 Yy

(*Brother-Sister Matings*)

Parent Type	P	F_1	F_2	F_3	F_4	Limit
		Generation				
YY	0	1/4	3/8	5/16	11/32...................	1/2 YY
yy	0	1/4	3/8	5/16	11/32...................	1/2 yy
Yy	1	1/2	1/4	3/8	5/16...................	0 Yy

The numbers represent the fraction of the population made up of the genotypes in question. P represents the parents, F_1, F_2, successive inbred generations.

and Jones (12), all found that there was an average decline in vigor in the course of inbreeding when the degree of inbreeding was very close. This can be attributed to the action of genes which are harmless or inactive in the heterozygous state but which actually reduce vigor when homozygous. Wright (30) has suggested that the degree of inbreeding which a population can withstand is related to the amount of inbreeding it has already undergone. Inbreeding has been made use of by plant and animal breeders in the creation of certain breeds; such breeds have got rid of the more deleterious genes, and consequently can stand a good deal of inbreeding. But in the case of chickens, where inbreeding has not been a common practice and, as a consequence, the elimination of recessive genes which would be harmful in the homozygous state has not proceeded far, it is well known that "new blood" should be imported into the flock at intervals, and Wright states that nearly any breed of chickens will "go to pieces" under a regime of continued close inbreeding.

The first generation of crossbreeding generally shows beneficial effects (heterosis or hybrid vigor, p. 124), but in populations containing harmful recessives, later generations may show a decline. It has been suggested by some writers that inbreeding in human populations would eventually show harmful effects, but there seems little proof that it ever has. Selection acts so severely on most human populations, however, that it is likely that such harmful recessives would ordinarily be swiftly eliminated, and the net effect would be beneficial. The existence of vigorous hybrid stocks in man, many of which have made notable contributions to civilization (such as the ancient Greeks, the French, the English, and the Germans), has been attributed by some to heterosis. Of course nobody doubts that rare human genes exist which produce very undesirable effects when present in double dose (homozygous) and consequently, for the sake of the immediate offspring, mating among relatives who possess, or might possess, any of these genes is to be discouraged. This fact has little bearing on the question of the evolutionary effect on whole populations of continued inbreeding.

Some anthropologists have written as if they considered that human inbreeding has been a good thing, or at least that it has been in large part responsible for the formation of the present human races (which may or may not be a good thing). Such writers apparently either misused the term, and meant by it simply endogamy, isolation, or something of the sort, or were not familiar with the actual genetic consequences, as just outlined. In particular they probably did not really understand how transitory the changes produced by inbreeding may be.

Such writers probably reasoned from work on domestic animals, where it is true (see above) that inbreeding has sometimes been found to have profound effects and has resulted in the creation of some well-known domestic breeds such as the Guernsey and Jersey cows, for example. But in these cases man was assisting nature and was able deliberately to *eliminate* the undesirable phenotypes and *retain* those which had the characteristics which he preferred. In a wild species living in a state of nature, no permanent change in the gene frequencies will result from inbreeding, *unless deleterious recessives are present and are eliminated — in whole or in part — by natural selection*. There will only be an increase in the number of homozygotes and a decrease in the number of heterozygotes.

The importance which some writers formerly ascribed to human inbreeding and its supposed role in the formation of races is illustrated by suggestions made by some that in early times (say before the Industrial Revolution) the degree of inbreeding in Europe must have been very high. It is likely that such writers overestimated the degree of inbreeding which then existed (20, 9). At any rate no such high degree of inbreeding is found at the present time. It is not too easy to estimate the exact degree of inbreeding which prevails among modern human populations. However, it has been estimated by Dr. Julia Bell (2) that in the patients of certain Children's Hospitals located around London, out of 4053 patients, only 0.271 per cent were the offspring of first cousins. This seems to be the first published attempt to test the amount of inbreeding in a human population, as opposed to the armchair speculation which preceded it.

But was the degree of inbreeding ever so terribly high in Europe? Let us take a study of a small population which today has much the breeding structure of a medieval European village.

In 1941, Boyd and Boyd (6) reported the results of a study of the inhabitants of a Syrian village in the Anti-Lebanon Mountains, called Boarij, where the population was said to be highly inbred. From a study carried out there by Miss Anne Fuller it was known that marriages between cousins were very common, as were consanguineous marriages in general. In fact, almost the entire population of the village could be traced back to three or four family lines. Traditionally, the village "kept its blood pure," and marriages were usually between members of the village (although one of the young men occasionally brought back a bride from the valley below). It is hard to expect any higher degree of inbreeding to have prevailed in recent years, at least in Europe, than still prevailed in 1937 in this small Syrian village. An opportunity was therefore provided to check the effect of inbreeding on the characteristics of such a population.

In the case of the M and N blood types, the test for the effects of inbreeding is relatively easy to make. The heterozygote is type MN and types M and N are homozygous. If inbreeding had modified the frequencies in the population of Boarij very much, one would expect to find types M and N relatively more numerous than normally, so that we would have the relation $\sqrt{\overline{M}} + \sqrt{\overline{N}} > 1$. Actually it was found that the *heterozygote* MN was slightly (but not significantly) in excess of the theoretical maximum of 50 per cent, so that contrary to expectation, the following relationship was found:

$$\sqrt{\overline{M}} + \sqrt{\overline{N}} = 0.972 < 1$$

Thus these results did not provide any evidence that the degree of inbreeding which had prevailed in Boarij had been sufficient to increase significantly the proportion of individuals homozygous for M or N.

In the case of the A, B, O blood groups, the only group which can be known immediately from serological evidence to be heterozygous is group AB. If inbreeding had significantly affected the frequencies of these groups, one would expect the frequency of the blood group AB to be less than that calculated from the values of the O, A, and B group frequencies. The calculated value is $2pq$ where p and q are the frequencies of the genes for A and B respectively, calculated by the equations $p = \sqrt{\overline{O} + \overline{A}} - \sqrt{\overline{O}}$, $q = \sqrt{\overline{O} + \overline{B}} - \sqrt{\overline{O}}$, where the symbols $\overline{O}$, $\overline{A}$, and $\overline{B}$ represent frequencies (per cent divided by 100) of the respective types. It was found in fact that the calculated value of $2pq$ was 0.144 or 14.4 per cent, which was somewhat greater (but not significantly greater) than the value of 9.1 per cent actually found in the population of 131 which was examined.

Whether a person of group A or group B is heterozygous or homozygous cannot be told readily except by tests of his parents or offspring or both, and even then the test will of course often be inconclusive, since human families are often too small to furnish examples of all the types of children which a mating could produce. In the tests in Boarij, six families were examined in which one of the parents belonged to group A or group B. In four of these families, the groups of the children proved the A or B individual in question to have been heterozygous. This result does not suggest that the proportion of heterozygotes in the population had been notably decreased by inbreeding. Therefore, as judged by an actual test, the effects of inbreeding on a human population where the genetic mechanism of the character involved was known do not seem to have been very great. This is one of the few populations which have been tested, but it is not atypical, and it seems possible therefore that, although inbreeding may have played an important role in the development of certain breeds of domestic animals, it has not in most cases played a very important role in the development of any of the present human races. Later tests on the Navaho Indians at Ramah, New Mexico, also failed to show any notable effect of inbreeding.

It might also be pointed out that reducing the heterozygotes in a population and increasing the proportion of homozygotes, even if the process is carried to its *limit,* may not make a very great difference in phenotypic frequencies, when a number of genes is involved. From formulas such as those of Wright (27), (28), and Hogben (18), we may calculate that if we were to take a population such as the Indians examined by Nigg (24) at the Haskell Institute at Lawrence, Kansas, and mate first cousins for a very long time, which would be considered a very high degree of inbreeding for most human populations, the results would be to give us the population with blood group percentages as shown in Table 12. This

TABLE 12

Change in Blood Group Frequency with Long Continued First Cousin Matings

	O	A	B	AB
Initial percentage	70.9	27.2	1.6	0.3
Final percentage	84.2	14.9	0.9	0.0

change is probably much less than that which many readers would have anticipated.*

Now comes the most startling point of all. Even this change would remain constant only so long as the degree of inbreeding continued to be intense. If the reader will examine treatments of the results of random mating (17, 9, see App. IV-1) he will see that *a single generation of random mating would at once abolish the changes completely, and give us again the same proportion of phenotypes with which we started!*

REFERENCES FOR CHAPTER IV

1. Allen, F. W., and W. Schaeffer, *Univ. New Mexico Bull., 4,* No. 2, 3–29 (1935).

1a. Allen, F. W., and J. Korber, cited by: Allen and Schaeffer (1935).

2. Bell, J., *Ann. Eug., 10,* 370–391 (1940).

2a. Bernstein, F., *Zeitch. f. indukt. Abstamm. u.- Verer., 37,* 237–270 (1925).

2b. Bernstein, F., *Z. f. ind. Abstamm. u.- Verer., 56,* 233–273 (1930).

2c. Bernstein, F., *Die geographisch Verteilung der Blutgruppen und ihre Anthropologische Bedeutung. Comitato Italiano per lo Studio dei Problemi della Populazione.* Rome, 1931.

3. Boyd, W. C., *Am. J. Phys. Anthrop., 25,* 215–235 (1939).

4. Boyd, W. C., and L. G. Boyd, *Am. J. Phys. Anthrop., 23,* 49–70 (1937).

4a. Boyd, W. C., *Tabulae Biologicae, 17,* 113–240 (1939).

5. Boyd, W. C., *Am. J. Phys. Anthrop., 27,* 333–344 (1940).

6. Boyd, W. C., and L. G. Boyd, *Am. J. Phys. Anthrop., 28,* 319–330 (1941).

7. Boyd, W. C., and L. G. Boyd, *Am. J. Phys. Anthrop., 7,* 569–574 (1949).

8. Candela, P. B., *Human Biol., 14,* 413–433 (1942).

9. Dahlberg, G., *Genetics, 14,* 421 (1929).

10. Dobzhansky, Th., *The Teaching Biologist, 12,* 98–106 (1943).

11. Dunn, L. C., and Th. Dobzhansky, *Heredity, Race, and Society.* Penguin Books, Inc., New York, 1946.

12. East, E. M., and D. F. Jones, *Inbreeding and Outbreeding.* Lippincott, Philadelphia, 1919.

13. Elsdon-Dew, R., *Sou. Afr. J. Med. Sci., 1,* 184–190 (1936).

13a. Fabricius-Hansen, V., *J. Imm., 36,* 523–530 (1939).

13b. Fales, H. A., and F. Kenny, *Inorganic Quantitative Analysis.* D. Appleton-Century, New York, 1939.

---

* We are assuming that the mechanism of random genetic drift (the "Sewall Wright effect") has not operated to abolish either the O, A or B gene.

13c. Fisher, R. A., *Ann. Eug., 13,* 150–155 (1946).

13d. Fisher, R. A., *Ann. Eug., 13,* 223–224 (1947).

14. Geppert, H., and S. Koller, *Erbmathematik.* Verlag von Quelle & Meyer, Leipzig, 1938.

15. Haldane, J. B. S., *Human Biol., 12,* 457–480 (1940).

16. Hardy, G. H., *Science, 28,* 49–50 (1908).

17. Hogben, L., *Genetic Principles in Medicine and Social Science.* Williams and Norgate, Ltd., London, 1931.

18. Hogben, L., *Proc. Roy. Soc. Edinburgh, 80,* 7 (1932–1933).

19. Hogben, L., *Nature and Nurture.* W. W. Norton & Co., New York, 1933.

20. Hogben, L., *Mathematical Genetics.* W. W. Norton & Co., New York, 1946.

21. Huxley, J. S., *Evolution: the Modern Synthesis.* Harper & Bros., New York and London, 1942.

22. Jonsson, S., *Hospitalstid., 66,* 45–50 (1923).

23. Laughlin, W. S., cited by: Romero, de Terra, and Stewart, Viking Fund *Publications in Anthropology, 11,* 132–135 (1949).

23a. Laughlin, W. S., personal communication (1949).

24. Nigg, C., *J. Imm., 11,* 319–322 (1926).

24a. Ottensooser, F., *Rev. Bras. Biol., 4,* 531–537 (1944).

25. Pearson, K., *Philos. Trans. Roy. Soc., A, 203,* 53–86 (1904).

25a. da Silva, E. M., *Am. J. Phys. Anthrop., 6,* 423–428 (1948).

25b. Stevens, W. L., *Ann. Eug., 8,* 362–375 (1938).

26. Weinberg, W., *Verein für vaterländische Naturkunde in Württemberg, 64,* 368–382 (1908).

26a. Wiener, A. S., *Blood Groups and Transfusion.* Charles C. Thomas, Springfield, 1943.

26b. Wiener, A. S., M. Lederer, and S. H. Polayes, *J. Imm., 17,* 357–360 (1929).

26c. Wiener, A. S., and E. B. Sonn, *Ann. N. Y. Acad. Sci., 46,* 969–992 (1946).

27. Wright, S., *Genetics, 6,* 111 (1921).

28. Wright, S., *Am. Nat., 56,* 330 (1922).

29. Wright, S., *U. S. Dept. Agric. Bull., 1090* (1922).

30. Wright, S., *J. Heredity, 33,* 333–334 (1942).

Factors Modifying Gene
Frequencies (Evolution)

> The paleontologist is given only phenotypes, and attempts to
> relate these to genotypes have so far had little success. But here
> genetics can provide him with the essential facts.
> — SIMPSON: *Tempo and Mode in Evolution*

EVOLUTION, essentially, is nothing but a change in gene frequencies
(15, 83). Since we are only beginning to understand the genetic
mechanism underlying a great many human characteristics, it is not
surprising that research in physical anthropology, though always
concerned to a greater or less degree with human evolution, should
only recently have come to be based largely on genetic concepts.
At the present time, however, we find anthropologists asking themselves more and more frequently: By what processes of genetic
change were certain variations brought about? When evolution goes
on for long periods of time, varieties of animals which were originally similar or identical may become extremely different from each
other. The number of genes eventually involved in such changes may
perhaps be rather large, and separate species may finally result.
Nevertheless, as far as we know at present, leaving aside chromosomal rearrangements with which we shall probably not have to
deal in the present discussion, all inherited modification is the result of (a) the production of new genes, (b) the loss of genes, and
(c) the accumulation of changes in gene frequencies. Let us represent the frequency of a gene (say the blood group B gene in human
populations) by the symbol q, and ask ourselves what might possibly happen to alter the frequency of this gene so that the ratio
$q:(1 - q)$ will become different. Whatever mechanisms we find in
operation will be, so far as we know, the same ones which have

altered the frequencies of other human genes in the past and are going to alter such frequencies in the future.

There seem to be four agencies which might be expected to alter the gene frequencies in human populations. They are:

1) *Mixture* of populations which are pure, in the sense that one possesses a gene (*B* for example) and the other does not possess *B*, or else of impure populations having different frequencies of *B*. The arithmetic of this has been discussed in Chapter IV. There may exist, under some circumstances, an "immigration pressure" tending to push a new gene into a population which does not have it, or has relatively little of it.

2) *Mutation,* which might increase the number of *B* genes in the populations from q to q', where q is the original frequency, which can be anything from zero to q', or might decrease the number as the result of mutation of the gene *B* to some other gene.

3) *Natural Selection* in an environment in which the gene is advantageous or disadvantageous to the individuals who possess it.

4) The phenomenon of *Genetic* or *Random Drift,* or *Random Variation* as it has been called by Sewall Wright (81, 80, 82, 84), which occurs in isolated populations of relatively small numbers.

We shall discuss each of these agencies in turn.

Mixture

The arithmetic of mixture of different populations in varying proportions has been treated in Chapter IV. In that chapter the result of mixture alone was being treated, so that it could be considered that no progressive change in gene frequencies took place (just as if we were suddenly to mix the contents of two bowls, one containing 100 red marbles, and one containing 100 green marbles; we still have 100 reds and 100 greens). It remains only to point out here that mixture is also a mechanism of race evolution, and in fact at the present time probably the most important agency which is bringing about changes in the frequency of genes in various populations. For, looking at any one local population, the gene frequencies in *it* can be modified by race mixture.

Mutation

The second mechanism by which evolution (that is, change of gene frequencies) operates is *mutation*. The term "mutation" has had a somewhat checkered career, and a number of misapprehensions concerning it have at one time or another been prevalent. In its current sense it may designate any one of the possible kinds of sudden genetic changes which may occur in an organism.

Mayr (51) has suggested that we may use the term "mutation" to designate any "discontinuous" chromosomal change with a genetic effect. Since the word "discontinuous" can hardly be meant here as the opposite of continuous, we might perhaps alter the phrase to read "any fresh chromosomal change with a genetic effect." This definition would apply to ordinary gene mutations (the only kind with which we shall deal here), chromosome mutations (including translocations, inversions, and so forth), and "genome" mutations which would include such phenomena as chromosomal losses and polyploidy. Mayr, in common with many other people, considers that the majority, perhaps the vast majority, of mutations are gene mutations, which might account for the fact that no other type has yet been certainly demonstrated in man. However, we must realize that the techniques for distinguishing gene mutations from other sorts of mutations are rarely applicable in man, and thus we cannot be certain that other types have not occurred in human families which have been studied. Polyploidy seems pretty well excluded, however.

If we assume that we are starting with the ordinary diploid form, the possible new types which may be produced by mutation may be classified as follows (72):

1. Changes in whole sets of chromosomes
   a. Polyploids
   b. Haploids
2. Changes in whole chromosomes
   a. Trisomics, tetrosomics, etc.
   b. Monosomics, nullosomics
3. Changes in amounts of portions of chromosomes
   a. Duplications
   b. Deficiencies

4. Changes in relations of parts of chromosomes
   a. Inversions (38, 48)
   b. Translocations
5. Changes in the composition of individual genes

Any of these changes may be termed mutations, but in this book we shall consider only the last, i.e., changes in the composition of individual genes. Little evidence has been adduced as yet that any of the other mechanisms of mutation (which are often observed in lower forms) have been in operation in human evolution, although there is little doubt that some of them will sooner or later be found to operate. Readers anxious to know more of this subject or hoping to anticipate possible future discoveries in human genetics may turn to some of the genetic textbooks already referred to (72, 74, 28).

For a time after the discovery of mutations some scientific workers doubted that mutations were really the primary material of evolution. They pointed out (61) that the mutations which had been studied experimentally (in lower forms) were produced often by unfavorable conditions or by destructive agents such as X-rays, and caused effects more like degeneration than evolution. And even spontaneously occurring mutations are generally slightly disadvantageous. Also the mutations found in the laboratory mostly had rather minor effects, not too obviously important for survival. Many serious workers doubted if evolution could really be based on such unpromising materials.

If we examine this objection carefully, we find — see Dobzhansky (14) — that it is invalidated by an analysis of the differences which exist between various races and between various species and other natural groups. These categories, we know, have diverged from each other by evolutionary mechanisms. But the only differences which distinguish one race from another or one species from another are found to be simply collections of the same sort of individual differences which mutations produce. At the present time we know of no other mechanism except mutation which *could* have produced such differences. Since these races and species have become differentiated by evolution, it follows that mutational changes can be and have been evolutionary material. Therefore, there is no reason to doubt the potential evolutionary force of the gene or chromosome changes which are observed to occur under laboratory conditions. Examples of such changes will be found in the genetics of the fruit fly Drosophila, the Jimson weed (*Datura stramonium*) (1), the mouse, etc.

The first mutation to be recorded in an animal appeared in 1791 in a male lamb belonging to the flock of Seth Wright, a Massachusetts farmer. As a result of this mutation, the lamb had very short bowed legs, and a special breed was developed from it, by deliberate selection, because it was an advantage to farmers to have short-legged sheep which were not able to jump the stone walls which surrounded the New England sheep pastures. This early breed eventually became extinct, but the same mutation later appeared a second time, this time in Norway, and the short-legged breed was reconstructed. Since that time numerous other mutations have been observed in animals, and we have some reason to believe that we know the exact origin of one or more of the mutations since found in man. A mutation of a normal to a hemophilia-producing gene is thought by some (39) to have occurred in the person of Queen Victoria, who transmitted it to many of her descendants, including members of the Russian and Spanish royal families.

Gene Mutations

The self-propagation of genes is one of the most remarkable things about them. Muller (58) has commented on the fact that not only is this self-propagation in itself remarkable, but the study of mutations reveals the still more remarkable fact that after mutation, when the chemical structure of the gene has changed, the gene still has the property of propagating itself, *its new self*. In other words, the change in gene structure, accidental as it presumably was, has somehow resulted in a change in the catalytic effect produced by the gene, a change of such an exactly appropriate nature that the new reactions are now accurately adapted to produce, among other things, new materials just like the modified gene itself.

Although a given gene may be changed in various ways, there is generally a strong tendency for any given gene to undergo changes of some particular kind (58); so that it usually mutates in some one direction rather than in another. The repeated mutation of the gene at a given locus in the same direction has often been observed in studying the heredity of various lower forms of life.

Although mutations certainly are not always mere losses of genetic material, nor do they always mean that some process or processes which were once part of the development of the organism have been lost, nevertheless mutations often produce effects in the organism which may be termed "losses." For instance, in the case of the mutant genes "bent" and "eyeless" in the fourth chromosome of Drosophila, it has been shown that the effects are exactly of the same kind, although of lesser degree, as those produced by the complete loss of the entire chromosome in which these genes lie (5). Flies having bent or eyeless genes in one chromosome and lacking the homologous "sister" chromosome are even more bent or even more eyeless than those having the homologous chromosome which contains the same gene. The fact that mutations are usually recessive is also evidence that the mutant gene in many cases fails to do something which in the presence of normal genes somehow gets accomplished. However, some dominant genes (e.g., dominant albinism) seem to prevent something from happening.

Muller (55) suggests that an animal is generally in such good equilibrium with its environment (as the result of countless generations of natural selection) that any change is likely to be a change for the bad. The chain of developmental processes goes better in some directions than in others. An alteration of one step in the scheme is likely to displace the whole complicated sequence in one of the many unfavorable directions, rather than in one of the few which would be favorable.

The extent of the change which a single gene mutation represents is evidently very restricted, for Muller has found that when a mutation occurs in one gene, the other gene of exactly the same kind lying nearby in the sister chromosome of the same cell remains unaffected. How extensive the change within an individual gene has to be, before we recognize it as a mutation, is still unknown. Muller thinks, however, that eventually it should be possible to decide whether the gene is composed of several molecules (or unit particles), one of which may change at a time.

Until researches such as those suggested by Muller and others have been carried out, we shall have to content ourselves with the supposition that a gene mutation is some sort of chemical alteration in the gene which causes the production of a different end product in the organism, under suitable environmental conditions. At present we do not know the exact nature of this alteration. We do know that it can be affected by outside agencies such as X-rays (56, 57, 59), and by the administration of certain toxic substances.

In a population living under normal conditions there seem to be certain normal rates of mutation for each gene. These may be so low that mutations are not observed in the normal course of events often enough to enable us to state what the normal rate of mutation is, although more extensive observations would nearly always enable us to ascertain this. Considering how little we know of human genetics, it is natural that there have not been many direct reports of new gene mutations (40, 53) in man but there is evidence (39) from reliable pedigrees that some human gene mutations are occurring with some frequency.

Haldane in 1935 (37) estimated that the normal allele of the hemophilic genes mutates to the hemophilic gene about once in 50,000 individuals per generation ($=$ a rate of 2×10^{-5}). Compared to the mutation rate in other forms of life, this is moderately high. Without such mutations, since hemophilia is a very serious disadvantage, and since the action of natural selection is to eliminate such a gene, the trait would certainly have disappeared long ago. Gunther and Penrose, about the same time (28a), estimated that the normal allele of the epiloia gene (epiloia is a rare disease in which mental defect and epilepsy are associated with tumor formation in the brain, the skin, and certain viscera) mutates to the gene for epiloia at a somewhat lower rate.

In a more recent paper (40) Haldane has re-estimated the mutation rate to hemophilia as 3.2×10^{-5}, a figure agreeing better with mutation rates observed in other organisms. He thinks the rate is higher, perhaps as much as ten times higher, in male X chromosomes than in female X chromosomes.

Since natural races of the lower forms, such as Drosophila, are regularly found on examination to contain a considerable number of lethal genes in the heterozygous state (14, 16), and since natural selection tends to eliminate these lethal genes, we may suppose that in all populations all over the world, mutations are occurring at a higher rate in some populations than in others, and affecting certain genes more frequently than they affect other genes.

It is possible that some mutations are irreversible, in the sense that when a gene has once mutated to a certain new form it cannot change back to the original form. The evolutionary effects of such a mechanism have been considered by Wright (85). However, there is reason to believe that in general mutations can occur in either direction, and that as a rule the mutant gene is potentially able to change back to the so-called "normal" gene. Changes in certain directions, however, are supposed by some (81) to be easier.

When mutation is reversible, there must be some gene frequency,

TABLE 13

Chances of Survival of an Individual Gene
(from Fisher (22))

Number of Generations	Probability of Survival	
	No Advantage	1 Per Cent Advantage
1	0.6321	0.6358
3	0.3741	0.3803
7	0.2095	0.2175
15	0.1127	0.1217
31	0.0589	0.0687
63	0.0302	0.0409
127	0.0153	0.0271
Limit	0.0000	0.0197

other than zero or one, which represents a stable equilibrium for the population, even though mutation, mixture, and selection may all be occurring simultaneously. The conditions of such a complex equilibrium have been worked out by Sewall Wright (89).

Just as in the case of small immigrations into a relatively large population (see p. 111), it is necessary to keep in mind that the appearance of a single mutation in a single individual, without the action of selection and other evolutionary mechanisms to build up the frequency, will not in itself be sufficient to cause this new gene to spread through the population. As will be seen below, even if a mutation has a slight but positive selective advantage, such a mutation occurring only once in a relatively small population is likely to end in ultimate extinction. A mutated gene with no advantage will probably be lost after relatively few generations; ultimately, it is sure to die out (22; see Table 13).

We see that in a large population even a gene with a 1 per cent advantage in selection — a relatively large advantage — has in the long run only a 0.0197 probability — less than 2 per cent — of establishing itself. But some genes mutate repeatedly. Formulas have been derived from which we may calculate the rate of increase of a gene which mutates repeatedly. The treatment, for the benefit of mathematically inclined readers, is given in Appendix V-1. It will be seen that the rate of spread is greater when the mutation rate is greater.

Mutation Equilibrium

If selection is acting in one direction (say to eliminate gene A) and mutation on the whole in another direction (say to increase the frequency of A) then an equilibrium will usually eventually result, for at some point the rate of elimination of the gene becomes equal to the rate of its replacement by mutation. We call this mutation equilibrium. (See App. V-1.) This can be illustrated diagrammatically (Fig. 20). See also Wright (88), Haldane (33, 39), and Fisher (22).

The mathematics of this problem are presented in Appendix V-2. We can conclude from the results that the frequency of the unfavorable "abnormal" gene varies with the mutation frequency.

Mutations are of course an absolute necessity for evolution, for they provide all of the "raw material." Very frequent mutations will provide a "mutation pressure" and may determine the direction of evolution.

However, in moderate-sized populations, Wright does not think that mutation pressure is as important an evolutionary force as is selection or random genetic drift (see p. 154). If a mutation occurs often enough, however, it will surely establish itself in the end, even if it is an unfavorable one (22). The chief difference in the points of view of Fisher and Wright is the emphasis of the latter on the greater effectiveness of selection operating on a population which is subdivided into many partially isolated local strains (81, 82, 88).

Spontaneous variability, just as Darwin supposed, provides the raw material for natural selection to operate on and thus is the basis of evolution. Darwin, writing before the real principles of heredity had been established, probably supposed that this variability was continuous, although on the basis of modern genetics we know it

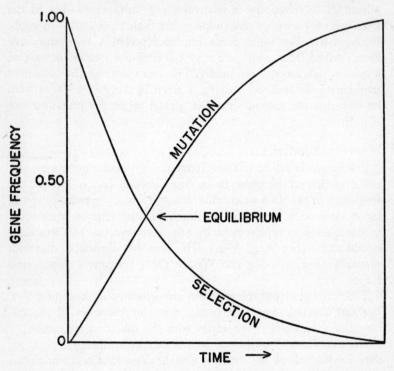

FIGURE 20. *Diagrammatic representation of the equilibrium between selection and mutation.*

to be discontinuous (i.e., due to genes and mutations). The changes produced by any individual mutation are usually so slight, however, that Darwin's ideas still apply very much as originally presented.

Selection

By selection we mean that organisms possessing certain characteristics survive in relatively larger numbers, and leave relatively more offspring, than do other organisms of the same kind possessing other characteristics. Selection is then said to be acting in favor of the first group of characteristics. The idea is simple, but the actual process as it occurs in nature is perhaps not so simple. Natural selection is an extremely complex process (89). Among the factors which may determine the relative contribution to the next generation by a given set of individuals, we may list: differences in mortality at practically any age; differences in age of onset and duration of sexual activity; differences in fertility; differences in emigration rates. Selection is constantly acting, and hardly any gene is neutral, selectively speaking. One of the objections to the theory of natural selection used to be that, even if we were to suppose that an individual who possessed some characteristics which gave him a very definite advantage over his fellows were to be born into a certain population, it would be very unlikely that the ultimate characteristics of the population would be influenced by this event. And it is perfectly true that a single individual, even one possessing considerable advantages over his fellows in the struggle for existence, might nevertheless be eliminated or fail to transmit the new characteristics to his offspring. Evolution probably makes very little progress by such accidental saltations.* We have seen above, however, that although mutations in general do not affect the characteristics of an individual very markedly, they do tend to occur repeatedly, so that any which are favorable from the point of view of natural selection are given a chance to become established in the population.

SELECTION RATE — MATHEMATICAL THEORIES

As Dobzhansky says, the main assumption which is made in the theory of natural selection is that some inherited traits of a species have an advantage over others, in survival or reproduction or both. If we could see the genes which an individual possesses (imagine for the moment that the organism is transparent and that the genes are of a conspicuous color and about the size of marbles), it would be possible to consider genetic selection directly, or in other words to treat cases where two alleles z and Z tend to be reproduced in each generation in the ratio $\dfrac{z}{Z} = (1 - k)$, where k is the so-called

---

* Changes of considerable magnitude, arising suddenly.

"selection coefficient." If, for instance, on the average there are retained only 999 gametes carrying z, where 1000 gametes carrying Z are retained, the value of k = 0.001. Some authors replace 1 − k by t, where t is defined as the "fitness," in the Darwinian-Spencerian sense, of the allele z compared to Z. But the mathematics of the present problem prove to be simpler if we retain the older (1 − k) notation, and this seems worth while, since by keeping the problem simple we may convince some readers that mathematical problems of selection are not necessarily too complex to understand.

The mathematical treatment is essentially a simple one, analogous to that used for the dynamics of other sorts of change. Equations are obtained which enable us to calculate the gene frequency after the lapse of a given number of generations, the rate of selection being known. This enables us to estimate the amount of change which would be produced in the periods of time known to be involved in the racial history of man. Some of the results are tabulated in Table 15. The derivations of the various equations will be found in Appendix V–3.

The equation of Haldane's given in Appendix V–3 holds pretty well for cases where the generations do not overlap and the selection is not too intense, that is, when the characteristic being considered does not have a selective advantage or disadvantage k in the formula greater than 0.1, or 10 per cent. (A 10 per cent advantage or disadvantage would be very large for any genes usually found in the heterozygous state in nature.)

In man, of course, the generations do overlap, and we can have matings possible between adults of practically all age groups. Some of these potential matings take place and offspring are produced. In a later paper (32) Haldane was able to show, however, that even if the generations do overlap, as in man, if we restrict our attention to populations nearly in equilibrium, so that the rate of selection is slow, and k is small (not over 10 per cent), we may still use the above formula, if we like, although this involves redefining a "generation" so that it now conforms to the mathematical equation and not exactly to the biological facts. The difference in magnitude between the two definitions seems likely to be small, and since we have every reason to believe that selection is acting only at a slow rate on most of the human characteristics we know about, it is probable that the results obtained from the equation fit the actual facts fairly closely.

In Appendix V–4 we consider briefly a case which is more general mathematically, and possibly more frequently met in nature — namely the case where the selective advantage is different for each genotype. We consider the possibility that different genotypes (say homozygous dominant and heterozygous dominant), although similar because of the effect of the dominant gene, are nevertheless not identical, and are acted on by selection at somewhat different rates. The results are more complicated, but similar to those obtained earlier for the simpler case in which heterozygote and homozygote are indistinguishable.

It should not be forgotten that it is possible for the heterozygotes to have advantages over either of the homozygotes. This situation is generally not found when we are dealing with mutant genes, since the mutant gene is usually deleterious or sometimes even lethal. But when dealing with old and well-established genes, such a situation is apparently sometimes found (91). Fisher, Ford, and Huxley (24) investigated the ability of chimpanzees to taste the chemical substance phenyl-thio-carbamide (which can be tasted by some men and not by others). They obtained results which indicated that some individuals of each species were able to taste it at about the same threshold as man, but some were not able to taste it. This suggested that the tasting gene has existed in man since the very earliest times when he diverged from the primordial anthropoid stock. If any selective disadvantage had attached to either gene, evolutionary mechanisms would certainly by this time have eliminated one of them, i.e., either the tasting gene or the nontasting gene. From this study, Fisher, Ford, and Huxley (24) inferred that the heterozygotes for this gene must have enjoyed some selective advantage over either of the homozygotes, thus explaining the preservation of both genes down to the present day in the human population. They had, of course, no idea of the nature of this advantage enjoyed by the heterozygote. Other geneticists such as Dobzhansky believe that the phenomena are more easily explained by assuming that the observed frequencies are the result of equilibrium of mutation rates.

The mathematical theory of selection has been discussed also by Geppert and Koller (27).

If combined with mutation, the process of selection might either be speeded up or slowed down, depending on the direction of mutation. If the direction of the mutation is chiefly "favorable," the speed of the evolutionary process is greatly increased, especially in the initial stage (14). Thus if we have a gene mutation to a gene X at a rate of 1 in 1 million, the change of the gene frequency from $q = 0.000,001$ to $q = 0.000,002$ is accomplished in a single generation, whereas a similar change resulting from the action of natural selection alone on a recessive gene having a selective advantage of 1 part in 1000 requires 321,444 generations!

APPLICATIONS TO MAN

If a certain dominant gene had a selective advantage over its recessive allele of only one part in 1000 (or 0.1 per cent), its frequency in the stock in question would be increased from 5 to 50 per cent in somewhat less than 3000 generations. In man this would correspond to a period of about 60,000 to 70,000 years. With the possible exception of the Rh blood factors, there is no evidence concerning anthropological characteristics which is exact enough to enable us to estimate whether any of them have a selective advantage as great or perhaps greater than this. It is extremely likely, as already pointed out, that some or most of them do. In particular the general relation between pigmentation and warm sunny climates suggests a selective advantage for pigmentation genes in such environments (p. 176). The frequency of blonds among the Scandinavians might suggest that in regions with deficient sunlight the reverse would also be true. The rather highly pigmented Eskimo seems to constitute an exception, but it is the opinion of some scholars that they have not inhabited their present cold environments for nearly as long as 75,000 years. Also, it will be seen that recessive genes, as most genes for light pigmentation seem to be, increase much more slowly than dominants, especially when they are rather scarce in the population to begin with.

In Haldane's equations it is only necessary to make k ($= 1 - t$) negative to calculate the effect of a selection which favors the recessives (at the expense of the dominants).

Even dominants increase rather slowly at first, and a population starting with 0.18 per cent of an advantageous dominant gene would require 3500 generations, with $k = 0.1$ per cent, to build the frequency of the new gene up to 5.62 per cent. If we start with 0.27 per cent of an advantageous recessive gene we find it would require 16,000 generations, or about 400,000 years, to increase it to 4.54 per cent. Perhaps the Eskimo started with too low a frequency of reces-

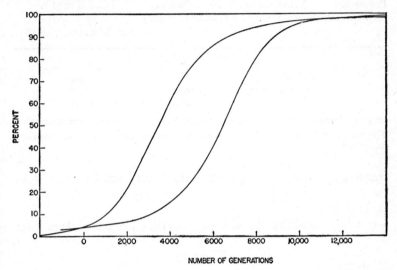

FIGURE 21. *The action of slow selection on a gene. Upper curve, dominants favored; lower curve, recessives favored. Abscissae, number of generations of selection, ordinates, per cent of population with favored character (after Haldane).*

sive genes for pigment, and mutations to genes for low pigmentation have rarely occurred in this stock. In Table 14 we give the probabilities that a recessive gene will become fixed in the population (that is, will completely replace the alternative gene or genes at the same chromosome locus) in various population sizes, considering three cases — a selective advantage of the double recessive of 0.01, a selective *disadvantage* of 0.01, and neutrality (that is, the case in which the gene is neither harmful nor beneficial). This table is taken from Wright (90).

Even with higher selective advantages, such as 1 per cent (which is probably relatively high), evolution due to selection when the

TABLE 14

Chances of "Fixation" of a Recessive Gene (90), Assuming One Such Gene in Populations of Various Sizes

Population Size	Advantage of $yy = 0.01$	No Advantage ("Neutral" Gene)	Disadvantage of $yy = 0.01$ (or Advantage $= -0.01$)
10	0.05	0.05	0.05
50	0.013	0.010	0.007
200	0.0057	0.0025	0.0003
800	0.0027	0.0006	0.0000

The symbol y represents the recessive gene, and yy the homozygous recessive type.

frequency of the gene being acted on is very small or very large (near zero or near 100 per cent) is extremely slow. This is shown in Table 15.

It will be noted that the table (see also the equations of App. V-4)

TABLE 15

Time Required for a Given Change in the Per Cent Frequency of a Gene Having a Selective Advantage of 0.01 (i.e. 1 Per Cent). Modified from Pätau (62)

Dominant Gene		Recessive Gene	
Change in Frequency from	Number of Generations	Change in Frequency from	Number of Generations
0.01–0.1	230	0.01–0.1	900,230
0.1–1.0	231	0.1–1.0	90,231
1.0–50.0	559	1.0–3.0	6,779
50.0–97.0	3,481	3.0–50.0	3,481
97.0–99.0	6,779	50.0–99.0	559
99.0–99.9	90,231	99.0–99.9	231
99.9–99.99	900,230	99.9–99.99	230

suggests that evolutionary change due to selection may be fairly rapid if the advantageous gene is moderately frequent.

In a later paper Haldane (36) derived an equation which describes the variation undergone by a population which mates at random and is subjected to intense selection. Since these calculations lead to the conclusion that, when the gene being acted upon is a recessive, the rate of selection is very much less rapid at first than if it is a dominant, Hogben (44) has mentioned that even if we were to sterilize all the possessors of an undesirable *rare* recessive gene, such as diabetics or people with Friedreich's ataxia, the reduction in incidence in these diseases would be very small, even after long periods of time, such as the whole length of the Christian era. Sterilization of all possessors of undesirable dominant genes, on the other hand, would completely eliminate them in one generation.

These facts have a bearing on the proposals of advocates of eugenics, but the important thing for us to notice at the moment is that there is considerable evidence that, in nature, natural selection can operate rather rapidly, in terms of the lengths of time which have elapsed, if an adequate supply of new genes, more suitable to changing environments, is available.

EFFECTIVENESS OF SELECTION

It used to be doubted if selection as we know it experimentally could really account for the sweeping changes which paleontological evidence indicates have gone on through various geological epochs; but at present, although we believe other agencies also to be operative, few serious workers in biology doubt the efficiency of selection in bringing about evolution.

In many cases we have actually been able to observe the process of evolution in lower forms, probably by selection, a privilege which was denied Darwin (13) and other pioneers in this field. One of the best-known examples is the increase in the incidence of dark coloring (referred to as the phenomenon of melanism) of certain moths. There seems to be no doubt that melanism among many species has become much more common in the last century, and that this change has been in some way connected with the progressive industrialization of the areas where these dark-colored moths are found, for the melanotics occur predominantly in and near large cities and in industrial areas. In some cases the entire population of an area has become melanotic. The history of this process has been described by Harrison (42) and the phenomenon on the continent of Europe has been described by Hasebroek (43). A summary of the genetic findings has been given by Ford (25).

It is worth noting that melanism in moths seems generally to be inherited as a dominant. We have seen from Haldane's formulas (p. 146) how rapidly selection would act to increase the frequency of a dominant gene which had an appreciable advantage in natural selection.

Another example of effective selection in producing adaptation is the increasing resistance of the scale insect, which attacks citrus fruit trees in California, to poisons, such as hydrocyanic acid, which are used to kill it. Quale (66) has shown that several strains of this insect pest have gradually developed a high degree of resistance to the hydrocyanic acid, a resistance which is transmitted genetically. In the microbiological field, modified strains of micro-organisms have repeatedly been encountered (52, 92, 71, 2, 7, 78), which have acquired resistance to various chemotherapeutic drugs such as the arsenicals, the sulfonamides, penicillin, and streptomycin.

Experiments with artificial selection have also demonstrated the rapidity with which evolutionary effects may be produced. As an example of this we may take changes in the numbers of scutellar bristles in Drosophila. In flies of the average laboratory stock, and in wild stock of Drosophila, this number is seldom other than four, but a fly with five bristles is occasionally found. Starting with a five-bristle female and a four-bristle male, Payne, by deliberate selection (63), raised the mean number to about 6.5 in eleven generations and to over nine in thirty generations. Sismanidis (70) has confirmed Payne's results and has even been able to assign the sudden response to selection to recombination in particular chromosomes. This is shown in Fig. 22 (50).

It is unfortunate that the examples of natural selection, resulting in the adaptation of the organism to its environment, which many textbooks choose to present, have been chosen chiefly from a highly specialized group of cases of what Huxley (46) calls the "wonders of nature" type, such as the resemblance of a butterfly to a dead leaf, complete with a mold spot and imitation holes, or the amazing contrivances of certain orchids to insure pollination by insects. The reader should realize that adaptation is not always as spectacular as this. In Chapter VIII of his book, *Evolution, the Modern Synthesis*, Huxley points to the widespread incidence of less fantastic but undoubted adaptations in nature. He includes such examples as the habits of birds living in nests, the acquisition by the giant panda

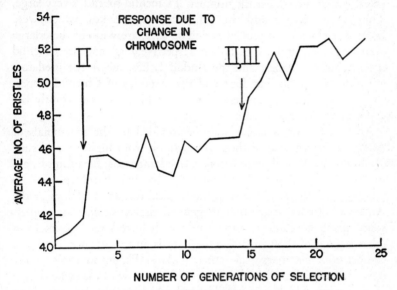

FIGURE 22. *Results of deliberate selection for number of scutellar bristles in* Drosophila (*see text*).

of the ability to hold the bamboo shoots which form the bulk of its diet, adaptations of parasites to the hosts which they inhabit and to the various stages in the development of these hosts, adaptations of certain plants and animals to the color of their environment, adaptation of certain plants to the mineral composition of the soil in which they grow, and adaptation to differences in the extent to which the fields in which they grow are grazed by animals.

Adaptation seems to be more perfect where the density of living forms and thus intensity of selection * is greater, as in the tropics.

* "Intensity of selection" = numbers of living individuals competing, on the average, for the same ecological niche.

Conversely, when selection pressure is lower and species are allowed to run "hog wild," without competition, they develop many varieties; but when they are subjected to rigorous selection, they will perpetuate only the most efficient forms. As an example of this principle, Huxley mentions the Chichlid fish of the African lakes. The large predatory fish which ordinarily eat the Chichlid are absent in certain lakes, and in these lakes the number of Chichlid species is very large. The Victoria-Kioga and the Edward-George Lakes, which were isolated in the second pluvial period or later, are without these large predatory fish, and they contain respectively 58 and 18 Chichlid species, but the Albert and the Rudolf Lakes, where the predators are present, contain but four and three species of Chichlid respectively, a decrease in numbers of species which seems obviously the result of vigorous selection.

An example on a larger scale is provided by the marsupials of Australia, which were without competition from higher forms such as placentals. According to Huxley, tree kangaroos, for example, are so imperfectly adapted to arboreal life that it is hardly possible to imagine their survival today in the tropical forests of Malaya or the Amazon. Huxley states that in general the Australian marsupials seem unable to compete successfully with introduced species from other regions of the world. In other words, in the absence of outside competition, the marsupial fauna of Australia, in an evolutionary sense, has not adapted itself to its environment with the same degree of perfection which was possible and which would doubtless have taken place had natural selection been more vigorously at work, constantly eliminating the unfit at a high rate. Lack of new mutations to select from may have been a factor.

Examples of Adaptive Factors in Man

We shall have, later on, to discuss the question of possible selective advantages or disadvantages belonging to certain physical characteristics of man. The blood grouping characteristics, with the possible exception of the Rh factors, seem to have been exonerated from being of much selective value in so far as we have been able to test them. The Rh factor is probably an exception, because Levine and others (49, 65) have demonstrated a close relationship between Rh incompatibility between mother and fetus and the disease called erythroblastosis fetalis, or hemolytic disease of the newborn, which is responsible for a certain number of stillbirths and neonatal deaths. Wiener (77) states that since all the affected infants are heterozygous, equal numbers (but different proportions of the total numbers) of Rh positive and Rh negative genes are lost in every generation. If we ignore the subgroups of the Rh factors, therefore, it is relatively easy to compute the effect of the loss of these genes on the distribution of Rh factors over a short period of time.

The mathematical treatment will be found in Appendix V–5. From it Wiener concluded that if the frequency of the Rh negative gene and the frequency of the Rh positive gene were equal, the action of selection would be zero. Therefore at this point we have an equilibrium. It is an unstable equilibrium, however, like a cone balanced on its tip, and a slight movement in either direction would start a process of continuing change. If the incidence of the two genes is unequal the less frequent gene would be affected to a greater extent than the more common gene, so that, in the absence of other influences, the less common gene would be gradually eliminated. The practically complete absence of the Rh negative gene in Australian, Indonesian, Asiatic, and American Indian populations (79, 65) might suggest it may already have taken place before the Australians, Indonesians, and American Indians left Asia. Because of the greater density of population, there is some reason to suppose that selection pressure may be higher in Asia than in sparsely populated parts of the world, and it is possible that it has long been higher. In a dense population, in which competition for food, etc., is intense, it might be thought that the survival of an individual implied a relative freedom from the effects of even slightly deleterious genes. Of course the "constant" C (see App. V–5) is really a function of the relative amounts of Rh positive and negative genes in the population, and its value would steadily fall off as either gene (Z and z in our notation) was eliminated. But since not all the Rh positive genes are equally likely to cause erythroblastosis, other uncertainties are also involved, so that the formula in Appendix V–5 can only be regarded as an approximation, even if it be true that the sort of selection Wiener considered really acts to reduce the frequency of the Rh negative gene. Some workers, such as Fisher (23), doubt that it does.

A treatment more in line with preceding examples has been given by Haldane (38). That certain early Europeans may have had high frequencies of Rh negative genes is suggested by recent studies on the Rh types of the Basques (21). Etcheverry reported 33.6 per cent Rh negatives among 128 persons of Basque descent living in Argentina, and as Mourant points out (54), if tests on larger numbers of subjects bear out this remarkable observation it will seem highly probable that the Rh negative gene in European populations is mainly derived from ancestors akin to the modern Basques.

Another probable example of the effect of selection on the "racial" characteristics of man is the gradual brachycephalization of Europe, especially among the Slavs. Or in other words, the Slavs (and other people in Central Europe) have gradually become more broadheaded (see Table 16).

TABLE 16

Change in Cranial Index of "Nordic" and East European Types (68)

Date	Cranial Index	
	"Nordic"	East European
1200 B.C.	69.2	76.1
300 A.D.	69.6	77.1
1200 A.D.	73.5	78.6
1935 A.D.	ca. 81.0	ca. 86.0

It has been mentioned by Schwidetsky (68) that well-documented series of skulls from Bohemia and from Russia show how this change has progressed from century to century, so that the average cranial index of 73–75 rose as high as 83 by the nineteenth century. Myslivec (60) suggests that a possible explanation of this phenomenon may be the dominance of the brachycephalic form of head over the dolichocephalic form.* It is to be feared, however, that Myslivec is here unconsciously relying on the imaginary phenomenon of

---

* The exact mechanism in which head form is inherited is unknown. Boas (3) thought environment affected the final result.

"genophagy." In view of what we have already said above about the rapidity with which gene equilibrium is obtained, in the absence of selection and mutation, we may doubt that this is really the explanation, for the brachycephalic genes would already have been in equilibrium with the dolichocephalic genes before our story began. As evidence for this statement, we may point to the blood group gene *B,* probably introduced (9) to Europe from Asia in historical times. This gene is dominant over gene *O.* Nevertheless, there is no evidence that the group O gene is tending to be swamped by *B* in Western Europe (or anywhere else). The most probable cause of recent brachycephalization would therefore seem to be the action of natural selection, which leads us to suppose that the brachycephalic individual has some advantage in the struggle for existence over the dolichocephalic individual. What this advantage is, we do not know. Weidenreich (76) suggests it is because the head of the brachycephalic is balanced better on the vertebral column.

Of course the objection has been raised that, in cases such as the above where we seem to see a secular change in the morphology of a population, the real process has been one of gradual replacement of a longheaded population (say) by a roundheaded one. Unfortunately this *is* always a possibility which we cannot deny, because man interbreeds so rapidly when given a chance, and because we never have data on any population certainly known to be isolated absolutely over a long period of time. But the way lower forms (e.g., horses) have undergone morphological change during the course of evolution leaves little doubt that such changes do occur, given sufficient time. It does not seem too much to suppose that similar evolutionary forces may act in similar ways in man.

Inapparent Adaptation

Although there is reason to believe that nearly all organisms are highly adapted to their environment, the way in which their various characteristics fit them for their locality and mode of life is not always apparent at first glance to the observer (46, 8), especially if they are seen outside their natural environment. Cott has analyzed in some detail the way in which design or color pattern, for instance, may be utilized to make an organism inconspicuous (or conspicuous), and Huxley comments on the fact that some organisms are usually nearly impossible to perceive, even when one is near them. Yet a casual observer, seeing the organism isolated from its normal environment, might conclude that there was no evidence of protective coloration or pattern. Knowledge acquired by workers such as Cott (12) is so "practical" that it has been utilized by man in the art of camouflage in war.

Some of the "racial" characters in man might very well be examples of inapparent adaptation. However, it must be admitted that this has not been demonstrated as yet. Nevertheless the possibility should be kept in mind.

SLIGHT ADVANTAGES IMPORTANT

A point which is often not clearly understood is that the fairly small advantage or disadvantage belonging to the possession of a given gene may cause a relatively rapid alteration in the frequencies of this gene. This has been illustrated in the calculations given above. It would not be very easy, with only the information at our disposal at present, to determine whether or not any of the human genes we know about possess a selective advantage or disadvantage of 1 part in 1000 or 0.1 per cent. Yet we have seen that under suitable conditions, selection of this order of magnitude would be adequate to secure the virtually complete elimination of an unfavorable gene in a few thousand generations.

Random Genetic Drift

The fourth evolutionary mechanism which we wish to consider is the Sewall Wright effect. Wright himself (79a) has called the phenomenon *random genetic drift*. This is the same as the mechanism of *isolation* (4), since it depends for its operation on the *isolation* of one small population from other populations with which it could interbreed. A number of biologists and anthropologists have realized, to some extent, the importance of isolation in evolution. For instance, Gates (26) stated that "isolation must have been a factor of extraordinary importance in the early history of man." According to Wright (82) Gulick fairly early recognized the importance of isolation in bringing about a nonadaptive differentiation of local races. The recognition of the great importance of the mechanism of *random drift* in evolution has been largely due to the mathematical work of Wright.

If we choose a very small population consisting, shall we say, of four women and four men, from a larger population which has about the usual European distribution of blood groups, and put them on a desert island, there to propagate themselves, it might easily happen that *no* individual of group B (which usually accounts for only 10–15 per cent of an average European population) would be represented. Even if a group B individual were by chance included he or she would most likely be a heterozygote, that is of the genotype *BO*,* and any child of his has a 50–50 chance of not belonging to blood group B (in other words of being A or O). Even if he had a fair number of children, therefore, the gene *B* might still not be represented in the new generation (the chances of no *B* in one child $= \frac{1}{2}$, of no *B* in four children $(\frac{1}{2})^4 = \frac{1}{16}$, not too unlikely [App. A] for the situation to occur occasionally), and as soon as this hypothetical original group B individual died, or passed the age of reproduction, the *B* gene would thus be irretrievably lost to the tribe, unless it were introduced again by mutation. And of course the group B individual might be killed before he reached the mating age, or might be sterile, or for some other reason fail to leave any offspring.

For such a small population, these conclusions are of course quite elementary. Wright, however, has shown mathematically that even in populations which we might not at first sight consider small, the chance fluctuation in gene frequencies with succeeding generations will often result in a gene being lost. A subdivision of species into isolated populations, plus time to allow a sufficient number of generations to elapse (the number of generations being a function of the population size), is all that is necessary for race formation. As Dobzhansky says (14), "The differentiation of a species into local or other races may take place without the action of natural selection." Possible operation of this mechanism on the blood group frequencies of early human history has been suggested (4).

The way in which the Wright effect may operate is illustrated in some experiments which are described in Appendix V–6.

---

*In the population of the United States, over 90 per cent of all group B individuals are heterozygous for this gene (45).

PERIODIC REDUCTION IN NUMBERS

It seems to be a fact, but one which has been insufficiently appreciated, that many natural populations, probably including, at least in prehistoric times, various groups of the human species also, are sometimes reduced to very small numbers. When this reduction in numbers does occur the mechanism of "genetic drift" has a good chance to operate. A quotation from the book on *Animal Ecology* by Elton (20) will illustrate this point:

> For our present purpose the important thing to bear in mind is the fact that at frequent intervals (frequent compared to the time which it would take for a species to change appreciably) the population of many animals is reduced to a very low ebb, and that this is followed by a more or less rapid expansion in numbers until the former state of abundance is reached once more. After a lemming year, with its inevitable epidemic killing off all but a few of the animals, the arctic tundra is almost empty of lemmings. The same thing can be said of the snowshoe rabbit. One year the country is pullulating with rabbits, the following year you may hunt for a whole summer and only see one. There is usually a rather rapid expansion after this minimum of numbers. In a stream near Liverpool studied by the writer, the whole fauna over a stretch of three miles was wiped out during the summer of 1921, by a severe drought. Recolonization took place from some deep ponds connected with the upper part of the stream, and after three or four years the population of molluscs, insects, crustaceans, fish, etc., had regained its "normal" density. A similar destruction of the fauna took place in 1921 in a small branch of the Thames near Oxford, but by 1925 the animals had reached "normal" numbers again (through immigration and natural increase). The *Gammarus pulex* were very scarce in 1922, but had reached great abundance by 1925, when they were again practically wiped out, this time by an epidemic.

Elton also says (20):

> One more example may be given. Carpenter, when carrying out a survey of the islands on Lake Victoria in order to discover the distribution and ecology of the tsetse fly, noted that islands below a certain size did not support any flies at all, although the conditions for breeding and feeding (which are well defined and regu-

lar) were otherwise apparently quite suitable. The explanation of this was probably that the fly population is subject to certain irregular checks upon numbers, and that any one population must be sufficiently large to survive these checks. There would not be a big enough margin of numbers on a very small island.

The reservoir of genes from which new populations are replenished in such cases of fluctuating populations is much smaller than one would think from a casual examination of the population in a good year, and Wright (80, 81, 87, 88) has shown that the effective population size, in this sense, is much nearer to the minimum than the maximum population (App. V–7).

SIZE OF BREEDING POPULATION

The breeding population, that is, the number of individuals which are potentially able to mate with each other, is in many cases smaller than we suspect. It is so obvious that we scarcely pause to think of it, that only a fraction of the total population can be effective, at any one time, for reproduction. Children below the age of puberty, women past the menopause (*usually*) and very old men, must all be excluded. And even persons past middle age, but still able to reproduce, may be much less effective, because fertility doubtless falls off rapidly with age (10, 69), and because of lowered physical and sexual energy, diminished physical attractiveness, glandular changes, etc. The relatively small size of human mating groups, even in large coeducational universities, has been rather amusingly pointed out by Cook (11), in commenting on a paper by Dudley and Allen (19), who reported that when older men and women were asked how many young people of the same age and opposite sex they had known well enough to consider as a possible husband or wife, their answers ranged around a dozen or so, with a maximum of two or three dozen. Of course they must have made the acquaintance of more than this number, but Cook points out that "not even the most active Lothario is going to take a hundred thousand girls on moonlight rides." Even in a large country with an urban and relatively mobile population such as we have in certain parts of the United States, the number of possible mates for a given individual is still pretty limited. In previous times, and under Old World social conditions, it must have been still smaller.

From the experiments of Dubinin and Romaschoff (App. V–6) we can see that the effectiveness of the Wright effect is much greater in small populations than in larger ones. In small populations, alleles favored by natural selection may actually be lost and disadvantageous alleles may become fixed. In such cases, evolutionary changes may even proceed against the direction of selection pressure.

Naturalists have known for a long time that island populations tend to have aberrant characteristics. This was observed by Darwin and started him thinking along lines which led eventually to the elaboration and publication of his book, *The Origin of Species* (13). Biologically, a cave is perhaps often as isolated as an island, and Mayr (51) suggests that this may explain at least to some extent the very aberrant developments of cave populations.

APPLICATIONS TO THEORIES OF EVOLUTION

In the evolution of actual populations (including man) all four of our main evolutionary mechanisms are probably in operation at once: *mixture, mutation, selection,* and *genetic drift.* The relative importance of each for the future of the group will depend partly upon the size of the population, and partly upon accident. The interaction of the various evolutionary forces is an interesting and important subject, and the mathematical questions involved have been examined by Wright in a series of papers (80, 81, 82, 84, 85, 87, 88), (30, 31, 32, 33, 34, 35, 36), (27) and by others.

The arguments of Wright are somewhat mathematical and will not be presented here, but the conclusions are fairly simple. In very large populations genetic drift has less importance, and very small selective advantages and disadvantages will eventually have their effect.

OTHER EVOLUTIONARY MECHANISMS

The forces of evolution we have surveyed in this chapter can produce races, and even new species, and have doubtless done so in the past. They do not exhaust the list of the evolutionary forces which may be acting, but comprise the ones which have probably been important in man. For a more thorough survey of evolutionary mechanisms, the reader is referred to Wright and to Huxley (46, 89), who discuss the problem in a more general way, and in particular consider mechanisms which, although so far as we know are of little or no importance in the recent evolution of man, are seen to be operating on plants and various other organisms.

REFERENCES FOR CHAPTER V

1. Blakeslee, A. F., *Proc. VI Cong. Gen., 1,* 104–120 (1932).
2. Bloomfield, A. L., W. M. M. Kirby, and C. D. Armstrong, *J. Am. Med. Assoc., 126,* 685–691 (1944).
3. Boas, F., *Changes in the Bodily Form of Descendants of Immigrants.* Columbia Univ. Press, New York, 1912.
4. Boyd, W. C., *A. J. P. A., 27,* 333–364 (1940).
5. Bridges, C. B., cited by Muller, H. J., *Genetics, 2,* 445–465 (1917).
6. Brooks, W. K., *The Foundations of Zoölogy.* Columbia Univ. Press by Macmillan Co., New York, 1899.
7. Buggs, C. W., B. Bronstein, J. W. Hirschfeld, and M. A. Pilling, *J. Am. Med. Assoc., 130,* 64–67 (1946).
8. Buxton, P. A., *Animal Life in Deserts.* London, 1923. Cited by (46).
9. Candela, P. B., *Human Biol., 14,* 413–443 (1942).
10. Child, C. G., *Sterility and Conception.* D. Appleton & Co., New York and London, 1931.
11. Cook, R. C., *J. Heredity, 33,* 332–333 (1942).
12. Cott, H. B., *Adaptive Coloration in Animals.* Methuen & Co., London, 1940.
13. Darwin, C. R., *The Origin of Species.* London, Murray, 1859.
14. Dobzhansky, Th., *Genetics and the Origin of Species.* Columbia Univ. Press, New York, 1941.
15. Dobzhansky, Th., *Teaching Biologist, 12,* 97–106 (1943).
16. Dobzhansky, Th., and S. Wright, *Genetics, 26,* 23–51 (1941).
17. Dubinin, N. P., cited by: Dobzhansky, Th., *Genetics and the Origin of Species.* Columbia Univ. Press, New York, 1941.
18. Dubinin, N. P., and D. D. Romaschoff, cited by: Dobzhansky, Th., *Genetics and the Origin of Species.* Columbia Univ. Press, New York, 1941.
19. Dudley, F. C., and W. Allan, *J. Heredity, 33,* 331–334 (1942).
20. Elton, C., *Animal Ecology.* Macmillan Co., New York, 1939.
21. Etcheverry, M. A., *El Día Médica, 17,* 1237–1251 (1945).
22. Fisher, R. A., *The Genetical Theory of Natural Selection.* Clarendon Press, Oxford, 1930.
23. Fisher, R. A., cited by: Race, R. R., *Brit. Med. Bull., 2,* #421, 165 (1944).
24. Fisher, R. A., E. B. Ford, and J. Huxley, *Nature, 144,* 750–751 (1939).

25. Ford, E. B., *Am. Nat., 64,* 560–566 (1930).
26. Gates, R. R., *Genetica, 18,* 47–65 (1936).
27. Geppert, H., and S. Koller, *Erbmatematik.* Verlag von Quelle & Meyer, Leipzig, 1938.
28. Glass, B., *Genes and the Man.* Columbia Univ. Press, New York, 1943.
28a. Gunther, M., and L. S. Penrose, *J. Genetics, 31,* 413–430 (1935).
29. Hagedoorn, A. L., and A. C. Hagedoorn, cited by: Dobzhansky, Th. (1941).
30. Haldane, J. B. S., *Trans. Camb. Phil. Soc., 23,* 19–41 (1924).
31. Haldane, J. B. S., *Proc. Camb. Phil. Soc., 1,* 158–163 (1924).
32. Haldane, J. B. S., *Proc. Camb. Phil. Soc., 23,* 607–615 (1926).
33. Haldane, J. B. S., *Proc. Camb. Phil. Soc., 23,* 838–844 (1927).
34. Haldane, J. B. S., *Proc. Camb. Phil. Soc., 27,* 131–136 (1931).
35. Haldane, J. B. S., *Proc. Camb. Phil. Soc., 27,* 137–142 (1931).
36. Haldane, J. B. S., *Proc. Camb. Phil. Soc., 28,* 244–248 (1932).
37. Haldane, J. B. S., *Nature, 135,* 907–908 (1935).
38. Haldane, J. B. S., *Ann. Eug., 11,* 333–342 (1942).
39. Haldane, J. B. S., *New Paths in Genetics.* Harper & Bros., New York and London, 1942.
40. Haldane, J. B. S., *Ann. Eug., 13,* 262–271 (1947).
41. Haldane, J. B. S., and P. Moshinsky, *Ann. Eug., 9,* 321–340 (1939).
42. Harrison, J. W. H., *Proc. Roy. Soc. B, 111,* 188–200 (1932).
43. Hasebroek, K., *Zool. Jahrbuch (Abt. Zool. Phys.), 53,* 411–460 (1934).
44. Hogben, L., *Genetic Principles in Medicine and Social Science.* Williams & Norgate, Ltd., 1931.
45. Hooker, S. B., and W. C. Boyd, *J. Imm., 16,* 451–468 (1929).
46. Huxley, J., *Evolution: the Modern Synthesis.* Harper & Bros., New York and London, 1942.
47. Koller, S., *Z. Rassenphysiol., 3,* 1–63 (1931).
48. Koller, P. C., *Proc. Roy. Soc. Edinburgh, 57,* 194–214 (1937).
49. Levine, P., and E. M. Katzin, *Proc. Soc. Exper. Biol. & Med., 45,* 343–346 (1940).
50. Mather, K., *Biol. Rev., 18,* 32–64 (1943).
51. Mayr, E., *Systematics and the Origin of Species.* Columbia Univ. Press, New York, 1942.
52. Miller, C. P., and M. Bohnhoff, *J. A. M. A., 130,* 485–488 (1946).
53. Mohr, O. L., *Heredity and Disease.* W. W. Norton & Co., New York, 1934.
54. Mourant, A. E., *Nature, 160,* 505–506 (1947).
55. Muller, H. J., *Am. Nat., 56,* 32–50 (1922).
56. Muller, H. J., *Science, 66,* 84–87 (1927).
57. Muller, H. J., *Proc. Nat. Acad. Sci., 14,* 714–726 (1928).
58. Muller, H. J., *Proc. Int. Cong. Plant Sci., 1,* 897–921 (1929).
59. Muller, H. J., *J. Genetics, 22,* 299–334 (1930).
60. Myslivec, V., *Fallacy and Reality.* Czechoslovak Research Institute, Fursecroft House, George St., London.

61. Osborn, H. F., *Am. Nat., 61,* 5–42 (1927).
62. Pätau, K., cited by: Dobzhansky, Th., *Genetics and the Origin of Species,* 1941.
63. Payne, F., *Indiana Univ. Stud., 5,* # 36, 1–45 (1918).
64. Penrose, L. S., and J. B. S. Haldane, *Nature, 135,* 907–908 (1935).
65. Potter, E. L., *Rh.* Year Book Publishers, Chicago, 1947.
66. Quayle, H. J., *Hilgardia, 11,* 183–210 (1938).
67. Romaschoff, D. D., cited by: Dobzhansky, Th., *Genetics and the Origin of Species,* 1941.
68. Schwidetzky, J., *Verband deutsche Gesellschaft für Rassen., 10,* 65–74 (1940).
69. Siegler, S. L., *Fertility in Women.* J. B. Lippincott Co., Philadelphia, London, Montreal, 1944.
70. Sismanidis, A., *J. Genetics, 44,* 204–215 (1942).
71. Spink, W. W., and J. J. Vivino, *Science, 98,* 44–45 (1943).
72. Sturtevant, A. H., and G. W. Beadle, *An Introduction to Genetics.* W. B. Saunders Co., Philadelphia, 1939.
73. Timofeeff-Ressovsky, N. W., *Proc. 6th Int. Cong. Gen., 1,* 308–330 (1932).
74. Waddington, C. H., *An Introduction to Modern Genetics.* Macmillan Co., New York, 1939.
75. Weidenreich, F., *Southwest J. Anthrop., 1,* 1–54 (1945).
76. Weidenreich, F., *Apes, Giants and Man.* Univ. Chicago Press, Chicago, 1946.
77. Wiener, A. S., *Science, 96,* 407–408 (1942).
78. Wilson, A. T., *Proc. Soc. Exp. Biol. Med., 58,* 130–133 (1945).
79. Wilson, H., J. J. Graydon, R. T. Simmons, and L. M. Bryce, *Med. J. Australia, II,* 581–589 (1944).
79a. Wright, S., *Am. Nat., 63,* 274–279 (1929).
80. Wright, S., *J. Am. Stat. Assoc., 26,* 201–208 (1931).
81. Wright, S., *Genetics, 16,* 97–159 (1931).
82. Wright, S., *Proc. 6th Int. Cong. Gen., 1,* 356–366 (1932).
83. Wright, S., *Proc. Nat. Acad. Sci., 19,* 411–420 (1933).
84. Wright, S., *J. Genetics, 30,* 257–266 (1935).
85. Wright, S., *Proc. Nat. Acad. Sci., 24,* 253–259 (1938).
86. Wright, S., personal communication, 1939.
87. Wright, S., *Am. Nat., 74,* 232–248 (1940).
88. Wright, S., in: *The New Systematics.* Ed. J. S. Huxley, Clarendon Press, Oxford, 1940.
89. Wright, S., *Bull. Am. Math. Soc., 48,* 223–246 (1942).
90. Wright, S., *J. Heredity, 33,* 333–334 (1942).
91. Wright, S., and Th. Dobzhansky, *Genetics, 31,* 125–156 (1946).
92. Youmans, G. P., *et al., Proc. Staff Meeting, Mayo Clinic, 21,* 126–127 (1946).

CHAPTER VI The Influence of Geography on Racial Distribution

> The bones of the slain lie scattered upon the field in two lots, those of the Persians in one place by themselves, as the bodies lay at the first — those of the Egyptians in another place apart from them: If, then, you strike the Persian skulls, even with a pebble, they are so weak that you break a hole in them; but the Egyptian skulls are so strong, that you may smite them with a stone and you will scarcely break them in.
>
> — HERODOTUS: *The History*

IN the distribution of human races and in the distribution of animal and plant species and subspecies, the influence of geography is often important. In the animal kingdom the most striking example is found in the continent of Australia, where, before the advent of man, placentals were unknown and marsupials occupied the ecological places which were occupied by mammalian placentals in the rest of the world. Because of their geographical isolation and consequent freedom from mammalian competition, the marsupials have been able to continue in Australia up to the present day, although with few exceptions they have been replaced by mammalian competitors in the rest of the world (6, 17).

The aberrant characteristics of island populations have already been commented on (p. 158). Mayr (19) has shown pretty conclusively that geographic isolation is nearly always the primary cause of racial or specific differentiation (17).

Geographical Influences

Geography may influence the distribution of races and species in at least three different ways. The first is the action of geographical barriers such as mountain ranges, oceans, desert regions, polar regions, to prevent interbreeding between populations and thus to allow differentiation by selection or the Wright effect (p. 51). Second is the indirect action of geography through its influence on the climate, and the influence of the climate on the evolution of species which live in a given locality. The third method is concerned with local chemical variations in key chemicals in the soil, and variations in other properties of the local terrain.

Let us take up first the role of geography as a barrier. Darwin discussed the subject in a way which can hardly be improved on, in his classic *Origin of Species* (6).

> . . . barriers of any kind, or obstacles to free migration, are related in a close and important manner to the differences between the productions [plant and animal life] of various regions. We see this in the great difference in nearly all the terrestrial productions of the New and Old Worlds, excepting in the northern parts, where the land almost joins, and where, under a slightly different climate, there might have been free migration for the northern temperate forms, as there now is for the strictly arctic productions. We see the same fact in the great difference between the inhabitants of Australia, Africa and South America under the same latitude; for these countries are almost as much isolated from each other as is possible. On each continent, also, we see the same fact; for on the opposite sides of lofty and continuous mountain-ranges, of great deserts and even of large rivers, we find different productions; though as mountain-chains, deserts, etc., are not as impassable, or likely to have endured so long, as the oceans separating continents, the differences are very inferior in degree to those characteristic of distinct continents.
>
> Turning to the sea, we find the same law. The marine inhabitants of the eastern and western shores of South America are very distinct, with extremely few shells, crustacea, or echinodermata in common; but Dr. Günther has recently shown that about thirty per cent of the fishes are the same on the opposite sides of the isthmus of Panama; and this fact has led naturalists to believe that the isthmus was formerly open. Westward of the shores of America, a wide space of open ocean extends, with not an island as a halting-place for emigrants; here we have a barrier of another kind, and as soon as this is passed we meet in the eastern islands of the Pacific with another and totally distinct fauna. So that three marine

faunas range northward and southward in parallel lines not far from each other, under corresponding climate; but from being separated from each other by impassable barriers, either of land or open sea, they are almost wholly distinct. On the other hand, proceeding still further westward from the eastern islands of the tropical parts of the Pacific, we encounter no impassable barriers, and we have innumerable islands as halting-places, or continuous coasts, until, after traveling over a hemisphere, we come to the shores of Africa; and over this vast space we meet with no well-defined and distinct marine faunas. Although so few marine animals are common to the above-named three approximate faunas of Eastern and Western America and the eastern Pacific islands, yet many fishes range from the Pacific into the Indian Ocean, and many shells are common to the eastern islands of the Pacific and the eastern shores of Africa on almost exactly opposite meridians of longitude.

Types of Barriers

What serves as a barrier for one species may not be effective as a barrier for another. For many species a body of water a few miles across, a mountain range, or a desert, may serve as a complete isolation barrier so that the two populations have no opportunity of interchanging genes with each other, even if that were possible physiologically.

The number of geographical barriers is probably greater than is implied by a simple list of oceans, mountain ranges, and deserts. Huxley (17) believes that complete geographical separation may sometimes occur for ecological reasons also. Thus the moth *Thera juniperata* when in the larval stage feeds entirely on juniper. In the English Midlands there is no juniper, therefore the British forms of this species are restricted to two separate areas, one in the north and one in the south, and as a result subspeciation has occurred.

Kinds of Influences Due to Barriers

We may consider four general ways in which geographical barriers could affect the evolution of a species: 1) they may tend to keep out new genes which would otherwise come from other populations; 2) they may tend to relax the pressure of the selection factor; 3) they may aid the Sewall Wright effect or "genetic drift" (by keeping the populations small numerically); 4) they may make it possible for sudden geographical change to produce changes in the distribution of the species, as by dividing an originally large homogeneous population into smaller isolated populations, or bringing together populations formerly isolated, or causing climatic changes which favor a slightly different type (see p. 173). It will be worth our while to consider each of these ideas in some detail.

We can conceive of a number of ways in which individuals of a given species could originally find themselves distributed in about equal numbers on either side of a geographical barrier. The important thing is that as soon as the geographical barrier becomes effective, it is clear that a gene mutation originating on one side of the barrier will not be able to penetrate to the other side, and consequently evolution on the two sides of the barrier will begin to go in different directions. Or, if we have a case where the barrier is not 100 per cent efficient and a few individuals cross it from time to time, there may be some introduction of newly mutated genes from one population to the other, but at too slow a rate to keep the populations in genetic equilibrium, so that, if enough time elapses, subspeciation or speciation will occur.

When the barrier is an effective one, the variation between the groups on either side is likely to be great and may be referred to as discontinuous. When the barrier is not very effective, the range between the extremes on either side may be bridged by intermediate types, as is generally the case with skin color in man, giving us a situation which we speak of as continuous variability. As an example of discontinuous variability, we may refer to the distribution of snails with a right-handed spiral in the shells and those with a left-handed spiral in the island of Moorea. Each valley has a characteristic frequency of snails with shells of either kind. In some places the population is purely dextral or purely sinistral. In other places a mixed population is found. In these cases the variation is really continuous, but since only two types of shell exist, we can recognize the mixed populations as such. Table 19 (taken from Dobzhansky) shows the distribution of the different types in the various localities. In human traits determined by the interaction of many genes, it is much more difficult to say which are the transitional populations.

Dobzhansky (8) points out that since in another species of snail it is known that the direction of coiling of the shell is determined by a single gene, the situation is very likely the same here, and the distribution therefore represents the effect of geographical variance in the distribution of a single gene. Eventually the difference will be so great that even should the geographical barrier disappear, the

TABLE 17

The Frequency (in Per Cents) of Dextral and Sinistral Shells of *Partula Suturalis* in Moorea (8)

Localities	Dextral	Sinistral	No. of Individuals Examined
Atimaha	100.0	0	277
Vaianai	100.0	0	369
Oio	98.7	1.3	612
Haapiti	93.0	7.0	241
Uufau	12.5	87.5	303
Moruui	0.1	99.9	537
Maraarii	0	100.0	788
Varari	0	100.0	578

two species will continue distinct and will not again mix with each other, unless, before differentiation has gone too far, some agency such as a geological upheaval again unites the two regions.

Even small geographical barriers are sufficient to restrict the spread of certain species. In a climate such as the present one it would be very remarkable, even if the British Isles were densely populated with elephants, for a single elephant to make his way, without the aid of man, across the English Channel to the Continent. Smaller species and especially flying creatures such as birds and insects would not find this distance at all prohibitive. It must never be forgotten that what constitutes a geographic barrier for one species may not be a serious barrier for another. One of the best examples of this perhaps is the fact that the various species of mushrooms which are known are practically the same throughout the world with very slight differences, the reason doubtless being that they are dispersed by spores which are very small, light, and numerous and can well travel great distances, so that mountain ranges and even oceans have not proved effective barriers. Therefore, in spite of the fact that *Amanita phalloides* is the most poisonous plant known, and some other mushrooms are far from wholesome, the native of Europe who knows his edible mushrooms can come to North America and, with but little danger, collect and eat edible mushrooms. In respect to barriers, man has occupied, at least in the past, an intermediate position, as we shall see.

Another effect of a barrier is the relaxation of selection pressure. Especially if one of the groups on one side is relatively small, it will not have to compete with corresponding members of the other group and the selection pressure will not be so intense. An example of this has already been given in the preceding chapter where we quoted the opinion of Huxley that certain marsupials of Australia would not be able to compete with the corresponding mammals of the same habitation in the rest of the world.

At the same time that the selection pressure is relaxed, and in fact as a consequence of it, the third factor will operate, namely the Wright effect, or genetic drift. A barrier will make each of the breeding populations effectively smaller than the original whole, and there will therefore be more opportunity for random drift and for the establishment in the population of genes which are perhaps neutral or even disadvantageous in an evolutionary sense.

If the geographical barrier suddenly changes, as might happen if there were a marked alteration of climate in some part of the world, or a new mountain range were thrown up, or a small body of water were suddenly to become much broader, then what had formerly been a minor and ineffective barrier in the genetic sense might become effective, and bar further interchange of genes between the two groups.

Overcoming of Barriers by Man

In considering the history of mankind we must of course take account of the fact that man, by his own ingenuity, has from time to time thought of devices enabling him to surmount barriers which

formerly could not be crossed. Among these devices we may list the
invention of the use of fire, of clothing, of the bow and arrow, of
canoes, boats and ships, and most recently of all of the airplane.
We probably shall never know exactly how man crossed the Bering
Strait into North America. He could perhaps have accomplished
the journey by walking across the ice (or a land bridge which has

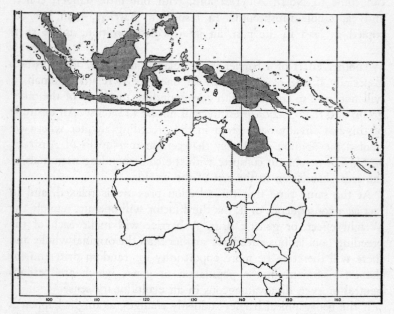

FIGURE 23. *Occurrence of blood group gene B in Australia
and islands to the north (after Graydon and Simmons).*

since disappeared) but it is certainly more likely that he crossed with
the aid of boats. The migration of the Polynesians from their original Asiatic homeland to the islands of the Pacific must certainly
have been accomplished by boats and would have been impossible
before the knowledge of these contrivances. From time to time man
has with relative suddenness abolished barriers which previously
forbade contact with other human groups in the rest of the world,
and at the present time we are forced to conclude that no group of
men in any part of the world can any longer be considered as isolated

from the rest. This is of course a fact of momentous genetic and evolutionary importance and it is difficult to foresee what the final consequences will be.

Before the invention of devices such as ships and airplanes, man's power of traversing geographical barriers, though greater than those of most other species possessing a body size at all comparable, was relatively limited, as is well shown by the well-established fact that man did not arrive in the New World until about 25,000 or so years ago (20). When a barrier is difficult to traverse, relatively few individuals will succeed in doing so, and the point in time at which the crossing is made may sometimes be deduced from studies of the subsequent composition of the population on the other side, as this may reflect the composition of the parent population at the time of separation. A good example of this is to be found in the Australian aborigines where blood group B was apparently unknown until relatively recent times, when it was introduced to a relatively narrow band on the northern coast of Australia, as is shown by the map (1, 22).

Modes of Penetrating a Barrier

There are of course various modes of entrance into a region protected by a geographical barrier. If the barrier consists of a large body of water, the point of entrance on the other side may seem rather random, although a study of the situation may show that landings were most frequently made at sheltered locations (harbors, etc.). In general one notes a tendency to prefer short voyages to long ones, so that the point of entrance into the new region will be relatively near the point of departure. The long voyages of the Vikings and the Polynesians are probably only apparent exceptions to this principle, for they were preceded by shorter trips, and the longer journeys which impress us today only followed as navigational skill increased. If the barrier is a mountain range, the point of entrance will probably be along a valley or a pass through the mountains (Fig. 24). If the barrier consists of desert the point of entrance is likely to be influenced by the position of the water supply across the desert, caravan trails, and the like.

Clines

When there is a continuous variation of a character from one geographical region to another it is convenient to speak of the range of variation as a *cline*.* Huxley, who proposed this name, points out

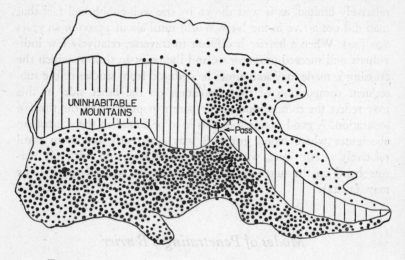

FIGURE 24. *Diagram showing the situation after a gene has crossed a barrier between two isolated populations. The degree of stippling roughly proportional to gene density on the two sides of the barrier.*

that such clines are fairly common, and on any general Darwinian view we would expect to find them as one of the general features of organic variation.

The adaptive characters directly affected may be visible characters, such as absolute size or relative size of some organ, or they may be invisible physiological features such as blood group frequencies, or the differences in temperature resistance in certain regional populations of Drosophila (9).

If members of one population succeed in crossing a barrier and

* A cline is a geographical transition from higher to lower incidence of a trait or gene (see Figs. 24 and 33b).

mingling genetically with the population on the other side of the barrier, they will generally follow the line of least resistance in making their way across, and will of course be more likely to mate with the inhabitants of the other population living nearest the barrier than with those further away; therefore we should expect to find clines set up which would give us some clue as to the point of entry of the characteristic which we are studying.

If the introduction of a physical characteristic is not too recent (or too remote), we may expect to learn a good deal about its point of entry, and perhaps even surmise what human groups introduced it by studying the cline or gradients in its distribution in the present day human populations. We may again refer to the introduction of blood group B into Europe (4).

When clines exist it must not be expected, unless the geographical barriers are 100 per cent effective (in which case we would not find clines, but absolutely discontinuous variation), that a cline for one characteristic will correspond to that for another. We may take the example given by Boyd (3) (Fig. 25) which shows how three different human characteristics in Europe vary independently of each other. An example of this same phenomenon in man is the distribution of the A and B blood groups in the vicinity of New Guinea. We find, for instance, in the Daru, Kikeri, and Kerema districts in Papua that there is considerable group B ($q = 0.52 - 0.72$); to explain this we might postulate that B was brought down from further north and east by peoples of the sort we find, for instance, in Java. However, the percentage of M in these Papuans is very low ($m = 0.06 - 0.24$), and in Java or in other regions from which our hypothetical bearers of blood group B might have come, M is high, so we are faced with the difficulty that if we postulate a migration of peoples containing B sufficient to account for the B in the Papuans, we are then confronted with the question, why do the Papuans not have a high frequency of M as well? Probably genetic drift, acting on populations which at the time were small, provides the answer (p. 154).

Some characters are more subject to the influence of geography than are others (19), and therefore one finds some characters varying more than others.

Geographic variation is nearly always accompanied by genetic

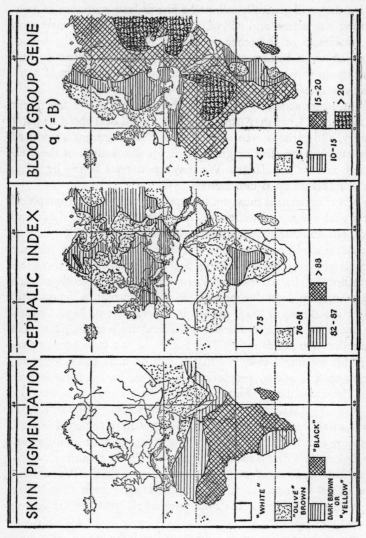

FIGURE 25. *Map showing independent distribution of variations in skin color, cranial index, and frequency of blood group B gene (q).*

variation but some animals are apparently more "plastic" than others. Mayr gives as an extreme example the raven, *Cervus corax,* which is found from the icy wastes of Greenland to the heart of the Sahara and the Arabian Desert. He states that it must be adapted in each region to a specific environment, but the raven is not a "plastic" bird, and the populations observed in these various regions are not very different one from the other. The desert birds are more brownish than the birds in the Far North, and somewhat smaller, with a relatively larger bill. Thus geographic variation is not very striking in this species.

Climate

As the second main example of the influence of geography on races we may take the influence which climate exerts directly. The climate may act by means of natural selection to discourage some characteristics in a population and to encourage others. In the polar regions the climate is cold and unsuited to many species which thrive in warm or temperate climates. In desert regions species which would find themselves at home in temperate, cool, humid climates are at a disadvantage.

As we traverse the surface of the earth from one pole to the other we pass from a region of polar cold with its characteristic distribution of animal life, to temperate zones — which seem most suitable for human activity (16) — into the tropics underneath or near the equator, down again into temperate zones, and finally again to another zone of polar cold. It is not surprising that the distributions of animals and plants are affected by these variations in climate. In Iceland, although the brief summer is relatively mild and pleasant, no trees are to be found, for the growing season is too short.

To a certain extent we may duplicate these changes by ascending a high mountain, where we may begin from a region which is tropical or at least temperate, and by climbing twenty thousand feet or so reach a region colder and more inhospitable than the poles themselves, and where animal life no longer is found (21). The familiar tree line which is found on high mountains is a good example of this phenomenon. Beyond a certain degree of cold trees simply will not grow. In other words, we can see geographical influences on flora and fauna produced by climatic variation due to altitude as well as to latitude. Not merely mountains but whole regions (plateaus, etc.) may show this.

We may therefore say that geography in general influences the environment and the environment in turn influences the organism. It is true that some organisms such as man prove relatively resistant to such modification. Within fairly recent times, geologically speaking, man has dispersed himself pretty much over the whole earth. The modifications he has suffered in the process have not been great enough to bring about differentiation into separate species. Many examples of adaptation in other species to the color or pattern of the environment are known. Huxley (17) cites numerous examples of the adaptations of desert insects, tree-dwelling insects, and many others. In the tropics, adaptation to warm climates and to the coloration prevailing in the tropical forests is found. The device of controlled body temperature found in birds and mammals, for example, is probably another instance of adaptation to warm climate. At a temperature where a rattlesnake will soon be killed if exposed to the direct rays of the sun, a mammal may survive and carry on his usual activities. It has even been postulated that the relatively sudden extinction of the dinosaurs was due to their lack of control of body temperatures, because like other reptiles they did not have the ability to keep themselves at a constant temperature, an advantage possessed by other groups of organisms such as mammals and birds. The thick fur coat of animals in the north may be looked upon as another example of adaptation to climate.

The influence of environment on animals is so well known that it has been formulated in a number of rules (19). There are rules applying to warm-blooded vertebrates for instance, including Bergman's rule, Allen's rule, and Gloger's rule.

Bergman's rule states that the smaller-sized geographical races of the species are found in the warmer parts of the range, the larger races in the cooler districts. Allen's rule states that protruding body parts such as tails, ears, bills, and extremities are relatively shorter in the cooler parts of the range of the species than in the warmer parts of the range. Gloger's rule states that the presence of melanin is greatest in the warm and humid parts of the range, whereas the reddish or yellowish-brown phaeomelanins prevail in arid climates where the blackish eumelanins are less prevalent. The phaeomelanins decrease in colder climates and in extreme cold so also do the eumelanins, giving us for instance the polar white.

It is obvious that if we were to take a homogeneous species of some animal and divide it into two roughly equal populations, and transport one of them to a cold humid climate and the other to a warm dry climate, for example, there are two sets of environmental effects which we might expect as a result of the geographical differences in location. The first of these would be a possibly direct but essentially transient effect due to the environment itself. It might well happen that certain melanin producing genes would be able to exert their effects more fully and more completely in the warm climate than in the cold. In the case of plants a longer growing season might make considerable difference in the appearance of the plant. It is obvious, however, that all of these effects would be reversed if we were to gather up our two hypothetical subpopulations and interchange them, putting the one which had formerly been in a warm dry climate into the cold humid climate and the other in its place. Therefore we may term the changes "transient."

In some cases, however, long-continued residence in a new environment does result in a permanent change in the species in question. In all cases in which we can make investigations, this has been shown to be due to an evolutionary change in the true sense, that is, some change in the genetic mechanism of the organism which causes it to perpetuate in another environment the characteristics acquired in the first.

Influence of Climate on Human Pigmentation

The most notable example of the influence of climate upon human characteristics is the influence of climate acting through natural selection on skin color. Since physical anthropologists were formerly convinced that racial classification should be based on characteristics which were not influenced by selection (p. 19), some of the older anthropologists are still convinced that skin color has no adaptive value. We are therefore forced to give the question serious consideration.

The arguments for the adaptive value of skin color fall into three classes: 1) evolutionary; 2) present distribution in the Old World; 3) present distribution in the New World.

Under 1) we must consider the arguments of thinkers such as Dobzhansky (7), who says that the simplest hypothesis to account

FIGURE 26. *Relation between pigmentation and ultraviolet radiation in Europe (after Fleure).*

for racial differences is that they have been brought about, in part at least, by natural selection. In other words, the existence of racial differences is presumptive evidence that these differences have different selective value in different environments. Dobzhansky has been able to confirm this in the case of many of the racial differences he has found in American *Drosophila;* confirmation in the case of man is more difficult, since the generations are so much longer, and we cannot make test matings at will.

Point 2) calls for a consideration of the present distribution of skin pigmentation in the Old World. A survey of the situation

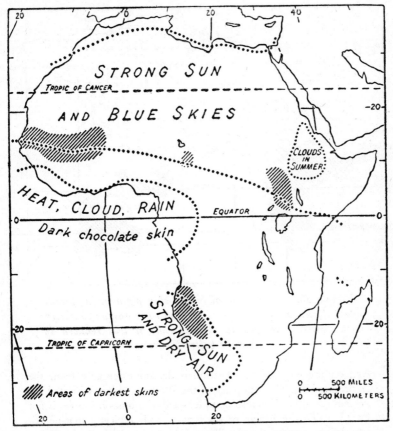

FIGURE 27. *Relation between skin pigmentation and ultra-violet radiation in Africa (after Fleure).*

leaves little doubt that there is a direct relation between the intensity of the ultraviolet radiation and the intensity of pigmentation. This is shown in Figures 26, 27, 28, and 29, based on Fleure (10). As Lyde (18) phrases it:

If pigment is developed according to need . . . we should expect
to find the "blackest" skins amongst men . . . in the hottest parts
of the world that are unforested; and this is precisely what we do
find — the real black man coming (except for a few small groups,

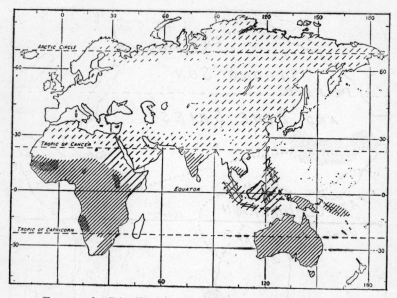

FIGURE 28. *Distribution of brown skin pigment in Eurasia
and Africa, suggesting that it was an early human characteristic, later intensified in Africa while it was reduced in
Europe (after Fleure).*

e.g., on the edge of the Australian desert) essentially from the
African savana. The rich black of the Western Sudan, with its high
percentage of bright sunshine to leeward of monsoon jungle, is not
found inside the jungle or on islands with typically marine climates. For instance, the negrilloes of the equatorial forest in Africa,
like the Sakai in the Malay jungle, are yellowish; the Samangs, like
most of the Australians, are dark chocolate; the Nilotic negroes are
reddish; the Indonesians are almost tawny.

Point 3) offers more of a problem. The aborigines of the New
World, though not by any means identical, agree in having on the
whole considerable skin pigmentation. If pigmentation is adaptive,

and conforms to climate, why are not the Eskimo and the inhabitants of Tierra del Fuego as light as Europeans? This looks like a
considerable difficulty, but the solution is probably comparatively
simple. The aborigines of the New World have not been here for

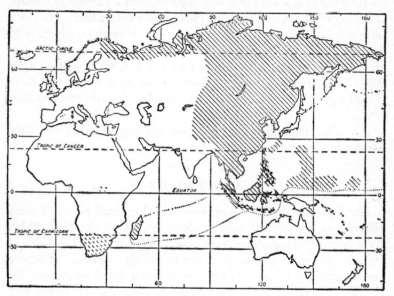

FIGURE 29. *Distribution of yellow pigment in the skin in
eastern Asia and Africa (after Fleure).*

more than about 25,000 years, or about 1000 generations. They are
by origin Asiatic, and in Asia skin pigmentation is fairly heavy.
Unless the selection of light skin as opposed to dark were fairly intense, the time elapsed has simply not been enough to allow for
much adaptation to occur (12). As a matter of fact, the populations
which might have been expected to become lighter, namely the
Fuegians and the Eskimo, have probably had a shorter time in which
to achieve this end than other American aborigines, for it is reasonable to suppose that the Fuegians did not reach their present home
until long after their northern neighbors were well installed. And
all students of the Eskimo (15) agree in recognizing them as probably the most recent (aside of course from the whites) arrivals in

America. It could well be that there has just not been enough time for selection to bleach the skins of the American aborigines. In any case, the pre-Columbian population was so sparse compared with that of Asia and India that on a statistical basis alone we should be justified in asserting that skin pigmentation conforms to climate. This has been denied chiefly by those who were concerned to prove skin color a non-adaptive character, so that it might safely be used in the classification of races (12). Since the more up-to-date students of anthropology have given up the idea of relying on non-adaptive characters, or even believing that such exist (13), there is no longer much dispute about the probable adaptive value of skin color.

It is altogether likely that hair and eye pigmentation also have some adaptive value (5).

Dwarf Forms

Island populations and populations of other small restricted areas often show a tendency towards dwarf forms. In the cases which have been investigated, we have reason to be convinced that this is because the dwarf forms, under the prevailing conditions of scanty food supply, or other influences, were better fitted to survive. By dwarf forms we of course understand *hereditary* dwarf forms, and ignore temporary changes brought about by such environmental limitations as lack of lime.

Other Effects

Geography does not operate solely through the influence of climate. There are effects of geography other than those caused by degrees of heat and cold or degrees of humidity. For instance, one important factor is the color of the soil on which the species lives, and it has been found that species of races living on lava flows are very often much darker than those living near by, even though sometimes they may live in the immediate vicinity, as in the sand-dune area. For one who has never had the experience of passing abruptly from a sandy desert to a great region of lava flow (as in northern Arabia) it is hard to appreciate the magnitude of the change in environment which is produced and how abrupt it is. It is obvious that selection by predators must have played an important role in the evolution of these localized color races. Direct background selection for micro-geographic races has also been demonstrated for a number of insects, particularly grasshoppers. Hovanitz (14) has analyzed a case in a Californian butterfly. Such analysis is often complicated by the fact that organisms other than man (and some of his relatives, may have poorly developed color vision, or may see parts of the color spectrum not visible to man.

So caution is required in extrapolating from our own perception of an organism to its own perception, or that of one of its enemies.

On the other hand, when the geographical variation is not sharp or discontinuous the variation of the animal in response may also be continuous rather than discontinuous. Blair (2) took four measurements — length of body, foot, parotid gland length and width — on about 5000 specimens of several species of North American toads. He found that each local population was characterized by a different set of constants, and that the measurements of body size, feet size, parotid gland length, and parotid gland width varied irregularly within the range of the species, and that the relative foot length and the amount of dorsal spotting tended to increase from the southwestern to the northeastern portions of the range. However, no pronounced break in any of these character combinations was noticeable anywhere.

Mayr (19) pointed out that intergradation between the subspecies of a species is frequently of the same continuous gliding nature as between various toad populations (*Bufo*), and he quotes from a case from Blair (2) which he considers particularly well analyzed.

Minerals of the Soil

Another way in which geography may influence the form or appearance of the species is through the mineral content of the soil. Huxley points out that plants provide numerous examples. Divergence in relation to the calcium content of the soil is fairly frequent. This again may simply affect the appearance of the full-grown plant, depending on whether the soil on which it is grown is rich

or poor in calcium, or selection may lead to the production of cal-
cipetal and calcifuge species or subspecies.

The way the mineral content of water may affect the forms of
individuals of species such as molluscs was mentioned in Chapter III.

Calcium is by no means the only mineral which is of importance
for the growth of animals and plants and an interesting example is
provided by a case from New Zealand. Among the animals, particularly the sheep, raised in certain regions of New Zealand a condition
known as bush sickness, or Tauranga disease, came to be recognized.
Eventually, it was found that this disease was not an infection but
was the result of some influence of the constituents of the plants on
which the animals fed and therefore indirectly an effect of the soil.
It was found * (11) that there existed "healthy" and "unhealthy"
lands, although the vegetation seemed to grow as luxuriantly in one
local region as in the other. The symptoms of the disease were similar to symptoms generally found in nutritional anemia and this suggested that the cause was possibly a deficiency of iron.

Experiments to test the effect of large doses of iron showed that
iron was sometimes helpful, but not always. In some cases the use of
iron (limonite) ore on the "unhealthy" land was sufficient to rem-
edy the deficiency, but in other experiments the same amount of
iron ore was not effective. Analytical determinations and fractiona-
tions were undertaken on the iron ores which were found to be the
most helpful in preventing the disease, and after a great deal of
costly and tedious work, it was finally shown that the effective element was cobalt, an element chemically similar to iron and sometimes associated with it. The iron minerals which had not been
effective were extremely low in cobalt, while those which had proved
helpful contained comparatively large amounts of this element. As
would then have been expected, it was later found that the soil in
the "unhealthy" areas contained only a trace of cobalt as compared
with the "healthy" areas. The unhealthy soil could be corrected by
the addition to it of small amounts of cobalt, or the cattle and sheep
showing the disease could be treated by the addition to their diet

* The role of cobalt in animal nutrition in New Zealand is discussed by various
authors in volumes *18* and *19* of the *New Zealand Journal of Science and Technology* (1936–1938).

of small amounts of cobalt, about one milligram per day. Traces of nickel also had some effect.

The anti-pernicious anemia factor in man has recently been found to be a cobalt compound.

REFERENCES FOR CHAPTER VI

1. Birdsell, J. B., and W. C. Boyd, *A. J. P. A.*, 27 (1), 69–90 (1940).
2. Blair, A. P., *Genetics*, 26, 398–417 (1941).
3. Boyd, W. C., *A. J. P. A.*, 27, 333–364 (1940).
4. Candela, P. B., *Human Biol.*, 14, 413–443 (1942).
5. Coon, C. S., *The Races of Europe*. Macmillan Co., New York, 1939.
6. Darwin, C. R., *The Origin of Species*. London, Murray, 1859.
7. Dobzhansky, Th., *A. J. P. A.*, 2, 251–265 (1944).
8. Dobzhansky, Th., *Genetics and the Origin of Species*. Columbia Univ. Press, New York, 1941.
9. Dobzhansky, Th., and C. Epling, Carnegie Inst. of Washington Publ., 554 (1944).
10. Fleure, H. J., *Geog. Rev.*, 35, 580–595 (1945).
12. Haddon, A. C., *The Races of Man*. Macmillan Co., New York, 1925.
13. Hooton, E. A., *Up from the Ape*. Macmillan Co., New York, 1946.
14. Hovanitz, W., *Ecology*, 21, 371–380 (1940).
15. Howells, W., *Mankind So Far*. Doubleday, Doran & Co., Inc., Garden City, New York, 1944.
16. Huntington, E., *Mainsprings of Civilization*. John Wiley & Sons, Inc., New York, 1945.
17. Huxley, J., *Evolution: The Modern Synthesis*. Harper & Bros., New York and London, 1942.
18. Lyde, L. W., *1st Universal Race Congress, London*. Pub. P. S. King & Son, London, 1911.
18a. Marett, J. R. de la H., *Race, Sex, and Environment*. London, 1936.
19. Mayr, E., *Systematics and the Origin of Species*. Columbia Univ. Press, New York, 1942.
20. Sauer, C. O., *Geog. Rev.*, 34, 529–573 (1944).
21. Ullman, J. R., *Kingdom of Adventure: Everest*. William Sloane Assoc., Inc., New York, 1947.
22. Wilson, H., J. J. Graydon, R. T. Simmons and L. M. Bryce, *Med. J. Australia*, 31, 581–589 (1944).

CHAPTER VII

The Concept of Race

A Hair perhaps divides the False and True;
Yes; and a single Alif were the clue . . .
— OMAR KHAYYÁM: *The Rubáiyát*

THE concept of race has probably been of some use in the past, employed as anthropologists formerly used it, although there are some today who would doubt that; but the word has latterly fallen into disfavor, partly because it has been much misused by fanatics and unscrupulous persons to further their purposes of gaining political power. Such persons apparently knew little, and cared less, about possible true scientific meanings of the term (22).

My own earliest memories of the use of the word "race" go back to a book, *The Clansman,* published by Thomas Dixon, Jr., in 1905. This volume was largely devoted to glorifying the exploits of the Ku Klux Klan, which sprang up in the South of the United States after the end of the Civil War. The author says in his note "To the Reader" that the exploits of the Klan form one of the most dramatic chapters in the history of the Aryan race (which Dixon evidently considered to include the white, but not the black, people living in the Southern states). This book, we should remember, was written long before Adolf Hitler's *Mein Kampf,* and though clearly they meant different things by "Aryan," both writers used the word to denote a "superior" group.

The term "Aryan" was introduced into modern usage by Professor Max Mueller, a German philologist who went to England and remained there the rest of his life. Later he energetically rejected the idea that it was proper to give the term any racial implications, and insisted that it should be applied only to a certain group of languages (the group includes Latin, Greek, Sanscrit, Slavic, etc.). The term, however, once released, proved to be a veritable monster of Frankenstein, and the monster has not yet been destroyed. Our generation, and perhaps still others to come, will have to pay with blood and tears for the delusions which resulted from its misuse.

According to Montagu (31), the common idea of race represents probably one of the most dangerous errors of our time, and the most tragic. Almost every person of the Western World seems to take it for granted that he knows what race means, and that scientific investigation has long ago proved the existence of differences, of a significant kind, between races. Anybody who has thoughtfully followed the political history of the last ten to twenty years can hardly fail to agree that deliberate misuse of the word "race" is indeed one of the most tragic crimes of our era. As a result of doctrines embodying the concept of race, but having no scientific foundation, millions of people have been tortured or killed. Yet nearly everyone, even the *victims* of this delusion, seemed to assume that distinct, physical races do exist and that each possesses well-defined differences in mental abilities and attitudes. Examination of the question will show, however, that it is by no means easy to differentiate mankind thus into sharply defined races with different mental attributes. The question of "racial" superiority, although often made use of by propagandists, has never really been examined scientifically.

In the Arabic world, even today, race differences are not felt to have much significance, but differences in religious belief are considered important. (The possible effects of the Palestine situation are too recent to treat here.) In medieval times, certainly, the Mohammedans in Egypt gladly accepted into Islam such Copts as were willing, without regard to presumably different racial backgrounds. Being accepted into the group depended on what one believed, not on one's chromosomes. Earlier, in the area where Greek was spoken, the inhabitants of the different city-states, though often at war with each other, did not consider that they belonged to different races. It is true that in ancient Europe as well as in modern Europe we find many examples of caste and class differences, and in India, particularly, an apparently rigid system of this sort was set up; but the concept of race, as an immutable physical entity, as we now know it, probably did not exist (34).

Origin of the Term "Race"

Lord Bryce has maintained (4) that even up to the time of the French Revolution there had been very little conscious racial feeling in any country at any time. However much men of different races may have fought with one another, it was seldom that any sense of racial opposition was a main factor behind this strife. They fought for land and they plundered one another. Patriotism and national feeling were often strong, but the peoples of that time did not think of themselves in terms of ethnology, and although they made war for various reasons, they did not make it because of consciousness of "racial" differences.

Montagu (31) believes that it was not until opposition developed against the inhuman traffic and trade in Negro slaves that the supporters of slavery, anxious to find some new arguments to bring against the powerful reasons urged against them, hit upon the argument of race. Since the slaves came from an inferior race, the dealers argued, they were certainly not as good as their masters; they deserved nothing better than slavery, and were incapable of the high ideals and thoughts of men of "higher" races. Such an argument satisfied disturbed conscience then, and often fulfills similar functions today.

The origin of the word "race" is somewhat obscure. It has been plausibly conjectured, however, that it derives from the Arabic word *râs,* which means "head, beginning," etc. From Arabic the word may have passed over into the Spanish and from there to the Italian and other languages (34a). The implication of separate origins for the different races came inevitably. The idea of diversity once established, the concepts of "superior" or "inferior" almost inevitably followed, the human ego being what it is. This is unfortunate. In one of the grandest periods of German history, the philosopher Herder, in his great book *Ideen zur Philosophie der Geschichte der Menschheit* (21), specifically stated, "I could wish the distinctions between the human species, that have been made from a laudable zeal for systematic science, not carried beyond due bounds. Some for instance have thought fit to employ the term *races* for four or five divisions, originally made on the basis of country or complexion:

but I see no reason for this appellation. Race refers to a difference of origin, which in our case simply does not exist, or in each of these countries, and under each of these complexions, comprises the most different races. In short, there are neither four or five races, nor exclusive varieties, on this earth. Complexions blend into each other; forms follow the genetic character; and, on the whole, all are at last but shades of the same great picture, extending over all ages and over all parts of the earth." Parenthetically, we may remark that whatever Herder meant by "genetic character," it can hardly be what would be meant today, since in his day the science of genetics, as we know it, did not exist. Otherwise the passage is a wonderfully clear statement of what should be our position today.

Do Human Races Exist?

If we choose the criteria we want, we can nearly always make races come out the way we think they ought to. If we are convinced that the "African race" exists, and is different from the "English race," we may concentrate our proof, for example, on criteria which will prove the inhabitants of central Africa to be quite different from those of England, and can view with alarm any claims that there are also great similarities between such populations.

It is the thesis of this book that racial categories, if they are to have a valid conceptual basis, must be made on the basis of man's genetic constitution. Until very recently, so scanty has been our knowledge of human heredity, the only classifications possible to the anthropologist have been those based on man's appearance, and on physical measurements. These methods have a limited usefulness, but are being superseded by our increasing knowledge of what is far more fundamental, man's genes and chromosomes.

How should races be defined? What are the differences, if any, which will cause us to arrange human beings in several distinct categories? First we may consider the ideas of the very naïve man, who is impressed by the way other people differ from him in language, complexion and stature, and he speaks of the "British race," the "French race," the "African race," the "Chinese race," etc., presumably meaning people whose ancestors were born and reared in Britain, France, Africa, China, etc. The common man, not being specially trained to face and solve logical puzzles, has not usually considered the ultimate consequences of such an attitude. A family from Great Britain, for example, goes to live in China and remains there for several generations, but carefully avoids marriage with any but persons of British origin. The descendants of this British family are born and reared not in England but in China. Are they British or Chinese? Confronted with such a case, the man in the street would probably say that the descendants still belonged to the British race, and he would give as evidence to support his judgment their obvious differences from the Chinese in skin color, hair color, eye fold, language, etc.

Now let us make the problem more difficult, and suppose that the British family settled, not in China, but in Germany; that they lost their knowledge of English, and that their descendants spoke only German. Would it then be possible to state that the family was still British, and not German? The ordinary person would probably not be prepared to say so readily how to distinguish members of the British race from all other Europeans, but he would probably suppose that of course the anthropologists, being scientists, had some way of easily answering such a question.

Race Defined by Anthropologists

Modern anthropologists, of course, have not been unaware of the possible bias involved in taking over the common man's ideas of race and incorporating them into anthropological treatises. Dahlberg (7) states that "the current race doctrines build . . . on pre-Mendelian views." Hooton (24) deplores the use of such terms as the "white race," the "Jewish race," the "Latin race," and the "Irish race," because these seem to imply, respectively, that race is a matter of skin pigmentation, of religion, of language, of geographical position, or perhaps of temperament.

Hooton thinks that all anthropologists agree that the proper criteria of race are physical characters. He has offered his own definition of race, which runs as follows:

> A race is a great division of mankind, the members of which, though individually varying, are characterized as a group by a certain combination of morphological and metrical features, prin-

cipally non-adaptive, which have been derived from their common descent.

A primary race is one which has been modified only by the operation of evolutionary factors, including the selection of its own intrinsic variations and of the modifications, adaptive or non-adaptive, possibly caused by environmental stimuli. . . .

A secondary or composite race is one in which a characteristic, stabilized combination of morphological and metrical features has been effected by a long-continued intermixture of two or more primary races within an area of relative isolation.

"Non-adaptive" evidently means not subject to the action of natural selection. Hooton has more recently stated (p. 19) that he no longer considers racial characteristics non-adaptive.

Hooton is obviously correct in supposing present-day races to have been formed, at least partly, by mixture. Whether the racial ingredients which went into the mixture were ever themselves pure is still a question (p. 190).

So far as common descent goes, this can often be inferred, but seldom proved. Even when geographical differentiation is observed in the species, this does not definitely prove common descent for the population in the area in question. Climatic and ecological conditions are constantly changing, and when these operate so as to open up a new area to a certain species, only certain types of combinations (of a probably highly variable population) would be able to spread into new areas. Suitable types might come from more than one race. These might later on come to constitute a single geographical and genetic group but would not have a single common origin. This question has been discussed by Huxley and Haddon (28). Therefore, there is no necessary justification in assuming that a group of people we consider sufficiently alike to constitute a race do actually derive from a common origin, unless we can prove it by historical or paleontological evidence.

Less exacting definitions of a "pure race" have been offered; Scheidt (16) simply requires that the several contributing elements have become so completely blended that correlation fails to reveal their original combinations. If by blending we understand independent assortment of Mendelian factors, this definition is unobjectionable, although probably not very useful in practice.

Coon, in his *Races of Europe* (6), also attempted to define the word "race." On page 3 he states that the concept of race is a general one and any attempt to bring it down to a more specific meaning represents a too rigid attempt at taxonomy. On page 11, however, he goes somewhat further and states that a race is a group of people who possess the majority of their physical characteristics in common. This definition might be unobjectionable if applied to species, but it is doubtful if it applies to races (p. 202). Coon further defines a pure race as one in which the several contributing elements have become so completely blended that tests for correlation (see App. A) fail to reveal their original combinations, while at the same time the processes of selection and the response to environmental influences have given the blend a distinctive character. Other anthropologists have also recognized the difficulty of defining the term "race" and Kluckhohn (29) has stated that he belongs to the group which considers that the term has, scientifically speaking, hardly any usefulness.

Those Original "Pure" Races

Since mankind has certainly existed for hundreds of thousands of years, and since during this time different groups have been to a greater or lesser extent in contact with each other by migration and conquest, the present human groups represent a pretty thorough, although not uniform, genetic mixture. This is admitted by Dixon, for instance (9), although even while he admits that such a thing as a pure race can hardly be expected to exist and that peoples of the world today are complex mixtures, he goes on to say that they are mixtures of original types and in these complex mixtures we must seek to discover, if we can, the constituent elements. Thus the obsession of our age with the idea of race, and particularly with the idea that there once existed *primitive pure human races,* whose mixtures produced the present-day human groups, is set forth once more.

Howells (26) suggests that beliefs in primitive "pure races" can be traced back to ideas expressed in the Bible, for we read there that the sons of Noah were Shem, Ham and Japheth, and that they, with their wives, repopulated the earth after the Flood. Later church scholars surmised that from Shem there were descended the peoples of Semitic speech, from Ham the peoples of Hamitic speech (which would include the ancient Egyptians), and the rest of the nations from Japheth.

It cannot be entirely the Biblical tradition, however, which causes people to postulate primitive pure races whose mixtures produced the modern peoples. Dahlberg (7) suggests that back of this line of reasoning lies the concept of pure substances, such as copper, tin, etc. The tendency to suppose that originally "pure" human races once existed seems to be an aspect of some almost instinctive process of the human mind, and evidently is by no means always the result of following tradition. The mathematician Bernstein (1), for example, in one of his early papers on blood groups, postulated the original existence of three "pure" human races, one belonging to blood group A, one to blood group B, and one to blood group O. Modern blood group distributions were supposed to be the results of various degrees of mixture of these primitive pure races. The results even of the investigations then known make the concept of Bernstein seem extremely unlikely, and subsequent research has not produced any evidence that any such pure primitive serological races ever existed.

At various other times, different workers have written in such a way as to imply the existence in antiquity of a pure Aryan race, a pure Alpine race, a pure Mediterranean race, etc.; apparently wishing to avoid at all costs facing the possibility that primitive man was nearly as diverse in physical characteristics as are men at the present time. The *reductio ad absurdum* of this tendency has been pointed out by Haldane (20), who mentions that if it were carried to its logical extreme we would have to suppose the existence at one time of an originally "pure" redheaded race to account for the redheaded people who exist in the world.

Other examples of the tendency to postulate originally pure races whose mixture resulted in modern mixed races may be found in Dart (8), who postulates that the Bantu type in Africa arose from the cross of Bushman and Negro, with infiltrations at intervals of "Caucasian" blood from the Nile Valley; and in the writings of Gates (17), who states that the modern European populations are so intermingled through processes that have been going on throughout history and pre-history that any geographic boundaries between Nordic, Alpine, and Mediterranean have largely ceased to exist. By this statement, Gates apparently intended to imply that such boundaries *did* exist at an earlier time, since he goes on to say that no one expects to find a relatively pure race except in local pockets, still relatively undisturbed.

Genetic Impossibility of Now Recognizing Original Strains

To a student familiar with genetics, or even merely with the bare outlines of heredity as expounded in Chapter II of this book, it should immediately be clear that any attempt to sort out the original characteristics of the originally pure racial components (even if they had ever existed), through a phenotypical study of modern mixtures, is bound to be fruitless.

The independent assortment of chromosomes in inheritance and the possibility that genes can cross over between pairs of chromosomes are alone sufficient to show the futility of trying to recognize remote ancestral types in a modern population. In a population of "mulattoes," for instance, it would be quite impossible to deduce the skin colors of their forebears, who might have been "pure" white and "pure" Negroes, or — mulattoes! Any types of mankind with differences pronounced enough really to constitute races must in most cases differ in a number of genes (see below). In a mixture of two or more races, independent assortment and crossing-over would soon mix up these genes to such a degree that it is very unlikely that any ancestral type would emerge, except perhaps very rarely, in a population descended from such a mixture. This was pointed out by East and Jones (15) in 1919:

> Traits originally characteristic of certain peoples because of isolation and the consequent inbreeding have been shifted back and forth, combined and recombined . . . Even if it were known what the average values of the various characters of these early strains were, there is little reason for believing that a present-day individual bearing one or two particularly striking traits should be felt to hold any closer relationship to the strain in which these traits are supposed to have arisen than his neighbors who are without them.

. . . It is positively misleading, therefore, to classify Englishmen
as resembling Danish, Norman, Pictic, Celtic, or Bronze Age types,
as is done in more than one work of authority.

The verdict of the modern geneticist is expressed in Dobzhansky's
remarks (11) that the naïve concept of "pure" races must be replaced
by the more authentic one of the varying incidence of definite genes.
The attitude of the modern geneticist is clearly shown when Dobzhansky goes on to say (11) that the idea of a pure race is not even
a legitimate abstraction: it is a subterfuge used to cover up ignorance
of the nature of the phenomena of racial variation.

We must therefore abandon any idea that individuals in a modern
population who show any one particular morphological feature characteristic of some ancient race will be on the whole any more nearly
like this ancient race than are other individuals who do not show
the trait in question. The characteristic trait is probably determined
by only a few genes, or perhaps even by only one, whereas the
nature of the individual is determined by the action and interaction
of the whole twenty or forty thousand or more genes which he
possesses (36). In other words, having a Roman nose does not make
you a Roman.

No One Criterion Enough

All anthropologists understand, but some laymen apparently do
not, that no one physical characteristic is going to be enough to
enable us to distinguish the various races of man, one from another.
There are people who mistakenly believe that Negroid ancestry in
people of mixed white and Negro descent can always be detected
by the fact that such hybrids always show black pigment underneath their fingernails. Other people believe that the color of skin
or the possession or lack of possession of wavy hair or some such
characteristic will enable race classification to be set up.

It requires only a very superficial acquaintance with the facts of
human descent to discover that these ideas are naïve and largely
unfounded. There are many people with some Negro ancestry who
definitely do not show any external Negroid characteristics. In the
U.S.A. a certain number of such hybrids "pass the color line" each
year. There are people of part Chinese ancestry who do not show

the Mongolian eye fold. Classifications based on the type of hair, whether straight, wavy or kinky, etc., are perhaps as satisfactory as any classification based on a single characteristic can be. But as soon as the whole population of the world is included in this scheme strange contradictions and inconsistencies begin to appear. Certain Pacific Islanders get lumped with the African Negroes largely because of their curly or kinky head hair. At the same time, we are obliged to classify many of the inhabitants of India with the natives of Central Asia and the aborigines of America, because of their straight hair and its complete lack of wave. If we use skin color, we find that we are obliged to classify the Australian aborigines (who are probably not a single race, anyhow, and who have many characteristics making them really much closer to the Ainu or even to the white races of Europe) with the natives of Africa, because of their skin color. It soon becomes very clear that no classification based on a single physical characteristic is going to be satisfactory, because no such classification fits with the geographical facts.

The "Racial" Constellation of Characters

Modern anthropologists, although they hold to no such naïve classification as those just suggested, still tend on the whole to believe that a classification of race can be achieved by considering a small number of characters together. Most of them feel that by defining the proper constellations of these characters, they somehow ought to delimit every "race" from each of the others. This idea is undoubtedly sound, but a wrong choice of the characters to be used in the classification can lead us completely astray.

As an example of what can happen, let us consider a brilliant but now almost completely discredited effort in the field.

Professor Dixon (who was however really a cultural, not a physical, anthropologist) in his book, *The Racial History of Mankind* (9), stated that our conception of race may be divided into two groups: 1) external and superficial, and 2) internal, structural and skeletal. The first group includes the characters which we have just been speaking of, such as pigmentation of the skin, eye, and hair, character of the hair, whether straight, curly, frizzly, or woolly, the character of the nose, whether aquiline or depressed, etc. Data on these characters are obtained primarily as a result of observations.

Dixon has a number of objections to criteria of this first sort. They can be used, he says, only in connection with living men and are useless for the study of the skeletal remains of ancient peoples. Also, although it is easy enough to distinguish a white skin from a black skin, or a light eye from a dark one, and straight hair from woolly or an aquiline from a pug nose, in practice it has been found extremely difficult to measure with any real accuracy the great number of intermediate conditions that are found. Thus while these purely observational, or external, criteria are of great value in distinguishing between groups of men, Dixon thought their use was surrounded by many practical difficulties and was restricted by serious limitations. Today we see that this is largely because we do not know the "unit factors" (genes) back of such characters. Yet an attempt to determine the genetic basis for such characters seems never to have occurred to Professor Dixon, although the fundamentals of genetics had been rediscovered over twenty years before he wrote.

Dixon, followed by many of the earlier physical anthropologists, preferred to base his criteria on the characters of the second group, that is on measurements. He says, very interestingly, that out of the very large number of measurements and ratios that have been tried and advocated at one time or another, a relatively small number have come to be accepted as undoubtedly of real significance in the determination and classification of races. Apart from structure, these are mainly concerned with the skull or head. Dixon does not state why certain criteria have come to be accepted while others have been rejected, but a little examination of anthropological writings of his time will, I think, reveal that the reason was essentially the same as the one advanced by Morant, who, in speaking of the blood grouping characteristics, said that to be useful they must be found to give "reasonable results" in practice. Those of the proposed criteria which were adopted are evidently those which were found to give "reasonable results" — that is, they brought home the bacon; so that in cases where the anthropologist was convinced race differences ought to exist, these criteria proved that they did. Unobliging criteria which seemed to show no differences between races "obviously" distinct, or which indicated differences within groups "obviously" homogeneous, have been tactfully relegated to the scrap heap (37).

It is true that criteria based on measurements have the advantage that at least some of them may be made both on skeletons and on living subjects. This enables us to compare modern peoples, in respect to these characteristics, with peoples of the past. Also, since such criteria are purely metrical in character, they are less subject to the uncertainties of the criteria which Dixon (9) called observational. (As a matter of fact, observational "all or none" characteristics are subject to the least uncertainty of all [3]).

Convinced, therefore, that racial differences ought to be detectable even in the admittedly mixed group of *H. sapiens* that now inhabits the earth, and convinced that the proper criteria to detect these differences were metrical averages, Dixon (9) made the rather bold experiment of attempting to classify *all* mankind on the basis of a combination of only three different morphological criteria: namely, the cranial, or cephalic, index; the altitudinal or length-height index of the skull; and the nasal index. The values obtained for each of these indices were subdivided into three ranges. All the possible combinations, $3 \times 3 \times 3$, made it possible to set up 27 different physical types. By looking up the combinations of these characters in various European, African, and other groups which he considered racially distinct, Dixon then proceeded to pick out arbitrarily certain ones of the 27 combinations as being characteristic of various races or "proto-races."

The results of this experiment in classification were astonishing, and somewhat sad, and in later years even Dixon himself somewhat ruefully referred to the book as "my crime." For example, when Dixon came to the aboriginal inhabitants of North America, he found that his system, from which he had resolved never to deviate, at least within the covers of *The Racial History of Mankind,* forced him to characterize some American Indians as Proto-Negroid, some as Proto-Australoid, some as Caspian, some as Mediterranean, etc., in spite of the abundant evidence, of which he was well aware, that the original inhabitants of North America could only have come from Asia by way of the Bering Strait and are therefore of Asiatic origin. If the categories of Dixon constitute races, then race is something which does not involve common descent. This clearly contradicts most common beliefs about the subject which were held at the time, and it was at this point that Dixon and the orthodox physical anthropologists came to the parting of the ways. But Dixon's work was only an extension, and really a most ingenious and logical one, of the trends of the physical anthropology of his time; however, it was frankly experimental, and most anthropologists of today regard it as a sort of blind alley. Few paused to reflect that the absurdity of many of Dixon's conclusions was fundamentally based not on errors in his use of method, or on his failure to understand the fundamental assumptions which underlay the physical anthropology of that time, but on the absurdity of these assumptions themselves.

Modern anthropologists have rejected Dixon's work, because of their appreciation of the fact that belonging to the same race usually implies community of descent.

Fallacy of "Ideal Types"

Boas (2) pointed out in one of his last papers that, although the logical way to express differences between different human groups was by determining the frequency with which various forms occurred in each group, this apparently is not the way the minds of many anthropologists tend to work. The anthropologist tends to be impressed by the forms which appear most commonly, and tends to combine these frequent forms in his mind into one imaginary individual which he calls THE TYPE. It is easy to show that such a type is a concept which has no reality. For instance, Professor Sargeant (35) established the ideal type of the Harvard student by having a sculptor make a figure of a youth whose body measurements corresponded to the average of the measurements obtained on a large number of Harvard students from about the year 1892, but he would certainly have been unable to find many individuals strictly corresponding to that type.

Suppose we are liberal, and say that a man is like the ideal in respect to any given measurement if he does not deviate more than do 50 per cent of the total examined; we should nevertheless find, as Boas points out, that the number of measurements is such and the number of their combinations is so great that Sargeant would have found, on the average, among 1024 individuals taken at random at Harvard just *one* who corresponded to his ideal type. Thus it is clear that ideal types have no real bearing on the racial classification of human populations as they actually exist. Instead we must deal with the variations in frequencies of various factors in different populations.

Paucity of Specimens

An accurate and scientific division of mankind into races must obviously be based on an adequate number of observations. The fact is, however, that in man, and even in many other species, attempts at classification have all too often been based on very scanty material. Mayr (30) points out that, even in well-worked taxonomic orders and classes, as for example some of the birds, new species and subspecies are occasionally described on the basis of a single museum specimen or at the most a few specimens. Even the American Museum of Natural History in New York City, which has what is probably the largest and most complete bird collection in the world, has only about 800,000 skins, which means about 1000 skins per species and about 30 specimens per subspecies. Yet many of the anthropological endeavors of the past were based on even scantier material. It has not been uncommon for races of man to be described on the basis of the examination of 20 or 30 skulls, and some of the fossil races are represented by a few specimens, or sometimes by a single specimen. With so little material, of course, the normal range of variation of the population which the specimens represent cannot possibly be known, and if one of our isolated skulls should by chance come from an abnormal or diseased individual, his true place in the total scheme could easily be misunderstood.

Reality of Species as Opposed to Races

The difficulty which we experience in trying to classify man, or any other species, into races is quite different from the problem of classifying organisms into species. Naturalists have not usually had any great difficulty in distinguishing the different species. Thus as Dobzhansky says (12), although any two cats are individually distinguishable one from the other and this is probably equally true of any two lions, nevertheless, no living feline individual has ever been seen which could cause in the mind of the observer any doubt as to whether it belonged to the species cluster of cats, *Felis domestica,* or to the species cluster of lions, *Felis leo.* The two clusters are entirely separate because there are *no intermediates,* and we can say with perfect safety that *any possible cat* is different from any possible lion, and that cats as a group are different from lions as a group. The reality of the difference between *Felis domestica* and *Felis leo* is entirely independent of the artificiality of any ideal cat or ideal lion which some particular observer may set up in his mind as the exemplification of the species. The objective reality of the differentiation of the human species into various races, however, cannot be similarly asserted, and it is important for us to recognize the radically different nature of the problem which confronts us. Certainly we should avoid any such nonsense as saying that "the different races of mankind are really different species in spite of the fact that they can interbreed" (17, 18). Any statement of this sort betrays a fundamental lack of understanding of the basic principles of taxonomy and evolution.

It would seem, on considering mankind as a whole, that we have only one polytypic species. Some of our races are sympatric (30) in the sense that they occupy the same locality, or at least that their habitats overlap; others are allopatric, in the sense that their habitats do not overlap.

Species may sometimes arise from races. According to Dobzhansky (10), species differ from races in the fact that the former are isolated reproductively (this does not mean that they cannot interbreed, but that for one or more reasons they seldom do) while races are not. In other words, a species is a genetically closed system, because species do not regularly exchange genes. Because of this fact, any given individual, with the exception of hybrids between species, always belongs to one certain species and never to two or more. Races, on the other hand, are more or less genetically open systems. Their populations are channels through which genes can and do flow from race to race. Since the genes may vary independently one from the other, an individual may carry some genes which occur more frequently in the representatives of one population or race, and other genes which are more characteristic of another. Such an individual could be said to belong to two or more races (depending on our definition of race) at the same time, since he is in fact compounded of elements of both.

Over-All Race Difference Small

Modern man represents an amalgam of elements which has been in the process of formation for thousands of years. Some human stocks have been isolated long enough for some evolutionary differentiation to go on, but at the same time inherited traits have been constantly interchanged, especially since the mass displacements of populations which have gone on in historical times. The forces making for eventual homogeneity are undoubtedly stronger today than the evolutionary forces allowing differentiation. So we should not be surprised if identical genes crop up in all corners of the earth, or if the over-all racial differences we detect prove to be small. We do not know the total number of gene differences which mark off a Negro of the Alur tribe in the Belgian Congo from a white native of Haderslev, Denmark. Glass (19) has suggested that the number of gene differences even in such a case is probably small. Besides a few genes for skin color, he thinks that there may be a dominant gene for kinky hair and a pair or two of genes for facial features. He considers it unlikely that there are *more than six pairs of genes* in which the white race differs *characteristically* from the black. This estimate errs somewhat on the small side, in the opinion of the present writer. Probably, however, it is of the right order of magnitude, and any outraged conviction that the difference between the two races must be much greater than this, which some persons might feel, is likely to be based on emotional, rather than rational, factors. In lower forms, even different species may sometimes differ by only a few genes (5).

Taken in conjunction with the fact that individual members of the same race, e.g., the white race, or the black race, as a rule differ from each other by many more genes than this, the foregoing estimate makes it seem quite probable that the intrinsic differences between the various races are not large or important in the genetical sense. The genetic differences between different individuals of the same race can often, even with our present limited knowledge of human genetics, be demonstrated to be as large as ten to twenty genes. Considering the enormous number of hereditary differences still unanalyzed (Ch. XI), it is likely that two human beings can differ in respect to a thousand or more genes, without seeming to us to be different enough to put into different racial categories. An inherited difference becomes vital as marking off a race only when someone chooses to treat it as vital, as Hitler did with the Jews in Germany, or as some individuals in the United States have chosen to do in the case of the Negro. A Semitic nose, or a black skin, is no more significant in the evolution of the species than a head of flaming red hair.

Genetic Definition of "Race"

In contrast to some anthropologists, the geneticists as a whole have not found it so difficult or so embarrassing to define the word "race," have not developed such timidity about using it, and have not used it in such a loose manner. They have had the advantage, of course, of dealing almost entirely with races which occur in species of lower organisms. Human emotions and prejudices have thus not influenced their thinking so much. But the difference is also partly due to the fact that the geneticists have based their definitions on more objective and scientific foundations. If the science of genetics had developed before physical anthropology, we might now be using the concept of race, as defined by geneticists, and applying it to the human species. As many writers, Hogben (23) for example, have pointed out, all of the existing human types are interfertile and constitute a single Linnaean species. Within this species there are various groups which differ from each other to a greater or less degree and some of these we may, if we choose, define as races.

It must not be supposed that the genetic definition of race would naturally be "a group of individuals with identical genetic constitutions." This would not be a good definition, for, as pointed out by Dobzhansky and Epling (14), groups of identical individuals are simply never found, for there is a great deal of genetic variation even within the confines of a race. If we should frame our definition of race along these lines, every single individual would have to belong to a separate race, of which he was the only member. (Identical twins might belong to the same race.) Dobzhansky and Epling (14) also point out that it would be equally fallacious to define a race as a group of individuals having some single gene in common, or some chromosome structure in common. Since so many variable genes and chromosome structures exist and since these different genes and chromosome structures can form a large variety of combinations, we should be certain to find individuals classified as belonging to one race in so far as some gene, say *F*, was concerned, but who would belong to a different race in regard to the gene *G*, and a still different race in regard to the gene *H*. A race (14) is not an individual and it is not a single genotype, but it is a group of individuals, more or less from the same geographical area (a population), usually with a number of identical genes, but in which many different types may occur.

Dobzhansky and Epling (14) propose to define races as (different) populations which are characterized by different frequencies of variable genes and/or chromosome structures. Dahlberg (7) has proposed a definition of race which amounts to much the same thing. He says "a race is an isolate or a collection of isolates." By an isolate is implied a group of individuals isolated geographically or socially or in some other way from surrounding peoples, and who consequently do not freely exchange genes with them. But within the isolate, mating occurs more or less at random. In the ideal case, one would take account of *all* the variable genes and chromosome structures in order to describe a given race. At present, we are unable to do this, even in the lower forms such as Drosophila, where the genetics are much more thoroughly understood than they are with man. Because of the incompleteness of our knowledge, we have to base our classifications on certain genetic differences which we do know about.

We still have to decide *how much* difference there must be in the distribution of the known variable genes and chromosome structures between two populations before we decide to call them two different races. According to Charles and Goodwin (5), in some cases the number of genes differentiating two different *species* may be of the order of 40. Statistically significant (App. A) differences (14) may occur between populations of Drosophila in localities only a dozen miles apart. Therefore we could if we liked say that these populations are racially distinct. If the concept of race is to be taxonomically useful, however, we should not use the term quite so freely, for otherwise we shall have too many races within each species, and the term will lose much of its value for purposes of classification. Dobzhansky and Epling go into some detail to show that in Drosophila, where far more is known about the genetic structure than in man, it would be quite useless to decide to base the concept of race on the possession of any one gene or any one particular arrangement of genes in any one particular chromosome. Individuals identical in respect to this chromosome would frequently be found to differ profoundly in respect to the arrangement of genes in some other chromosome. To make the race concept useful, we must look for some additional feature to use in defining it. In the species of *Drosophila pseudoobscura* (14) there is a rather conspicuous break between the populations of the Pacific Coast of the United States and those of the Intermontane Plateau; between those of the Intermontane Plateau and those of the Rocky Mountains and Texas; and between those of the United States and those of Mexico and Guatemala. Thus we can readily distinguish four races of *Drosophila pseudoobscura*. In addition, within at least two of those four races, there are rather clear secondary discontinuities. Thus one student might choose to distinguish four or seven or even more races in this species; whereas another, feeling in a different mood, and recalling that the major as well as the minor races are connected by gradients, might refuse to delimit any races at all.

When we take account of the various intermediate grades which are possible, and which often exist, between groups which appear to be distinctively different, the differences sometimes begin to seem considerably less. For instance, the titmouse of Asia, *Parus minor*, and the titmouse of Europe, *Parus major*, differ (10, 27) to such an extent that if there were no intermediate forms they could be considered "good" species, especially since they are physiologically isolated and can exist in the same territory without crossing. Nevertheless, the Asiatic titmouse occupies the territory from Amur and Japan to southern China, where it intergrades with *Parus bokharensis*. The latter inhabits southern Asia from the Sunda Islands through India to Turkestan, and in Persia it intergrades with the European form, *Parus major*, which extends across Siberia. In the Amur region it meets the distribution of *Parus minor* and in this region both forms occupy the same territory without intergradation. (This overlapping is probably recent; that is, since the last Ice Age.) Nevertheless it is clearly impossible to draw a sharp line anywhere between *Parus major* and *Parus minor*.

If we examine the population of a good many localities, it may happen (14) that the frequencies of some genes or of some chromosome structures change gradually in various geographical directions, so that the differences between populations are proportional to the distances between the localities which they inhabit. When this is true we have a geographical gradient (a cline), analogous to the slopes shown by the contour lines on topographical maps, or the temperature gradients crossing the isotherms on weather maps. Examples for the human population are given in Figures 33a, 33b. The populations at the two ends of such a gradient may be profoundly different in genetic constitution, but they may be connected by all grades of genetic variation between the two. In such a case, whether or not the systematist decides to break up the population into two or more sections and designate them as races is quite arbitrary. *This decision will be based upon considerations of expediency and nothing else.* In favor of defining two or more races there will be the advantage of having simple reference names which apply to the various populations. Among the disadvantages there will be the difficulties caused by the existence of populations which are intermediate between the arbitrary racial types.

Dobzhansky and Epling note (14) that the gene frequency gradient between some populations may be relatively steep, and that in some cases these gradients are steep enough (contour lines close together) to justify taking some point on the steep portion as a boundary and thus breaking up the species into one or more discrete arrays of populations which will have few intermediates. In such a situation we have little hesitation in defining races. Each major population array becomes a race, and these arrays can be delimited, counted, and named. The mean differences between these population arrays may not necessarily be any greater than those between the end members of a continuous population chain which we may prefer to call one (variable) race, but if nature, by providing us with complete or nearly complete discontinuities between the arrays, has to a large extent eliminated the arbitrary human element otherwise involved in drawing dividing lines between populations, we feel justified in referring to these arrays (isolates) as races.

In nature the geographic gradients in gene frequencies are seldom quite uniform on the one hand and are seldom entirely discontinuous on the other, so we have usually to deal with a somewhat intermediate situation. Therefore it is not at all uncommon to find within a single species that two certain races may be easily separated from each other, while two other races show only a slight discontinuity where their populations meet or overlap.

Whatever the course adopted in devising names for the populations (14), the realities of the situation are not altered in the least. It still remains a fact that the species *Drosophila pseudoobscura* is geographically differentiated, and that populations of different territories differ in regard to the relative frequencies of chromosome types (and genes). And this is exactly what the geneticist means by racial differentiation. The differences are usually gene differences, not differences in whole chromosomes, but the principle is the same. Dobzhansky has often used chromosome arrangements in *D. pseudoobscura* because these can be identified directly by microscopic examination, without breeding experiments.

Given an individual from any part of the distribution area, we can predict the probability that it will have a given gene, or to take *D. pseudoobscura* as an example again, a given gene arrangement in the third chromosome. Or, given a population sample from a well-known locality, we can predict the probable frequencies of the different varieties of chromosomes which will be found in it. Or if we are told the genetic constitution of a population sample, we may guess at the probable location from which it has originated. To that extent racial studies in Drosophila may be said to be successful. It is certainly doubtful if racial studies in man can ever be expected to be any more successful than this.

Race Only a "Constellation of Characters"

The moral to be drawn from the above considerations of independent variation is that if we make a thorough study of man, genetically and morphologically, we must not expect that the various data collected will all be mutually "consistent." In fact, we must be prepared to find that populations in Greenland and in Australia agree quite well in regard to blood grouping frequencies (A, B, O at least) (Table 31) while they markedly disagree in regard to the M and N blood types, in regard to skin color, hair form, and other characteristics. Most contemporary physical anthropologists will probably accept this as a necessary and not illogical situation.

If we may again illustrate with an example from the study of lower forms, a specimen of *Drosophila pseudoobscura* (14) from California, which carries the "Santa Cruz" gene arrangement in the third chromosome, is *in that respect* more similar to specimens from Mexico which have the Santa Cruz gene arrangement than it is to other California specimens which do not, more similar perhaps than even to some of its own brothers and sisters, which may carry some of the other gene arrangements. In other words, although the genotype of an individual is derived from the population from which it sprang, it is not absolutely predetermined by the genetic composition of this population (except of course in respect to genes for which the population is homozygous). And the extent to which the individual can vary in turn depends on the degree of genetic variability which is present in the species in question.

It is to be feared that many anthropologists, and many laymen, nevertheless have continued to hope that human races are so different basically that the differences will show up, almost irrespective of what sort of observations we make on populations. This attitude interposes an unfortunate obstacle to progress towards a really objective concept of human races.

Fleure says (16): "Skin color and hair form have been used in the classification of mankind, and they are, it is true, obvious and distinguishing marks; but there is a danger in such usage. We too easily slip into the habit of considering, for example, that the peoples with dark skin and kinky hair form a profoundly distinct group marked off by all their characteristics from the rest of the human race and that the so-called Nordic race can be described simply as light colored of hair, eyes, and skin." Some writers are not satisfied with the simple observation that a Negro has a black skin, whereas Europeans are "white," but are convinced (probably without adequate evidence) that each organ and each bone of a Negro will, when properly scrutinized, show some characteristic Negroid traits. Professor R. R. Gates (18) has carried this tendency about to the limit in claiming that the various races of man are really different species.

As data on the physical characteristics of the human race have accumulated, however, and it has become clear how they are mostly independent of each other, this point of view has become more and more patently absurd, and it has gradually become clear that whatever races we choose to distinguish will be almost entirely arbitrary, and their distribution will depend on the particular characteristics on which we choose to base them. Dahlberg (7) reminds us that the finding of one "racial" difference does not mean we can forthwith assume that many other differences must exist. The observed difference may be the chief or even the only difference. The only instances in which we may expect a "dividend" of additional similarities will be those in which we are studying populations which have long been isolated genetically, and thus have had time to undergo considerable differentiation. The situation is entirely different from the case of the chemical elements, where, when we find one test which clearly differentiates sodium and arsenic, for example, we can safely infer the existence of many other important differences.

We may define a human race as a population which differs significantly from other human populations in regard to the frequency of one or more of the genes it possesses. It is an arbitrary matter which, and how many, gene loci we choose to consider as a significant "constellation"; but it seems better, on the one hand, not to designate a multiplicity of races which differ only in regard to a single pair or a single set of allelic genes; and on the other, not to insist that the races we define must differ from each other with respect to all their genes. An actual race classification will be attempted in Chapter IX.

References for Chapter VII

1. Bernstein, F., *Z. Indukt. Abstamm. & Vererbungsl.*, *37*, 237–270 (1925).
2. Boas, F., *Science*, *98*, 311–314; 334–337 (1943).
3. Boyd, W. C., *A. J. P. A.*, *27*, 333–364 (1940).
4. Bryce, J., *Race Sentiment as a Factor in History*. Univ. of London Press, London, 1915.
5. Charles, D. R., and R. H. Goodwin, *Am. Nat.* *77*, 53–69 (1943).
6. Coon, C. S., *The Races of Europe*. Macmillan Co., New York, 1939.
7. Dahlberg, G., *Human Biol.*, *14*, 372–385 (1942).
8. Dart, R. A., *J. Roy. Anthrop. Inst.*, *70*, 13–27 (1940).
9. Dixon, R. B., *The Racial History of Man*. Charles Scribner's Sons, New York, 1923.
10. Dobzhansky, Th., *Genetics and the Origin of Species*. Columbia Univ. Press, New York, 1941.
11. Dobzhansky, Th., *Sci. Monthly*, *52*, 161–165 (1941).
12. Dobzhansky, Th., *Trans. N. Y. Acad. Sci.*, Ser. II, *4*, 115–128 (1942).
13. Dobzhansky, Th., *A. J. P. A.*, *2*, 251–265 (1944).
14. Dobzhansky, Th., and C. Epling, *Carnegie Inst. Wash. Pub.*, *554* (1944).
15. East, F. M., and D. F. Jones, *Inbreeding and Outbreeding*. J. B. Lippincott Co., Philadelphia, 1919.
16. Fleure, H. J., *Geog. Rev.*, *35*, 580–595 (1945).
17. Gates, R. R., *A. J. P. A.*, *2*, 279–291 (1944).
18. Gates, R. R., *Human Ancestry*. Harvard Univ. Press, Cambridge, 1948.
19. Glass, B., *Genes and the Man*. Columbia Univ. Press, New York, 1943.
20. Haldane, J. B. S., *C. R. Cong. Int. Sci. Anthrop. & Ethnol.* (I London), *53* (1934).
21. Herder, J. G., *Ideen zur Philosophie der Geschichte der Menschheit*. C. G. Schmieder, Carlsruhe, 1794.
22. Hitler, A., *Mein Kampf*. Reynal & Hitchcock, New York, 1940.
23. Hogben, L., *Genetic Principles in Medicine and Social Science*. Williams & Norgate, London, 1931.
24. Hooton, E. A., *Up from the Ape*. Macmillan Co., New York, 1946.
25. Howells, W. W., *Physical Determination of Race in Contemporary Social Theory*. D. Appleton Century Co., New York, 1940.
26. Howells, W. W., *Mankind So Far*. Doubleday, Doran & Co., Inc., New York, 1944.
27. Huxley, J., *Evolution: The Modern Synthesis*. Harper & Bros., New York and London, 1942.
28. Huxley, J. S., and A. C. Haddon, *We Europeans*. J. Cape, London, 1935.
29. Kluckhohn, C., *The Science of Man in the World Crisis*. Ed., Ralph Linton. Columbia Univ. Press, New York, 1945.
30. Mayr, E., *Systematics and the Origin of Species*. Columbia Univ. Press, New York, 1942.

31. Montagu, M. F. A., *Man's Most Dangerous Myth: The Fallacy of Race*. Columbia Univ. Press, New York, 1945.
32. Morant, G. M., *Man, 34,* 99 (1934).
33. Morant, G. M., *The Races of Central Europe*. George Allen & Unwin, Ltd., London, 1939.
34. Nehru, J., *The Discovery of India*. John Day Co., New York, 1946.
34a. Oberhummer, E., *Z. Rassenkunde, 1,* 92–93 (1935).
35. Sargeant, D., cited by: Hooton, E. A., *Up from the Ape*. Macmillan Co., New York, 1931.
36. Spuhler, J. N., *Science, 108,* 279–280 (1948).
37. Young, M., *Man, 28,* nos. 116, 127 (1928).

CHAPTER VIII

Blood Groups

> Since species are characterized not only by morphological attributes but by their specific biochemical constitution as well, it seems evident that the somatic and functional development of the organic world was paralleled by a biochemical evolution. . . .
>
> — KARL LANDSTEINER

Three Types of Hereditary Characteristics

IN the first chapter, it was pointed out that the best physical anthropological classification of men must be based on genetic characters. Having surveyed, although somewhat briefly, the subject of genetics in the second chapter, we may at this point inquire: how much is known about genes which act to determine human constitution, and which genetically determined characters are best adapted for use as the basis for a physical classification? In answering this question, we may divide the inherited characters into three categories: characters which are fairly common and variable, believed to be inherited although the mechanism is still to be worked out; rare pathological conditions whose mechanism of inheritance is known, and normal physiological characters inherited by a known genetic mechanism. Let us first consider the first category.

Perhaps nearly all human characteristics are at least in a sense inherited, for they are the end result of the action of certain genes acting in a given environment. Facial features, such as the shape of the nose, and the color of the hair, skin, and eyes, are good examples. All the genes which affect physical appearance, the various skeletal and morphological features, etc., belong in this category. But human genetics has been investigated to such a slight extent that in very few, if any, of these cases do we know the genetic mechanism, i.e., the number and behavior of the genes involved, whether they are on one or several chromosome pairs, what dominance relations exist, and so on. Whether personality traits are inherited is still a very controversial issue.

The second category contains a rather large group of fairly uncommon genes which may produce certain pathological conditions. For example, there are a large number of inherited abnormalities of the eye for which the genetic mechanism has been worked out (19). Another good example is the gene which, when present in double dose (homozygous), makes the individual unable to oxidize phenyl pyruvic acid, and at the same time, whether as a consequence of this metabolic failure is not known, causes the affected person to be an idiot (22). The frequency of any one of these genes in any given population is very low.

In the third category there are a few characteristics which do not affect the appearance of an individual, but which are relatively common, and whose genetic mechanism is fully understood. These genes have been identified in the course of physiological and pathological research, or sometimes purely as the result of an accidental observation.

The members of the second group are too rare in the human population to be of any great value for purposes of classification. It is fairly obvious that a fruitful classification cannot be based upon the frequency of same rare gene which, although it always produces some disease or abnormality, occurs in only about one person out of 50,000. Our knowledge of the behavior of these human genes, although of interest to the student of pure genetics, is of no use to us as anthropologists because of the rarity of these genes. The first class of general heritable features has heretofore been the one most used as a basis for the defining of human races. Classification of men into racial categories on the basis of such characteristics has been attempted by a great many authors. Nevertheless, all of these characters fall far short of meeting all the specifications for a really valuable criterion of classification which we discussed in Chapter I. They are most unsatisfactory in one particular aspect: the exact manner of their inheritance is not known.

Only the third group of characteristics seems to meet the qualifications we laid down in Chapter I. It is just an accident, stemming from the rather haphazard way in which our knowledge of human genetics developed, that all of this group are the result of discoveries made in the laboratory (although most of them can be investigated under field conditions) and a slight amount of specialized knowledge is required to understand their significance. The simplest and most important of these are the blood groups. It may be wise to present at first a somewhat oversimplified explanation of the blood groups, and to fill this out later on, as the reader becomes better acquainted with the ideas involved.

The A, B, O Blood Groups

The four classical blood groups, O, A, B, AB, were discovered in 1900–1902 (12, 27, 28) by Dr. Karl Landsteiner and pupils. They depend upon the circumstance that the red blood corpuscles of certain individuals are acted upon by substances present in the fluid part of the blood (i.e., plasma or serum) of certain other persons in such a way that they stick together to form clusters and clumps. These clumps are at first so small that they can be seen only under the microscope, but when the reaction is strong they grow to a size easily discernible by the naked eye. The chemical substances in the red corpuscles which permit their being agglutinated in this way are called antigens, and there are two of them, designated as A and B. In serum, substances which react with these substances may be formed, and there are two of these, designated as anti-A and anti-B.

The division of all persons into four blood groups depends upon the fact that the two different blood corpuscle characteristics, A and B, can be present singly or together, or can be absent. If we designate the absence of both by O, we have four possibilities:

1. Blood corpuscles contain O
2. Blood corpuscles contain A
3. Blood corpuscles contain B
4. Blood corpuscles contain A and B

These four possibilities correspond to the four blood groups which are now by international agreement designated briefly by the above mentioned letters, thus:

O   A   B   AB

The relation of the serum agglutinins anti-A and anti-B to the characteristic blood corpuscle substances of the individual is given by the Landsteiner rule: *there is always found that agglutinin or*

TABLE 18

The Human Blood Groups

Blood Group	Agglutinogen in Corpuscles	Agglutinin in Serum
O	O	anti-A + anti-B
A	A	anti-B
B	B	anti-A
AB	A + B	—

agglutinins which could co-exist physiologically with the blood corpuscle characteristic which is present. Thus, for example, anti-A is found in the presence of O and B, but not of A. These relations are illustrated by Table 18, in the last column of which the blood group serum characteristics are represented. (Cf. Fig. 30.)

Procedure of Testing

The technic of blood group determination will not be described in detail here. Detailed descriptions will be found in (48, 56). In determining blood groups, the corpuscle suspension of the person to be tested is allowed to react, preferably in the test tube (29, 48, 56), with sera which have the property of agglutinating cells containing blood group factors A and B respectively. It is customary to put in each test tube one drop each of cell suspension, serum, and saline (0.9 per cent sodium chloride solution). The contents of the tubes are then thoroughly mixed. If no centrifuge is available, the tests are read after the lapse of 15 minutes to one half hour, depending on the strength of the sera and the behavior of the controls (bloods of known group tested simultaneously). Typical agglutination is shown in Figure 31. The group is determined by the simple scheme shown in Table 19.

Blood grouping tests can also be carried out on glass slides, in-

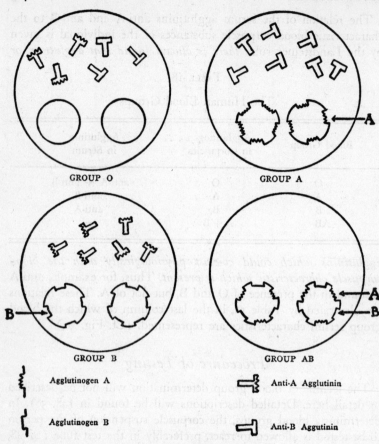

GROUP O   GROUP A

GROUP B   GROUP AB

{ Agglutinogen A   Anti-A Agglutinin

{ Agglutinogen B   Anti-B Aggutinin

FIGURE 30. *Schematic representation of red blood agglutinogens (antigens) and agglutinins.*

stead of in test tubes. This method is often used for clinical tests in
hospitals. An idea of the appearance of the reactions to the naked
eye and under the microscope is given in Figure 32.

Inheritance

It was fairly soon found that the blood groups were inherited,
but at first the exact mechanism was not fully understood. The

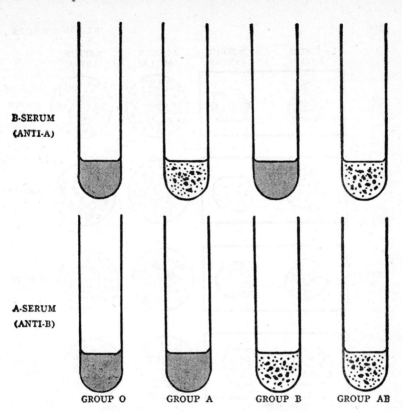

B-SERUM
(ANTI-A)

A-SERUM
(ANTI-B)

GROUP O   GROUP A   GROUP B   GROUP AB

FIGURE 31. *Schematic representation of blood grouping as carried out in test tubes.*

TABLE 19

Determination of Groups with Two Test Sera,
Anti-A and Anti-B

	Known Serum Anti-A	Known Serum Anti-B	Group
Agglutination of the unknown blood corpuscles	−	−	O
	+	−	A
	−	+	B
	+	+	AB

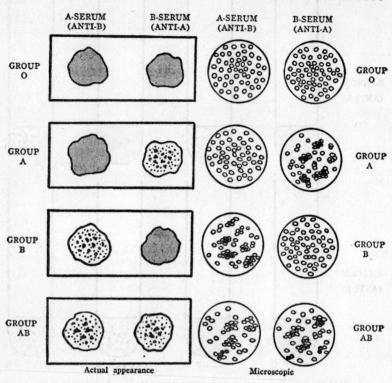

FIGURE 32. *Schematic representation of blood grouping on slides.*

earliest theory of blood group inheritance, proposed by von Dungern and Hirszfeld (16), postulated that the blood groups were inherited by means of two independent pairs of genes. The correct mechanism of inheritance was shown by Bernstein (1) to depend upon a series of three allelic genes, that is, three genes which can occupy the same locus on a certain chromosome, which are generally designated as A, B, and O. From Chapter II, we know that each person must possess some combination of two of these genes. Six different combinations, OO, AA, AO, BB, BO, and AB are possible. Since, however, the factor O seems to be recessive to both A and B (or at least its presence in the genetic make-up of the individual does not interfere with the full expression of the A or B characteristic), the heterozygotes AO and BO are indistinguishable from the homozygotes AA or BB respectively, and the six gene combinations produce only four distinguishable groups, as shown in Table 20.

TABLE 20

Genotypes and Phenotypes of Blood Group Genes

Genotype	Blood Group (Phenotype)
OO	O
{ AA ⎰ AO	A
{ BB ⎰ BO	B
AB	AB

Because of the length of human generations, and because of the impossibility of making direct experimental crosses, the methods of human genetics are necessarily somewhat different from those commonly employed in the study of the lower forms. It is, therefore, worth while to consider briefly how Bernstein demonstrated that the blood groups are inherited by a series of three allelomorphs and not by two pairs of independent factors on different chromosomes, as had been previously suggested (16) by von Dungern and Hirszfeld, whose theory led to the predicted genotypes and phenotypes shown in Table 21. According to this theory, parents of blood group AB could have children of any of the four groups.

According to Bernstein's theory, group AB is homogeneous, in the sense that all individuals in the group are alike in having one A gene and one B gene. Individuals of group AB could therefore never become the parents of a child of group O. (The blood group of an individual never changes from infancy to old age.) Careful study of a large number of human families revealed that this was true, for although a few such children had been reported before Bernstein's hypothesis was proposed, later studies, made with more

TABLE 21

Genotypes and Phenotypes According to the (Obsolete) von Dungern and Hirszfeld Hypothesis

Genotype	Blood Group (Phenotype)
aabb	O
{ AAbb { Aabb	A
{ aaBB { aaBb	B
AABB AaBB AABb AaBb	AB

careful technic, carried out by workers knowing the Bernstein hypothesis (who therefore were led to retest any apparent exceptions), have revealed that children of group O are never born to individuals of group AB. It is true that since the enunciation of Bernstein's hypothesis some families have been reported with the *father* of group AB and a child of group O, but no authenticated case is known of a mother of group AB having a normal child of group O. It seems pretty clear that the children in the former cases were illegitimate. The accompanying Table 22 shows how nearly the experimental results conform to the Bernstein theory.

Another way in which the von Dungern and Hirszfeld theory proved inadequate and the Bernstein theory correct was shown by the statistical study of populations (p. 401).

From the absence of normal children who have a blood group incompatible with that of their mother (and the same argument applies to the M, N types discussed on page 232), we may infer that the blood group genes do not mutate at any rapid rate, for otherwise children incompatible with their mothers would have been observed. Blood groups thus may be more "conservative" characters than

TABLE 22

Inheritance of Blood Groups, as Found in Actual
Studies (48)

Groups of Parents	Number of Families	Number of Children in Group				
		O	A	B	AB	Total
O × O	1405	3355	(14)	(9)	0	3378
O × A	2647	2486	3389	(10)	(2)	5887
O × B	1365	1315	(7)	1690	(1)	3013
O × AB	504	(6)	607	612	(3)	1228
A × A	1270	516	2354	0	(1)	2871
A × B	1299	561	908	734	782	2985
A × AB	419	0	478	238	279	995
B × B	536	188	(1)	975	0	1164
B × AB	304	(2)	171	383	225	781
AB × AB	57	0	26	36	63	125
Totals	9806	8429	7955	4687	1356	22,427

Numbers in parentheses are apparent exceptions to the accepted theory of blood group inheritance proposed by Bernstein. They are doubtless due to faulty technic in making the tests, or to illegitimacy.

albinism and hemophilia, both of which seem to be recruited steadily by mutations from the normal gene (p. 137).

The genes A and B cause the production in the red blood cells of the individual of the chemical substances known as A and B respectively. The chemical nature of these substances has been investigated (24) by Kabat and by Morgan. They are nitrogen-containing carbohydrates. If gene A or B is not present, the individual does not develop the corresponding blood group characteristic, and a person who has neither the A nor the B gene has neither antigen A nor B, and therefore belongs to group O.

Blood Transfusion

From Table 18 it will be understood that if we inject the blood of an individual of group A into the circulation of an individual of group B, the anti-A agglutinins in the plasma of the group B recipient will agglutinate the A cells which were injected. It has been found from experience that a serious, or indeed often a fatal reaction may result from such a transfusion, especially if much of the incompatible blood is injected. It is for this reason that blood transfusions can be performed safely only when the blood groups of the individuals have been previously determined.

In making a transfusion, the preferred procedure is to use blood of the same group to which the recipient belongs. If the scheme in the above table is studied, however, it will be seen that there are a number of combinations in which the cells of the donor will not be agglutinated by any agglutinins present in the circulation of the recipient. The converse possibility, namely, that the agglutinins of the donor may agglutinate the cells of the recipient, is generally not so important, because the amount of blood injected from the donor is equivalent in amount to only a small fraction of the recipient's circulation, and the agglutinins introduced by it get diluted (and probably to some extent neutralized) by substances in the recipient's plasma and tissues. The possibilities of transfusion which are thus allowable are shown in the accompanying scheme. It should be remarked, however, that transfusions carried out according to this scheme, such as using persons belonging to group O as so-called

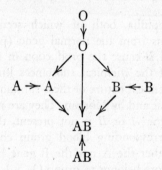

"universal donors," have not always been successful, and there is some evidence that certain individuals of this group are dangerous when used as donors for persons of other groups (40), since their agglutinins are strong enough to destroy some of the recipient's cells. There is no evidence that the results of transfusion depend upon race. If you need a blood transfusion, the blood of a healthy Negro or Chinese, if he is of the same blood group as you, will be of the same clinical value as the blood of a "Caucasian," and the blood of your brother or sister, if of the wrong group, may kill you.

The effect of the blood group genes is manifested in each individual in any and all environments. So far as we know, neither climate nor diet, nor any other outside factor, can affect the blood group, which is determined by heredity alone.

Racial Classification

Tens of thousands of individuals have been "blood grouped" since 1900. The very early tests did not seem to reveal very much difference in the frequencies of the four groups in various nationalities, but during the First World War two Polish doctors named Hirszfeld, working on the Macedonian battle front, made the discovery that the percentages of the four groups varied considerably in different races, and later, after some discouraging experiences, they finally got their findings accepted and published in 1919 (23). A summary of their results will be found in (48). This new anthropological technic was at first hailed enthusiastically by some anthropologists and other scientists (43, 50, 51) as a wonderful way of detecting races by characters "hidden in their blood," but since the conclusions which had to be drawn from the blood group observations in many cases did not coincide with ideas based on earlier work such as morphological studies, already thought to be firmly established, there was later on a reaction against the use of blood groups in anthropology; the enthusiasm faded to a puzzled bewilderment, and anthropologists became suspicious of the whole subject. Now the pendulum is beginning to swing in the other direction again, and many geneticists and anthropologists are maintaining that blood groups constitute the best basis, at present, on which to frame a racial classification (6, 15).

As characters for use in anthropological classification, the blood groups offer several advantages (26): (a) They are inherited in a known way according to Mendelian principles. (b) They are not altered by differences in climate, food, illness, or medical treatment. (c) Their frequency in a population is a very stable characteristic.

(d) They probably arose very early in the course of man's evolution. (e) There is a considerable correlation between geography and the distribution of the blood groups. (f) The blood groups are sharply distinguishable "all-or-none" characters which do not grade into each other.

Since every human individual has to belong to one or another of the four blood groups, the only racial differences we find, or can expect to find, will be differences in *frequencies* of the four groups among various populations. It would be a very simple situation if, for example, all the people in Asia belonged to blood group B, all the Indians in America to blood group A, and all the aborigines in Australia to blood group O. This is not exactly what we find, however, and a little reflection will show us that it is not the sort of thing we should expect to find. The human species is an ancient one, and has presumably dispersed to its present habitats from some relatively restricted area or areas in which it originated by evolution from its ancestral anthropoid stock or stocks. In the process of this dispersal there has constantly been a great deal of mixture among different groups of men, and unless the blood groups were something of very recent origin, and in addition had some feature which enabled them, once introduced, to spread rapidly through a population — and we see in Chapter IV that they do not have these characteristics — we would not expect any such simple situation as that outlined above.

A relatively enormous mass of data on blood group frequencies in various ethnic groups has accumulated since 1919 (over 1500 series of observations). The results of all blood group studies on different populations up to about the middle of 1938 have been summarized in another place (3). Other important results for Africa are summarized by Elsdon-Dew (17), for India by Sarkar (47), and for Australia and the Pacific area in various issues of the *Medical Journal of Australia* published during the past few years. They are not reproduced here because of considerations of space. Results by reliable workers for typical populations are shown in Table 23. These figures are necessarily a rather arbitrary selection from the mass of data available. When possible, a series which can be found in one of the present author's monographs, or in the *Medical Journal of Australia,* where some of the best recent work

TABLE 23

Frequencies of Blood Groups O, A, B, and AB in Typical Populations

Population	Place	Number Tested	O	A	B	AB	p	q	r
Low A, Virtually No B									
Am. Indians (Utes)	Montana	138	97.4	2.6	0	0	0.013	0.0	0.987
Am. Indians (Toba)	Argentina	194	98.5	1.5	0	0	0.007	0	0.993
Am. Indians (Sioux)	S. Dakota	100	91.0	7.0	2.0	0	0.035	0.010	0.955
Am. Indians (Kwakiutl)	B. Columbia	123	85.4	12.2	2.4	0	0.063	0.013	0.926
Moderate A, Virtually No B									
Am. Indians (Navaho)	N. Mexico	359	77.7	22.5	0	0	0.125	0	0.875
Am. Indians (Pueblo)	Jemez etc. N. M.	310	78.4	20.0	1.6	0	0.105	0.007	0.885
High A, Little B									
Am. Indians (Bloods)	Montana	69	17.4	81.2	0	1.4	0.583	0	0.417
Am. Indians (Blackfeet)	Montana	115	23.5	76.5	0	0	0.515	0	0.485
Australian Aborigines	South Australia	54	42.6	57.4	0	0	0.346	0	0.654
Australian Aborigines	West Australia	243	48.1	51.9	0	0	0.306	0	0.694
Basques	San Sebastián	91	57.2	41.7	1.1	0	0.239	0.008	0.756
Am. Indians (Shoshone)	Wyoming	60	51.6	45.0	1.6	1.6	0.264	0.011	0.718
Polynesians	Hawaii	413	36.5	60.8	2.2	0.5	0.382	0.018	0.604
Eskimo	Cape Farewell	484	41.1	53.8	3.5	1.4	0.333	0.027	0.642
Australian Aborigines	Queensland	447	58.6	37.8	3.6	0	0.216	0.023	0.766
Am. Indians (Flatheads)	Montana	258	51.5	42.2	4.7	1.6	0.250	0.032	0.718

TABLE 23 (*Continued*)

Frequencies of Blood Groups O, A, B, and AB in
Typical Populations

Population	Place	Number Tested	O	A	B	AB	p	q	r
		Fairly High A, and Some B							
W. Georgians	Tiflis	707	59.1	34.4	6.1	0.4	0.198	0.038	0.769
English	London	422	47.9	42.4	8.3	1.4	0.250	0.050	0.692
Belgians	Liége	3500	46.7	41.9	8.3	3.1	0.257	0.058	0.684
Spanish	Spain	1172	41.5	46.5	9.2	2.2	0.294	0.068	0.645
Swedes	Stockholm	633	37.9	46.1	9.5	6.5	0.301	0.073	0.616
Icelanders	Iceland	800	55.7	32.1	9.6	2.6	0.190	0.062	0.747
Danes	Copenhagen	1261	40.7	45.3	10.5	3.5	0.290	0.078	0.638
French	Paris	1265	39.8	42.3	11.8	6.1	0.276	0.088	0.632
Armenians	fr. Turkey	330	27.3	53.9	12.7	6.1	0.379	0.110	0.523
Irish	Dublin	399	55.2	31.1	12.1	1.7	0.186	0.076	0.744
Lapps	Finland	94	33.0	52.1	12.8	2.1	0.323	0.078	0.574
Melanesians	New Guinea	500	37.6	44.4	13.2	4.8	0.293	0.099	0.613
Micronesians	Saipan	293	50.5	33.8	14.0	1.7	0.207	0.093	0.711
Greeks	Athens	1200	42.0	39.6	14.2	3.7	0.254	0.102	0.648
Germans	Berlin	39,174	36.5	42.5	14.5	6.5	0.285	0.110	0.604
Turks	Istamboul	500	33.8	42.6	14.8	8.8	0.293	0.116	0.581
		High A and High B							
E. Georgians	Tiflis	1274	36.8	42.3	15.0	5.9	0.283	0.113	0.607
Bulgarians	Sofia	6060	32.1	44.4	15.4	8.1	0.308	0.123	0.567
Hungarians	Budapest	624	36.1	41.8	15.9	6.2	0.282	0.120	0.601
Welsh	N. towns	192	47.9	32.8	16.2	3.1	0.206	0.108	0.692
Italians	Sicily	540	45.9	33.4	17.3	3.4	0.213	0.118	0.678
Siamese	Bangkok	213	37.1	17.8	35.2	9.9	0.148	0.257	0.595
Syrians	Meshghara	300	39.3	39.0	17.1	4.6	0.258	0.124	0.628
Finns	Häme	972	34.0	42.4	17.1	6.5	0.285	0.126	0.583
"Berbers"	Algiers	300	39.0	37.6	18.6	4.6	0.251	0.134	0.625
Germans	Danzig	1888	33.1	41.6	18.0	7.3	0.288	0.139	0.575
Ukrainians	Kharkov	310	36.4	38.4	21.6	3.6	0.261	0.158	0.604
Japanese	Tokyo	29,799	30.1	38.4	21.9	9.7	0.279	0.172	0.549
Japanese	Kyoto	6205	29.2	38.0	22.2	10.6	0.279	0.177	0.541
Estonians	Estonia	1844	32.3	36.6	22.4	8.7	0.261	0.170	0.589
Madagascans	Madagascar	266	45.5	27.5	22.5	4.5	0.180	0.151	0.674
Russians	n. Moscow	489	31.9	34.4	24.9	8.8	0.250	0.189	0.565
Abyssinians	Abyssinia	400	42.8	26.5	25.3	5.0	0.178	0.172	0.654
Egyptians	Cairo	502	27.3	38.5	25.5	8.8	0.288	0.203	0.523

Table 23 (*Continued*)

Frequencies of Blood Groups O, A, B, and AB in Typical Populations

Population	Place	Number Tested	O	A	B	AB	p	q	r
Bogobos	Philippines	302	53.6	16.9	26.5	3.0	0.107	0.163	0.732
Chinese	Huang-Ho R.	2127	34.2	30.8	27.7	7.3	0.220	0.201	0.587
'Iraqis	Baghdad	386	33.7	31.4	28.2	6.7	0.226	0.208	0.581
Tatars	Kazan	500	27.8	30.0	28.8	13.4	0.233	0.225	0.527
Pygmies	Belgian Congo	1032	30.6	30.3	29.1	10.0	0.227	0.219	0.554
Arabs, Bedouin (Rwala)	Syrian Desert	208	43.3	22.1	30.3	4.3	0.151	0.200	0.658
Egyptians	Assiut	419	24.6	34.4	31.0	10.0	0.272	0.250	0.459
Kirghiz	USSR	500	31.6	27.4	32.2	8.8	0.206	0.236	0.563
Asiatic Indians	Goa	400	29.2	26.8	34.0	10.0	0.208	0.254	0.540
Chinese	Peking	1000	30.7	25.1	34.2	10.0	0.193	0.250	0.554
Javanese	Ampelgading	450	30.4	24.7	37.3	7.6	0.190	0.271	0.552
Buriats	N. Irkutsk	1320	32.4	20.2	39.2	8.2	0.156	0.277	0.570
Asiatic Indians	Bengal	160	32.5	20.0	39.4	8.1	0.154	0.278	0.571

N. signifies north, S., W., and E. south, west, and east respectively. fr. signifies from. n. signifies near. In this table the frequencies of the blood groups O, A, B, and AB are given in per cents, but the gene frequencies (see p. 108) are given as straight frequencies, following common practice. The symbol p represents the frequency of the gene A, q the frequency of the gene B, and r the frequency of the gene O.

Apropos of this and succeeding tables in this chapter, we may remark again that no one characteristic is enough to differentiate races satisfactorily. Therefore populations obviously not closely related are found cheek by jowl in these tables. But in Chapter IX, in which we try to synthesize all this information and make use of it, it will be found that the various serological characteristics taken together do make classification of mankind into races possible, and that the resulting classification is far from nonsensical.

has been published, has been chosen. Figures which suggest accuracy, either by statistical test (3) or by the reputation of the authors, have been given preference. Large series have been chosen as against small series, unless the only data for a significant population were limited. The arrangement into categories is quite arbitrary, and only achieves a kind of justification in Chapter IX, where an attempt is made to define race on a genetic basis.

Let us recall that the blood groups depend upon the presence of a pair of genes derived from three members of the allelomorphic series: A, B, and O. From the frequencies (per cents are frequencies multiplied by 100) of the blood groups in any population, the frequency of these genes which we designate as p, q, and r may be estimated by simple formulas (App. A). The sum of the actual gene frequencies will equal 1.000. If the usual formulas are used, the resulting *estimated* gene frequencies may not add up exactly to 1.000, but the discrepancy will fall within certain limits (App. A). As an illustration we may mention that in London (52) the percentages of the four blood groups are O, 47.9 per cent; A, 42.4 per cent; B, 8.3 per cent and AB, 1.4 per cent. From these values we calculate $p = 0.250$, $q = 0.050$, $r = 0.692$. In Kharkov (USSR) the respective percentages were found to be 36.4 per cent, 38.4 per cent, 21.6 per cent, and 3.6 per cent (9). From these values we estimate p, q, and r to be 0.261, 0.158, and 0.604. The higher value of q (frequency of the B gene) in the Ukrainian population is apparent. This suggests that the best way to present the net result of blood grouping studies is by putting them in cartographical form, plotting the gene frequencies.

Isogenes

In the map (Figs. 33a and 33b) are shown the results of blood grouping determinations on populations all over the world. Lines are drawn through points where the gene frequency is supposed to be the same. These lines are analogous with the isotherms and isobars which we find on weather maps, and can be referred to as isogenes. From them a picture of the geographical distribution of the three blood group genes may be obtained. Since we are not most interested in recent historical migrations, we have tried to avoid the confusing effect of recording data on recent migrants, and for America, the Pacific Islands, and Australia, we have plotted information only on the aborigines, omitting the results for the modern inhabitants, whose blood group frequencies, of course, are characteristic of their origins. We are not interested at present, for example, in the frequency of the four blood groups in the white inhabitants of Montana, but we are interested in the frequencies in the Indians who originally inhabited this state.

The general situation is easily summarized. Looking at the isogenes for B, we notice that the highest incidence of B occurs in certain parts of Asia, and that in all directions as we go away from central Asia the incidence of group B declines. There is a subsidiary high center in Africa (and this seems to include the Nile Valley), although the frequency of q does not reach the highest levels we have seen in Asia. We find that the lowest figures in the Old World are reached in the Scandinavian countries, in the British Isles and the Spanish peninsula, where the percentage of the gene for B falls below 5 per cent. In Australia the gene seems to have been absent until very recent times and there is every reason to believe that its introduction into a part of the northern coastal area is the result of fairly recent migration from the islands of the East Indies to the north and east (cf. Fig. 23).

In the living aborigines of North America also we note a complete absence of the gene for B, except possibly in the Far North, and of course in Indians of part European ancestry group B is sometimes encountered. In South America the gene for B seems to be present only sporadically, if at all. One early report of a high percentage of group B in the Indians of Tierra del Fuego (45) has not been confirmed on retest (39, 46). Another observation of B in South American Indians (20) was made with carefully checked reagents, but in view of the surprising nature of the results should nevertheless be redone. Certain Peruvian mummies, supposedly pre-Columbian, seemed to possess the B factor (8), but more careful examination of the exact source of the specimens would be desirable before any sweeping conclusions are drawn from this observation.

The map showing the incidence of the gene A presents a rather different situation. There is no large area of the world where A is

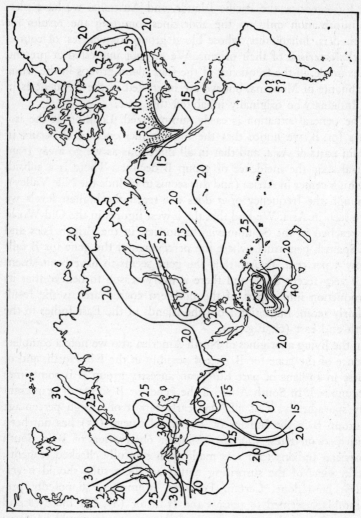

FIGURE 33a. "Isogenes" for blood group gene A.

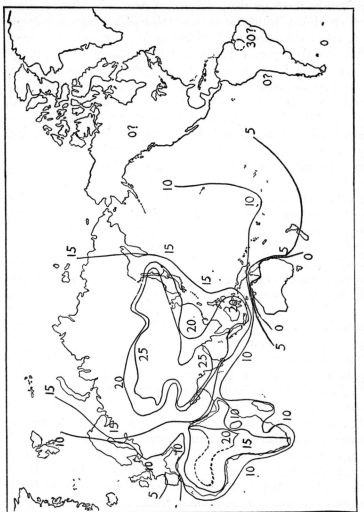

FIGURE 33b. "Isogenes" for blood group gene B.

absent, at least in the modern inhabitants. Among the North American Indians there are sharp differences from tribe to tribe. Some tribes are almost lacking in A; some tribes possess high percentages of A, and the Bloods and Blackfeet have percentages of A even higher than those possessed by any white population.

It would hardly be possible or even desirable to discuss completely here the variations in blood group gene frequencies which exist in the various parts of the world which have been studied, but in addition to the general remarks already offered, we may mention a few results as typical. In Europe, for example, we find that in Germany the frequency of the B gene increases as we go from west to east, so that the Prussians of East Prussia have a higher frequency of group B (a typically Asiatic factor) than do the Jews of Berlin, in spite of whatever "Semitic" (and thus Asiatic) ancestry the latter group may have (3). This increase in B frequency continues on into Poland and Russia. The probable origin of this gradient is discussed in Chapter XII.

Conversely, the frequency of B falls off as we go west in the Spanish peninsula, and is subject to local variations such as a possibly complete absence of B in the Basques (9). In Italy the frequency of B increases as one goes from north to south (33, 3). In England a consistent gradient of the frequency of the gene A exists, with A increasing from north to south (18).

The Japanese, before the Second World War, had already thoroughly determined the frequencies of the blood group genes throughout the home islands, and the accompanying map (Fig. 34) shows the data for the gene A.

The highest large concentration is in the area around the city Matsuye, on the island of Honshu, although there is another smaller concentration of A on the neighboring island of Kyushu. Going towards the north and east, the A concentration falls, although there is a secondary high center around Tokyo, and the lowest frequencies are reached in northeast Honshu, in the vicinity of the city of Morioka. The great regularity and fineness of the gradations in frequencies is only partly shown on the map reproduced here, which is based on a more complicated map in color published by Komatsu and Ito (25).

If we think of mankind as having originated in Asia, it would look as if the gene *A* were possessed by the earliest wanderers from the original homeland, so that it is now widely dispersed, and on the whole common, although still a bit "patchy" in its distribution. Gene *B*, on the other hand, is still most concentrated in the areas in which we think the human race may have had its origin. Early writers thought that this signified a late origin for *B*, but studies

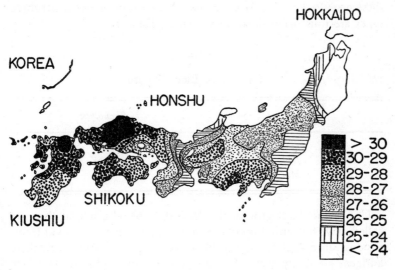

FIGURE 34. *Distribution of blood group A in Japan (Schiff and Boyd).*

on anthropoids would suggest that *B* is no less ancient than *A*, and that it is largely accidental that the *A* gene spread so early and so widely, whereas the evidence clearly shows that *B* is in many places a recent importation. In all probability, both genes are older than the human species.

The distribution of *B* in decreasing quantities around a center has led to its being called centripetal, and the wide-flung distribution of *A* has caused it to be called centrifugal (48).

Other Blood Types

The A, B, O series of allelomorphs does not by any means exhaust the list of genes which influence the blood antigens. Another series discovered in 1927 is known as M and N (31). These letters represent inherited antigens, detectable in human blood by the use of agglutinins formed by rabbits injected with M positive (or N positive) human red cells. These antigens have been reported by some to be present in tissues other than red cells, but other workers have not found them outside the blood. Each human being has two of these genes, either two *M* genes, two *N* genes, or one of each; three types are thus determined, as shown in Table 24.

TABLE 24

The M, N Blood Types

Genotype	Phenotype
MM	M
NN	N
MN	MN

Unlike the A, B groups, the M and N blood types, as they are called, have but little importance in the performance of blood transfusions, since agglutinins capable of reacting specifically with these antigens are rarely if ever found in normal human blood. This lack of medical importance has somewhat limited the amount of information which we have about this newer gene series, since investigations by medical men have been, so far at least, the chief source of data concerning blood groups. But enough is known to make possible the outline which is shown in the accompanying map. For example, the *M* and *N* frequencies are quite well known for the native inhabitants of one whole continent, Australia, and for some adjacent populations. (See Fig. 35.) Since only two genes are involved and the sum of their frequencies must equal unity, to give an adequate picture it is sufficient to plot the frequency of either gene alone, and we have shown here the frequency of the gene *M*. In Table 25, *M* and *N* gene frequencies for the whole world are shown. If we ignore certain slight variations in small groups of people who have been tested in Europe and Asia, we can make the following general statement: the genes *M* and *N* are roughly of

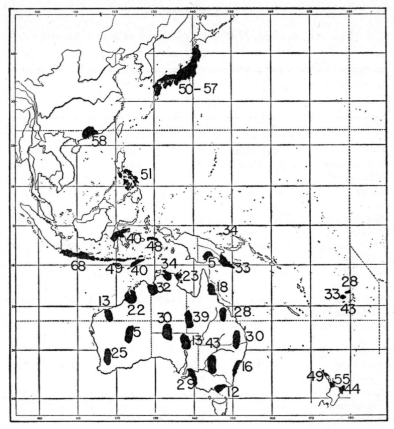

FIGURE 35. *Frequencies of blood group gene M in Australia and regions to the north (after Graydon and Simmons).*

equal frequency in both Europe and Asia but in the aborigines of America the gene for *N* is relatively rare. In the aborigines of Australia, as we have seen, however, the gene for *N* is very common, while the gene *M* is very rare, and it is even possible that in certain earlier times, the gene, though probably originally present, was totally lost by certain populations in Australia (2), presumably by "random genetic drift" (p. 154).

The A and B, M and N factors in human blood still by no means exhaust the list of antigenic differences which have been found in

TABLE 25

Frequencies of M, N Blood Types, and *M* and *N* Genes, in Various Populations

Population	Place	Number Tested	M	MN	N	*m*	*n*
Populations with Low N and Therefore High M							
Eskimo	E. Greenland	569	83.5	15.6	0.9	0.913	0.087
Am. Indians (Navaho)	New Mexico	361	84.5	14.4	1.1	0.917	0.083
Aleuts	Aleutian Islands	132	67.5	29.4	3.2	0.822	0.179
Am. Indians (Utes)	Utah	104	58.7	34.6	6.7	0.600	0.240
Arabs, Bedouin (Rwala)	n. Damascus	208	57.5	36.7	5.8	0.758	0.241
Am. Indians (Pueblo)	New Mexico	140	59.3	32.8	7.9	0.757	0.243
Am. Indians (Blackfeet)	Montana	95	54.7	40.0	5.3	0.747	0.253
Arabs (Bedouin)	n. Damascus	80	51.3	40.0	8.7	0.713	0.287
Populations with Low M (High N)							
Australian aborigines	N. S. Wales	28	0	32.1	67.9	0.160	0.840
Australian aborigines	Queensland	372	2.4	30.4	67.2	0.176	0.824
Papuans	Papua	200	7.0	24.0	69.0	0.190	0.810
Fijians	Fiji	200	11.0	44.5	44.5	0.332	0.667
Ainu	Shizunai	504	17.9	50.2	31.9	0.430	0.570
Populations with "Normal" M and N Frequencies							
Negroes	N.Y.C.	730			28.1	ca. 0.530	
Basques	Spain	91	23.1	51.6	25.3	0.489	0.511
Spanish (m)	Spain	134	26.9	55.2	17.9	0.545	0.455
Syrians	Boarij	131	24.4	52.7	22.9	0.508	0.492
Filipinos	Leyte, Samar, etc.	382	25.9	50.3	23.8	0.510	0.490
Egyptians	Cairo	502	27.8	48.9	23.3	0.522	0.477
English	London	422	28.7	47.4	23.9	0.524	0.476
Lapps	Inari, Finland	56	28.6	48.2	23.2	0.527	0.473

TABLE 25 (*Continued*)

Frequencies of M, N Blood Types, and *M* and *N* Genes, in Various Populations

Population	Place	Number Tested	M	MN	N	*m*	*n*
Poles	Poland	600	28.2	49.0	22.8	0.527	0.473
Egyptians	Assiut	419	26.2	53.1	20.7	0.527	0.472
Indonesians	Java, etc.	296	30.4	45.6	24.0	0.532	0.468
Irish	Dublin	399	30.0	46.7	23.3	0.533	0.466
Danes	Copenhagen	2023	29.1	49.5	21.4	0.538	0.461
Belgians	Liége	3100	28.9	50.3	20.8	0.540	0.460
Germans	Berlin	8144	29.7	50.7	19.6	0.550	0.449
Japanese	Kyoto	430	32.0	46.1	21.9	0.551	0.449
Russians	Leningrad	701	32.0	46.7	21.3	0.553	0.446
Yugoslavs	Moravska	256	30.5	50.0	19.5	0.555	0.445
Germans	Danzig	2018	30.6	50.4	19.0	0.558	0.442
French	Paris	400	33.0	45.8	21.2	0.559	0.441
Italians	Sicily	300	32.0	48.0	20.0	0.560	0.440
Japanese	Tokyo	1100	32.4	47.2	20.4	0.560	0.440
Syrians	Meshghara	306	30.7	52.0	17.3	0.567	0.433
Armenians	fr. Turkey	339	34.2	45.4	20.4	0.569	0.431
Hungarians	Budapest	624	33.5	47.9	18.6	0.574	0.425
Chinese	Hong Kong	1029	33.2	48.6	18.2	0.575	0.425
Ukrainians	Kharkov	310	36.1	44.3	19.6	0.583	0.417
Welsh	N. towns	192	30.7	55.3	14.0	0.583	0.416
Scots	Glasgow	456	35.0	47.9	17.1	0.589	0.410
Swedes	Sweden	1200	36.1	47.0	16.9	0.596	0.404
Estonians	Estonia	310	34.8	49.7	15.5	0.596	0.403
'Iraqis	Baghdad	387	37.0	47.0	16.0	0.605	0.395
Finns	Uusimaa	1050	37.1	47.2	15.7	0.607	0.393
Arabs, Bedouin (Jabour)	n. Mosul	206	36.9	49.5	13.6	0.616	0.383
Russians	n. Moscow	489	39.9	44.0	16.1	0.619	0.381
E. Caucasians	Tiflis	134	38.8	47.8	13.4	0.627	0.373
W. Caucasians	Tiflis	245	40.0	46.5	13.5	0.632	0.367
Finns	Karjala	398	45.7	43.2	11.1	0.673	0.327

(m) signifies mixed; N. signifies north, E. signifies east, W. signifies west; n. signifies near; ca. signifies approximately; fr. signifies from. M, MN, and N stand for the percentages of the M, MN, and N blood types, *m* stands for the frequency of the gene for M, *n* for the frequency of the gene for N.

normal human blood. Subgroups of A (30) and probably of B exist. Subgroups of N have been reported. We shall discuss the subgroups later in this chapter. The inheritance of these subgroups is not quite so well established as that of the main groups (48, 56). Also factors designated by the letters P, G, H, X, Q, E, and Rh have been described by various workers (48, 56). More recently English workers (10, 13, 42) have discovered other previously unknown blood grouping factors. It is known that racial differences exist in the frequencies of these other blood grouping factors and that the factor P, for instance, is much more common in the blood of Negroes, or at least American Negroes, than in the blood of American whites. The other factors, with the exception of Rh, have not yet been sufficiently studied to have any value in anthropological classification.

Subgroups

The blood factor A is not always exactly the same in different individual human bloods. For a number of years it has been known that there were two main varieties of A which are designated as A_1 and A_2 (30). Of these, the latter gives weaker reactions with the average anti-A reagent, and the former gives stronger reactions. Since this is not a textbook on serology, we will not go further into the nature of the differences between the two subgroups of the gene A. For a recent study see (5). The variations are expressed also in the group AB, so that we find two subgroups, A_1B and A_2B, where the difference in the A antigen is very much the same as it was in group A, save that in certain instances the A reaction in individuals of subgroup A_2B may be weaker than in any individual of group A_1, or even A_2. It has been proposed (53, 54) that the subgroups of A are inherited in the following way (Table 26): instead of the gene series A, B, and O, suppose we have a series of four allelomorphs, A_1, A_2, B, and O, with A_1 being dominant over A_2, and A_1, A_2 and B all being dominant over O. This theory on the whole seems to fit most of the observations satisfactorily, although it does not account for the rather wide variability in sensitivity to anti-A agglutinins of cells of individuals belonging to the subgroups A_2 and A_2B (5).

TABLE 26

Supposed Mechanism of Inheritance of Subgroups

Mating	Children Possible
$A_2 \times O$	O, A_2
$A_2 \times A_2$	O, A_2
$A_2 \times B$	O, A_2, B, A_2B
$A_2B \times O$	A_2, B
$A_2B \times A_2$	A_2, B, A_2B
$A_2B \times B$	A_2, B, A_2B
$A_2B \times A_2B$	A_2, B, A_2B
$A_1B \times O$	A_1, B
$A_1B \times A_1$	A_1, B, A_2B, A_1B
$A_1B \times A_2$	A_1, B, A_2B
$A_1B \times A_2B$	A_1, B, A_2B, A_1B
$A_1B \times B$	A_1, B, A_1B
$A_1B \times A_1B$	A_1, B, A_1B
$A_1 \times O$	O, A_1, A_2
$A_1 \times A_1$	O, A_1, A_2
$A_1 \times A_2$	O, A_1, A_2
$A_1 \times B$	$O, A_1, A_2, B, A_1B, A_2B$
$A_1 \times A_2B$	A_1, A_2, B, A_1B, A_2B

Subgroups of the group A, which are even weaker than A_2, designated as A_3 and A_4, have been reported, but they are quite rare, and it seems unlikely that their existence is going to be of any particular importance to anthropologists (cf. 48, 56).

Studies to determine the relative proportion of A_1 and A_2 in different populations have been carried out, however, and the results are shown in Table 27. It is a striking fact that the subtype A_2 does not seem to occur in the Australian aborigines, in China, Japan, in the American Indians, or in the natives of the islands of the Pacific, in so far as can be determined from the somewhat sketchy studies made up to the present time. Simmons et al. (49) remark that these observations indicate that the subgroups of A will become a point of greater importance than heretofore in the study of races. Contrast, for example, the relatively high proportion of A_2 in Negroes with its total absence in Papuans.

TABLE 27

Subgroups of A and AB in Various Populations
(Arranged in order of increasing ratio A_2/A_1)

Population	Place	Number Tested	O	A_1	A_2	B	A_1B	A_2B	Ratio A_2/A_1
Eskimo	Alaska	254	43.3	42.5	0	11.9	2.4	0	0
Am. Indians	Tacoma, Wash.	120	73.3	25.8	0	0.8	0	0	0
Am. Indians (Utes)	Utah	104	98.1	1.9	0	0	0	0	0
Am. Indians (Navaho)	N. Mexico	228	76.7	23.3	0	0	0	0	0
Japanese	Japan	400	30.8	37.2	0	22.0	9.5	0.5	0
Chinese	N.Y.C.	138	31.2	32.6	0	27.5	8.7	0	0
Polynesians	Hawaii	413	36.5	60.8	0	2.2	0.5	0	0
Indonesians	Java, etc.	296	51.8	22.6	0	21.3	4.4	0	0
Papuans	New Guinea	200	45.5	28.5	0	19.0	7.0	0	0
Fijians	Fiji	200	43.5	34.0	0	16.5	6.0	0	0
Polynesians	Easter Island	22	54.5	45.5	0	0	0	0	0
Australian aborigines	Australia	649	56.1	43.9	0	0	0	0	0
Filipinos	Leyte, Samar, etc.	382	45.0	21.7	0.3	27.0	6.0	0	0.01
Am. Indians (Mapuches)	Chile	205	86.8	8.3	0.5	3.4	1.0	0	0.06
Asiatic Indians		156	34.0	23.1	1.9	37.2	3.2	0.6	0.08
Latvians		172	32.0	37.4	2.9	19.2	7.8	0.8	0.08
Egyptians	Cairo	378	27.8	37.0	3.2	24.6	5.6	1.8	0.09
Syrians	Boarij	127	24.4	32.3	3.2	3.1	7.9	1.6	0.10
E. Georgeans	Tiflis	138	39.8	31.9	3.6	18.8	3.6	2.2	0.11
Armenians	fr. Turkey	340	27.6	49.1	4.4	13.2	4.1	1.5	0.11
Egyptians	Assiut	412	24.6	30.4	3.6	31.6	6.1	3.9	0.12
Arabs, Bedouin	n. Baghdad	418	29.4	31.1	3.6	24.9	10.1	1.0	0.12
Arabs, Bedouin (Rwala)	Syrian Desert	208	43.3	19.3	2.9	30.3	2.4	1.9	0.15
Ukrainians	Kharkov	310	36.5	33.9	5.1	21.3	2.3	1.0	0.15
W. Georgians	Tiflis	268	57.5	25.4	3.7	10.1	1.9	1.5	0.15
'Iraqis	Baghdad	386	33.7	26.9	4.4	28.2	5.7	1.0	0.16
Syrians	Meshghara	199	44.7	34.2	6.0	11.6	1.5	2.0	0.18
Germans	Germany	417	40.1	37.5	7.0	11.3	3.3	0.8	0.19
English	London	345	46.4	35.9	7.5	8.4	1.2	0.6	0.21
Russians	n. Moscow	500	32.0	28.5	6.5	24.2	6.0	2.8	0.22

TABLE 27 (*Continued*)

Subgroups of A and AB in Various Populations
(Arranged in order of increasing ratio A_2/A_1)

Population	Place	Number Tested	O	A_1	A_2	B	A_1B	A_2B	Ratio A_2/A_1
English	Sheffield	421	34.0	43.2	10.2	10.0	2.1	0.5	0.23
Egyptians	Cairo	516	26.6	29.1	6.6	27.1	7.0	3.5	0.25
Russians	Leningrad	763	33.7	30.8	7.6	20.8	4.0	3.1	0.25
Swedes	Sweden	1200	37.9	36.9	9.8	10.3	3.9	1.2	0.27
Danes	Copenhagen	1835	40.0	32.7	9.8	12.4	2.8	2.3	0.30
Finns	Finland	7120	33.9	32.3	10.7	15.8	4.4	2.9	0.33
Spanish (m)	San Sebastián	161	47.2	34.8	11.8	5.0	1.2	0	0.34
Am. Negroes	N.Y.C.	189	48.1	19.6	6.8	22.8	1.6	1.1	0.35
Asiatic Indians	Calcutta	50							0.36
Irish	Dublin	399	55.2	21.7	9.5	11.8	1.0	0.8	0.44
Welsh	N. Towns	190	47.3	21.6	11.6	16.3	2.6	0.5	0.54
Basques	San Sebastián	64	51.5	31.2	15.6	1.6	0	0	0.54

N signifies north, E east, W west. The symbol n. signifies near, (m) signifies mixed, fr. signifies from.

From a table such as Table 27, it is possible to calculate the gene frequencies p_1, and p_2, and if we were more certain of the mechanism of inheritance of the subgroups and of the correctness with which early workers distinguished A_1 and A_2 (cf. 5), it would be desirable to do so. As it is, however, the most important thing one learns from the table is that nearly all non-European and non-African stocks possess no A_2, i.e., $p_2 = 0$.

The situation in Africa is not yet fully understood, but in American Negroes at any rate, both A_1 and A_2 occur, the latter fairly frequently, and Wiener believes that an intermediate type of blood which is also found occasionally among whites, designated by him as $A_{1.2}$, occurs much more commonly among Negroes. The expression of the subtype of the gene A which we knew as A_2 seems to be chiefly a European and African characteristic, and it would enable us, if we wanted to, to mark off such populations from all others, on this basis alone. It will be seen later that other serological properties permit a similar distinction to be made.

The antigen N has been shown to have a rare variant N_2 which has been detected in the heterozygote MN_2 (48, 56).

A serum which subdivides both antigens M and N into two varieties has been found (55), so that instead of two genes at the M, N locus, there would seem to be four, tentatively designated as M, MS, N, NS. If such sera ever become available to anthropologists, they may greatly extend the usefulness of the M, N series of alleles.

The Rh Series of Genes

In 1940 Landsteiner and Wiener (32) reported the discovery of a new blood group antigen. It was discovered that the serum of a rabbit which had been injected with the blood of a rhesus monkey would agglutinate certain human bloods, and not agglutinate others, irrespective of the A, B, O group, or M, N type of these bloods. The new factor was designated Rh, for the first two letters of rhesus. Human bloods tested with this serum could be differentiated into two types, Rh positive, and Rh negative. It is probable that agglutinins which reacted with the Rh antigen had been previously observed (4), for on looking back it can be seen that this is the most probable explanation of certain blood incompatibilities encountered by some of the earlier workers, and several such cases (36, 4) were retested and shown to be due to Rh incompatibility.

The Rh factor might not have excited any more attention than its practically stillborn brethren G, H, X, Q, and E had it not been for the demonstration by Levine and others (35) that Rh incompatibility between mother and child was very often the cause of a rare but fairly serious disease of infants known as *erythroblastosis fetalis,* or hemolytic disease of the newborn. Wiener and others (57) also showed that incompatibilities in which the recipient had received repeated transfusions were often due to the Rh factor.

The way in which Rh incompatibility operates to produce *erythroblastosis* is briefly this: if the mother is Rh negative and the fetus Rh positive (having inherited the Rh factor from the father), Rh-containing cells, or Rh antigen, may get through the placenta from the circulation of the fetus into that of the mother. The mother's agglutinin-forming mechanisms may respond by the production of anti-Rh agglutinins. (This does not always happen, but it may —

say in about 1 out of 200–400 pregnancies.) Agglutinins diffuse readily through the placenta, so some of the anti-Rh formed by the mother diffuses into the fetal circulation. There it combines with the fetal red cells, damaging them, causing hemolysis and damaging the liver and other organs.

At first it was believed that Rh was inherited as a simple Mendelian pair, *rh* and *Rh,* the latter gene causing the Rh positive condition, and being dominant over rh. Three different genotypes would be possible, rhrh (Rh negative), and Rhrh and RhRh (both of the latter Rh positive). On this theory, the inheritance would be very simple, the various matings and their possible outcomes being:

$$RhRh \times RhRh \rightarrow 100\%\, RhRh$$
$$RhRh \times Rhrh \rightarrow 50\%\, RhRh \text{ and } 50\%\, Rhrh$$
$$Rhrh \times Rhrh \rightarrow 25\%\, RhRh, 50\%\, Rhrh \text{ and } 25\%\, rhrh$$
$$RhRh \times rhrh \rightarrow 100\%\, Rhrh$$
$$Rhrh \times rhrh \rightarrow 50\%\, Rhrh \text{ and } 50\,\%\, rhrh$$
$$rhrh \times rhrh \rightarrow 100\%\, rhrh$$

However, it was soon found that the Rh factor was antigenically and genetically complex. The steps by which this knowledge was acquired belong to history and not to the present exposition. Let us simply say that Wiener (58) now supposes that at least six allelomorphic genes are involved, as follows:

$$Rh_1, Rh_2, Rh^\circ, rh', rh'', rh$$

All of the first five are supposed to be dominant over *rh,* but not over each other. The genes Rh_1 and Rh_2 are "double acting" genes, the former producing the antigens rh′ and Rh°, the latter rh″ and Rh°.

The discovery of an agglutinin which reacted regularly with Rh negative bloods led to the postulate that Rh negative bloods contained an Hr factor (Hr being the letters Rh in reverse). But this agglutinin also reacts with some of the Rh positive bloods. These observations led Fisher (44) to propose that the Rh types were determined by a series of three pairs of alleles, at distinct loci, but so close together on the chromosome that crossing-over would occur very rarely. Fisher proposed to represent each different Rh antigen by a different letter, and propounded this scheme: $C,c; D,[d]; E[e]$.

The letters [d] and [e] are enclosed in brackets because at the time they were proposed they were purely hypothetical. Agglutinins which react with them have since been discovered (21, 41). The various combinations of C, D, E, c, d, and e are eight in number (Table 28), which led to the prediction of two new Rh genes, designated as Rh^y and Rh^z, both of which have since been discovered (58).*

The way in which the Fisher scheme corresponds to the Wiener scheme is shown in Table 28. Each scheme supposes six antigens

TABLE 28

Gene Present (Wiener)	Genes Present (Fisher)	Agglutinins and Their Reactions					
		anti-rh' anti-C	anti-hr' anti-c	anti-Rh° anti-D	anti-Hr° anti-d	anti-rh" anti-E	anti-hr" anti-e
R^z	CDE	+	−	+	−	+	−
R^1	CDe	+	−	+	−	−	+
R^y	CdE	+	−	−	+	+	−
r'	Cde	+	−	−	+	−	+
R^2	cDE	−	+	+	−	+	−
R^o	cDe	−	+	+	−	−	+
r''	cdE	−	+	−	+	+	−
r	cde	−	+	−	+	−	+

Use of the three common sera which are now available for testing for Rh [anti-rh' (anti-C), anti-Rh° (anti-D), anti-rh" (anti-E)] enables eight subtypes to be determined. Use of anti-hr' (anti-c) enables the types positive for rh' (C) to be subdivided, giving twelve subtypes. The eight postulated genes would produce thirty-six different genotypes, and twenty-seven different distinguishable serological types, if all of the six sera shown in the table were available.

to exist, and the chief difference is in the proposal of Fisher to designate each antigen by a separate letter. The schemes of inheritance, although apparently very different, reduce to the same thing if Fisher's C, D, and E loci are so close that crossing-over *never*

* As a matter of historical fact, R^z was discovered before Fisher proposed his theory. Two of its reactions were predicted by him before they were confirmed experimentally.

occurs, and in that case the genetic predictions are the same. Blood group workers are not in full accord as to which nomenclature, if either, is to be preferred (13).

By making all the possible combinations, two at a time, of the Rh genes shown in Table 28, the reader will be able to write out the thirty-six possible genotypes which can result from the combinations of the eight genes presented there. He will note that not all of the thirty-six are distinguishable serologically, even by use of all the six antisera whose reactions are shown. For instance, genotypes CDE/cde and Cde/cDE both give positive reactions with all six antisera. Twenty-seven phenotypes can be distinguished.

When not all the possible antisera are available, the number of serologically distinguishable phenotypes is still less. When only four sera (anti-C, anti-D, anti-E, and anti-c) are available, as is usual at present, twelve phenotypes can be distinguished. These are usually abbreviated, using either the most common genotype expressed in the English system, or a shorthand expression derived from Wiener's system. Not all authors give the frequencies of all the phenotypes their sera would have revealed, so in Table 29 we present only nine phenotypes. The classes Rh_1 (CDe) and $rh'rh''$ (Cde/cdE) are actually composites of distinguishable types. Rh_1Rh_z (CDe/CDE), and Rh_1Rh_2 (CDe/cDE) are separated, because the incidence of the gene R^z seems to have some racial significance.

It was soon found that the frequency of the Rh types was different in different races. Data on various ethnic groups gradually accumulated as the complexity of the Rh situation was recognized. As yet, there has not been time for a survey to be conducted of all the interesting populations making use of all the available antisera. However, certain data are available, and are summarized in Table 29.

As a first approximation, we may note that the Rh negative gene (cde) is distributed differently in different ethnic groups. (a) Peoples of European stock, by which we mean modern inhabitants of Europe and the white inhabitants of America, possess considerable amounts of the Rh negative phenotype, amounting to 13 to 17 per cent. (b) The situation in Africa is not clear because of lack of information, but from studies on American Negroes (57) and South African Bantu (38) it seems likely that some Rh negative

TABLE 29

Distribution of the Rh-Hr Blood Types
(Arranged in order of decreasing rh negative)

Population	Number of Persons Tested	Frequencies of Rh Types (Per Cent)								
		rh cde	Rh₁ CDe	Rh₂ cDE	Rh₁Rh₂ CDe/cDE	Rh₀ cDe	rh' Cde	rh" cdE	rh'rh" Cde/cdE	Rh₁Rh₁ CDe/CDE
Basques	167	28.8	55.1	7.8	6.0	0.6	1.8	0.8	0	0
"Whites" (France)	501	17.0	51.7	13.6	13.0	3.6	0.4	0.6	0	0.6
Czechs (Prague)	181	16.0	50.3	11.6	11.6	1.1	0.6	0.6	0	0
"Whites" (Hollanders)	200	15.4	51.5	12.3	17.7	1.5	1.5	0	0	0
"Whites" (England)	1,038	15.3	54.8	14.7	11.6	2.3	0.6	0.7	0	0.7
S. Paulo (Brazil)	138	15.2	55.2	10.1	11.6	5.8	1.4	0.7	0	0.7
"Whites" (Australia)	350	14.9	54.0	12.6	16.6	0.6	0.9	0.6	0	0
"Whites" (England)	927	14.8	54.9	12.2	13.6	2.5	0.7	1.3	0	0.1
"Whites" (U.S.A.)	7,317	14.7	53.5	15.0	12.9	2.2	1.1	0.6	0.01	
Spanish (Barcelona)	223	13.0	63.2	13.0	9.4	0.5	0	0.5	0	0.5
"Whites" (U.S.A.)	766	12.5	54.7	14.9	13.9	2.2	0.9	0.5	0	0.1
"Arabs" (Baghdad)	300	10.3	50.3	13.7	15.7	8.3	1.0	0.7	0	0
Porto Ricans	179	10.1	39.1	19.6	14.0	15.1	1.7	0.5	0	0
Negroes (U.S.A.)	223	8.1	20.2	22.4	5.4	41.2	2.7	0.7	0	0
Negroes (U.S.A.)	135	7.4	23.7	16.3	4.4	45.9	1.5	0.7	0	0
Asiatic Indians (Moslems)	156	7.1	70.5	5.1	12.8	1.9	2.6	0	0	0
S. African Bantu	300	5.3	27.0	0	2.3	64.3	1.0	0	0	0

TABLE 29 (Continued)

Population	Number of Persons Tested	rh cde	Rh₁ CDe	Rh₂ cDE	Rh₁Rh₂ CDe/cDE	Rh₀ cDe	rh' Cde	rh" cdE	rh'rh" Cde/cdE	Rh₁Rh₂ CDe/CDE
Chinese	132	1.5	60.6	3.0	34.1	0.9	0	0	0	
Japanese	150	1.3	37.4	13.3	47.3	0	0	0	0	0.7
Japanese	180	0.6	51.7	8.3	39.4	0	0	0	0	
Am. Indians (Mexico, Tuxpan)	95	0	48.1	9.5	38.1	1.1	0	0	0	3.1
Am. Indians (Ramah, N. M.)	105	0	40.0	17.1	36.2	2.9	0.9	0	0	2.9
Am. Indians (Ramah, N. M.)	305	0	28.5	20.0	41.0	0.7	3.0	0	0.7	6.2
Am. Indians (Utah)	104	0	33.7	28.8	37.5	0	0	0	0	4.8
Am. Indians (Brazil)	238	0	22.7	19.3	53.2	0	0	0	0	0
Indonesians	200	0	74	2.5	22.5	0.5	0	0	0.5	
Filipinos	100	0	87.0	2.0	11.0	0	0	0	0	
Australian aborigines	100	0	53.0	21.0	15.0	4.0	1.0	0	0	6.0
Australian aborigines	234	0	58.2	8.5	30.4	1.3	1.7	0	0	
Papuans	100	0	93.0	0	4.0	0	0	0	0	3.0
Maoris	32	0	25.0	31.0	41.0	3.0	0	0	0	
Admiralty Islanders	112	0	92.9	.9	6.2	0	0	0	0	
Fijians	110	0	89.1	1.8	9.1	0	0	0	0	
New Caledonians (N and NW)	243	0	77.4	2.1	20.5	0	0	0	0	
Loyalty Islanders	103	0	77.7	2.9	19.4	0	0	0	0	
Siamese (Bangkok)	213	0	74.7	3.3	21.1	0.5	0	0	0	3.3

genes are present. (c) In all the rest of the world, the Rh negative gene is either extremely rare or nonexistent. As a corollary of this, of course, one would expect that the disease caused by Rh incompatibility between mother and fetus would be very rare in populations of non-European stock. So far as can be told by information at present available, this is the case. It will be seen that most of the Asiatic and Pacific populations tested (and the American Indians) possess essentially only two Rh genes, that is Rh_1 and Rh_2, so that three types result, Rh_1, Rh_2, and Rh_1Rh_2, much as in the M, N system. Other Rh genes are rare, or absent, in such populations, although one of the rare genes (Rh^z) is nevertheless commoner than in Europeans. (d) One population, the Basques, possesses a much higher per cent of the Rh negative gene than does any other yet tested. (e) The tremendously high incidence of the Rh° type in the Africans marks them off very distinctly from all other populations.

Serological Races

It is obvious that we could classify men into different races on the basis of blood groups. The races which would result from such a classification, however, would coincide only in part with the races of man as they have previously been delineated by anthropologists, and in some cases would conform better to geography than to the previously inferred history of the peoples.

The seeming contradictions to conventional physical anthropology of classifications based on the distribution of blood group genes have evidently been the cause of considerable discomfort to many writers. Thus Young, in a paper on racial significance of the blood groups which appeared in 1928 (59), was very pessimistic about their usefulness, because population samples which were different with respect to blood group distribution nevertheless appeared to belong to the same "race," while conversely, racial samples which were "racially" dissimilar by almost every recognized canon agreed sometimes in their blood group distribution within the limits of sampling error. Although he did not say so, it seems clear that Young concluded that blood group characters were of no value for use in racial classification. Young, of course, had available data only for the O, A, B blood groups, and an inspection of Table 31 will show the sort of situation he was confronted with.

Since 1928, however, a great deal of germ plasm has flowed under the genetic bridges and the situation is no longer one of muddy confusion. We should consider whether a classification based on blood groups might not actually be more, instead of less, significant than one based on the traditional standards. In Chapter IX, we shall find that a racial classification based on the frequency of the blood grouping genes makes rather good sense, and allows us to distinguish six races which were at one time separated, at least to a considerable extent, by geographical barriers, which is what would be expected from our analysis of the methods of race formation (Ch. IX).

It should be noted that our serological tests do not allow us to identify a single individual as belonging to a given race. More than one white European, among whose ancestors no Negro could be found in the last ten generations, belongs to blood group A_2 and Rh°.

Blood Group Archæology

For a long time it seemed impossible that we could ever expect to know the blood groups of any of the earlier world populations.

It was taken for granted that the blood groups of peoples of the past could not be determined, since all that ever remains of them are skeletons or bloodless mummies, but in actual fact even these dry relics may sometimes be made to reveal their blood groups. The chemical substances A and B are not restricted to the red cells of the individual, but exist throughout his whole body, in practically all of his cells and tissue fluids, and they are rather unusually stable antigens. They resist drying, heating, and exposure to a number of drastic chemical reagents which would quickly inactivate protein antigens (7). Dried tissues from human cadavers of known blood group have been found still to contain blood group substances (8), and there is good reason to suppose that the group substances might survive, once a carcass was thoroughly dried, for hundreds or even thousands of years.

The results of tests on mummified tissue (8) corresponded in general with the modern blood group picture, as is shown in Table 30. In Egyptians of the present day, A and B are relatively common, and in the ancient Egyptians A and B were found. There

Table 30

Classification of Material According to Origin and Blood Groups (8)

Number of Specimens

Egyptians

Period	Total	"O"	A	B	"AB"	Un-decided
Predynastic	6	3	0	1	2	0
Old Kingdom (I–VI dyn.)	7	4	0	1	1	1
Middle Kingdom	2	1	1	0	0	0
New Empire (XVIII–XXIII)	23	15	2	2	2	2
Later material	74	62	0	7	4	1
Unknown	10	8	0	1	0	1
Total	122	93	3	12	9	5

Americans

Period	Total	"O"	A	B	"AB"	Un-decided
Basket Maker	23	20	3	0	0	0
Big Bend Basket Maker	8	7	0	1	0	0
Pueblo I	1	1	0	0	0	0
Pueblo III	21	19	0	0	0	2
Pueblo IV	2	2	0	0	0	0
Peruvian	134	118	1	6	2	7
Alaskan	4	4	0	0	0	0
Others (or unknown)	12	12	0	0	0	0
Total	205	183	4	7	2	9

were some suggestions that the frequencies of A and B which were found in the mummy samples were not so high as in their modern descendants. This difference could be explained either by deficiencies in the technic, which might result in a number of incorrect diagnoses of group O, or by supposing that many of the mummies have at some time been exposed to unfavorable conditions, which have caused the antigens contained in them to deteriorate and lose their reactivity. Other considerations would lead one to doubt a third alternative which is the possibility that the genetic composition of the population of Egypt has greatly altered in the last few thousand years.

In the American Indian mummies of the Southwest of the United States, the antigen A was found, but relatively infrequently, and only one group B was reported from all the specimens studied (Table 30). This is consistent with the blood group situation among the present-day Indians of that region, for in these tribes the frequency of A is never great and is usually "patchy." Group B is perhaps entirely lacking in pure-blood Indians, at least in this area.

Candela (11) clearly demonstrated that it was possible, by suitable modifications of the mummy technic, to determine blood groups from specimens of ancient bone. Although it is not possible to assert that the blood groups of mummified or skeletal remains can be ascertained in all cases with complete exactness, it is obvious that blood groups are relatively almost as permanent as the morphological features of the skeleton. Recently Laughlin (34) has obtained an apparently positive blood group reaction from a bone specimen from Tepexpan man, an American specimen dated as being about 11,000 years old. Completely fossilized bone, of course, in which all the organic material has been replaced by minerals, cannot be expected to yield information about blood groups. It does not at present seem likely that the M and N types or the Rh factors, which are also important for racial classification, can be determined from ancient tissue or bone.

Because of paucity of specimens, it may never be possible to make world maps of the blood gene frequencies for remote periods of the past, but to some extent we evidently can, in the case of *A* and *B*, use these genes as markers in time as well as in space. Until a complete genetic analysis of the various factors which determine man's appearance and morphology is made, blood groups seem to offer us the most valuable information for purposes of racial anthropology.

References for Chapter VIII

1a. Altman, A., and E. G. Lewis, *So. Afr. J. Med. Sci.*, *10*, 137–140 (1945).

1. Bernstein, F., *Z. indukt. Abstamm. u. Verer.*, *37*, 237–270 (1925).

2. Birdsell, J. B., and W. C. Boyd, *A. J. P. A.*, *27*, 69–90 (1940).

3. Boyd, W. C., *Tabulae Biologicae*, *17*, 113–240 (1939).

4. Boyd, W. C., *Arch. Path.*, *40*, 114–127 (1945).

5. Boyd, W. C., *Ann. N. Y. Acad. of Sci.*, *46*, 927–937 (1946).

6. Boyd, W. C., *Southwest. J. Anthrop.*, *3*, 32–49 (1947).

7. Boyd, W. C., and L. G. Boyd, *Proc. Soc. Exp. Biol. & Med.*, *31*, 671–672 (1934).

8. Boyd, W. C., and L. G. Boyd, *J. Imm.*, *32*, 307–319 (1937).

9. Boyd, W. C., and L. G. Boyd, *A. J. P. A.*, *23*, 49–70 (1937).

10. Callendar, S., R. R. Race, and Z. V. Paykos, *Brit. Med. J.*, *II*, 83–84 (1945).

11. Candela, P. B., *Am. Antiquity*, *5*, 55–56 (1939).

12. DeCastello, and Sturli, *M.m. W.*, *54*, 1090 (1902).

13. Castle, W. B., M. M. Wintrobe, and L. H. Snyder, *Science*, *107*, 27–31 (1948).

14. Coombs, R. R. A., A. E. Mourant, and R. R. Race, *Lancet*, I, 264–271 (1946).

15. Dobzhansky, Th., *Genetics and the Origin of Species*. Columbia Univ. Press, New York, 1941.

16. von Dungern, E., and L. Hirszfeld, *Z. Imm. & Exp. Ther.*, *8*, 541–547 (1911).

17. Elsdon-Dew, R., *Pub. S. Afr. Inst. Med. Res.*, *9*, 29–94 (1939).

18. Fisher, R. A., and G. L. Taylor, *Nature*, *145*, 590 (1940).

19. Gates, R. R., *Human Genetics*. Macmillan Co., New York, 1946.

20. Golden, G., *Lancet*, *219*, II, 278–279 (1930).

21. Haberman, S., J. M. Hill, B. W. Everist, and J. W. Davenport, *Blood*, *3*, 682–688 (1948).

22. Haldane, J. B. S., *New Paths in Genetics*. Harper & Bros., New York and London, 1942.

23. Hirszfeld, L., and H. Hirszfeld, *Lancet*, *197*, II, 675–679 (1919).

24. Kabat, E. A., A. Bendich, A. E. Bezer, and S. M. Beiser, *J. E. M.*, *85*, 685–699 (1947).

25. Komatso, Y., and R. Ito, *Contrib. from Univ. Inst. Forensic Med.*, Kanazawa, 7 (1936).

26. Lahovary, N., *Les Peuples Européens*. La Baconnière, Neuchâtel, 1946.
27. Landsteiner, K., *Centr. Bakt. Orig., 27*, 357–362 (1900).
28. Landsteiner, K., *Wien. Klin. Woch., 14*, 1132–1134 (1901).
29. Landsteiner, K., in: *The Newer Knowledge of Bacteriology and Immunology*. Ed. by Jordan, E. O., and I. S. Falk. Chicago, 1928.
30. Landsteiner, K., and P. Levine, *Proc. Soc. Exp. Biol. & Med., 24*, 941–942 (1927).
31. Landsteiner, K., and P. Levine, *J. Exper. Med., 47*, 757–775 (1928).
32. Landsteiner, K., and A. S. Wiener, *Proc. Soc. Exp. Biol. & Med., 43*, 223–224 (1940).
33. Lattes, L., *Individuality of the Blood*. Oxford Univ. Press, 1932.
34. Laughlin, W. S., cited by: Romero, J., Viking Fund Publ. (1949).
35. Levine, P., and E. M. Katzin, *Proc. Soc. Exp. Biol. & Med., 45*, 343–346 (1940).
36. Levine, P., and R. E. Stetson, *J. A. M. A., 113*, 126–127 (1939).
37. Levine, V., in press, 1949.
38. See Altman and Lewis, No. 1a.
39. Lipschütz, A., G. Mostny, and L. Robin, *A. J. P. A., 4*, 301–321 (1946).
40. Malkiel, S., and W. C. Boyd, *J. A. M. A., 129*, 344–345 (1945).
41. Mourant, A. E., *Nature, 155*, 542 (1945).
42. Mourant, A. E., *Nature, 158*, 237–238 (1946).
43. Ottenberg, R., *J. A. M. A., 84*, 1393–1395 (1925).
44. Race, R. R., *Nature, 153*, 771–772 (1944).
45. Rahm, G., *Invest. y Prog., 5*, 160–162 (1931).
46. Santiana, A., *Los Fueguinos; sus grupos sanguíneos*, Quito, Imp. de la Univ., 1946.
47. Sarkar, S. S., *Trans. Bose Res. Inst., Calcutta, 12*, 89 (1936–1937).
48. Schiff, F., and W. C. Boyd, *Blood Grouping Technic*. Interscience Publishers, New York, 1942.
49. Simmons, R. T., J. J. Graydon, and C. Ouwehand, *Med. J. Australia, 32*, 108–110 (1945).
50. Snyder, L. H., *A. J. P. A., 9*, 233–263 (1926).
51. Snyder, L. H., *Human Biol., 2*, 128–133 (1930).
52. Taylor, G. L., and A. M. Prior, *Ann. Eug., 8*, 343–361 (1938).
53. Thomsen, O., V. Friedenreich, and E. Worsaae, *Acta path. et microbiol. Scandinav., 7*, 157 (1930).
54. Thomsen, O., V. Friedenreich, and E. Worsaae, *Klin. Woch., 9*, 67–69 (1930).
55. Walsh, R. J., and C. M. Montgomery, *Nature, 160*, 504 (1947).
56. Wiener, A. S., *Blood Groups and Transfusion*. Charles C Thomas, Springfield, 3rd ed., 1943.
57. Wiener, A. S., *Am. J. Clin. Path., 16*, 477–497 (1946).
58. Wiener, A. S., Wiener Laboratories Paper, #3, Aug. 1, 1948.
59. Young, M., *Man, 28*, No. 116, 153–No. 127, 171–176 (1928).
60. Zoutendyk, A., *So. Afr. J. Med. Sci., 12*, 167–169 (1947).

CHAPTER IX Use of Blood Groups in Human Classification

Will he not fancy that the shadows which he formerly saw
are truer than the objects which are now shown to him?
— PLATO, *The Republic*

Doubts

THERE have probably been some readers who experienced a feeling of disappointment on reading the end of the last chapter, and may have asked themselves questions such as the following: "Is this the best that blood grouping can do for anthropology?" or, "How are we going to establish races based on the sort of characteristics discussed here?" Others more accustomed to the older systems may have felt tempted to close the book and say flatly, "This is all extremely interesting but has absolutely nothing to do with race."

A careful analysis of the situation will show that such disappointment is based largely on two circumstances. First, there is the fact that the blood grouping genes affect invisible serological characteristics of the individual, and are thus never visible to the naked eye. It is to be feared that we are all too much inclined to be impressed by the visible as opposed to the invisible. Second, there is the fact that the layman's concept of race (which is that the human species can be divided up by valid, scientific methods, into various groups that are pretty different from each other and which will *look* pretty different from each other) has been unconsciously retained by many scientific workers, and the hypothetical dissenting readers are unconsciously expecting that the new systematics we propose to introduce will also provide us with startling differences in the appearance and behavior of the different "races" we define, and will feel let down to discover that the new classification does not, when all is said about it, reveal any very dramatic results.

If the blood grouping genes *had* affected, not characteristics of the blood, but prominent morphological or physical characteristics such as the shape of the head, color of the skin, etc., there cannot be the slightest question that they would already have been made the chief basis of a racial classification and would have been considered entirely adequate for that purpose.

Equivalence of Genes

From our knowledge of genetics (Ch. II) we may see that there is nothing fundamentally different between the blood grouping genes *as genes,* and the genes which do affect morphological features. It is simply a historical accident that fairly adequate information was obtained about the mode of transmission of blood grouping genes before any information at all equivalent in amount or value was obtained about the genes affecting physical appearance.

In view of these facts, and since there seems to be no reason to suppose that the location of a gene in a chromosome, or the nature of the particular chromosome in which the gene resides, determines in advance the main or even the subsidiary characteristics which are to be influenced by the gene, it might be instructive to let our imaginations roam a bit. The outwardly observable effects of the blood group genes are, so far as we know, zero. Therefore let us make some arbitrary assumptions as to the sort of effect which the blood grouping genes could have produced, supposing them to have affected some of the external and visible characteristics instead of serological characters which are ordinarily tested for only in a laboratory. The insight we shall thus acquire will throw considerable light on the real nature of anthropological genetic classification and the sort of information which can be expected from it.

Hypothetical Worlds

Let us suppose for the moment that the genes which at present operate to affect skin color and stature were to affect, instead, obscure serological properties of the blood or other relatively imperceptible physiological traits; and let us suppose that the present blood grouping genes affected, instead of the blood type, various morphological characteristics, easily distinguished by the casual observer. We now have considerable information about three series of serological allelomorphs. We can select three visible or measurable characteristics of the human being and suppose that each is affected by one of these series. It will probably be wise to oversimplify the picture considerably, and not try to take account of all the subtle serological differences and subgroups which can actually (p. 237) be identified within the blood grouping series of genes. It is clear, however, that if we were to take these into account we could, if we wished, considerably refine and complicate the picture which we are going to present now.

Since this situation is purely hypothetical we can make any assumptions we like and we shall probably do better to make some of the simpler ones. Let us suppose that individuals of the genetic constitution OO (which in actuality causes their blood to possess the properties which we know as group O) would possess a skin color about the Spanish, Italian or Arab degree of pigmentation; and that those possessing the gene A were somewhat darker in appearance; and that those possessing gene B were a somewhat dark yellow, such as certain Mongoloids of today, and that those who possessed the genetic constitution AB were quite dark, but not actually "black" in color. Genotype AO would be a brown lighter than AA, and the genotype BO would be browner and less yellow than the genotype BB.

The way in which the A and B genes, when both present together in the genotype AB, would interact in producing skin color would of course really depend upon the exact mechanism of their action in the organism, the various enzyme systems which they controlled, etc.

Polymorphism

One consequence of supposing that skin color was mainly determined by such a simple mechanism as this is, of course, that our various races would be polyphenic or "polymorphic" for skin color. This admission may at once cause some revulsion on the part of the reader who believes that all individuals of a given race should be alike in regard to the characters used in racial classification. Many examples of this tendency could be combed from the writings of early anthropologists, or from statements made by laymen today, but we may restrict ourselves to one. Franz Boas, in a book published in 1928, stated: "When we speak of racial characteristics we mean those traits that are determined by heredity in each race and in which all members of the race participate" (2). It is only fair to mention that Boas, one of our greatest anthropologists, later came to see the error inherent in this distinction of race. In earlier pages of this book (201, 202) we have quoted the opinions of geneticists such as Dobzhansky that such a definition of race is impracticable.

In reply to the objections raised by people who still take this old-fashioned point of view, we may point out that groups classified as "races" by physical anthropologists of the past, and even of the present day, are in fact often "polymorphic" for skin color. Examples are found in Russia and Arabia, China, etc. It is true that polymorphism may be the result of the mixture of racial groups of different degrees of pigmentation, as with American Negroes, and in hybrids in South Africa (8), but this is not always the case, and "pure" races are not always homogeneous for skin color. Polymorphism in regard to other characteristics is often found in ethnic groups regarded as homogeneous, but is hardly commented on. Eye color (blue, brown, gray, etc.) has been mentioned already (p. 201) as an example; type of body build ("somatotype") is another. In a number of racial groups several varieties of body build are found, as has been pointed out by Weidenreich (22). Stature also varies considerably, even in a relatively homogeneous group such as the Japanese (21).

If we were to suppose a somewhat different series of pigmentation effects to be produced by the blood group genes, and particularly if we were to suppose that gradations in skin color corresponding to the allelomorphic genes (O, A_4, A_3, A_2, A_1, B) determining the subgroups were produced, then the polymorphism which we should have to suppose as a result would be little if any greater than that which can actually be observed in many existing ethnic groups. So in all probability we may safely go ahead with our construction of hypothetical ethnic groups composed of individuals whose visible characteristics are determined chiefly by the blood group genes.

Let us further suppose specific hypothetical effects for the M and N genes. Let us imagine that the effect of the M gene was generally the production of a tall individual, whose stature, in the male, we may suppose would range from 168 to 172 centimeters or, in other words, from about 5 feet, 6 inches to about 5 feet, 7¾ inches.

Let us suppose that the gene for N resulted in short individuals with a height, in the male, varying from 148 centimeters to 158 centimeters, in other words about 4 feet, 10¼ inches to 5 feet, 2¼ inches. Let us further suppose that the heterozygotes MN would be intermediate in stature. (We may recall that there is some evidence that, serologically, the heterozygote MN gives reactions intermediate in strength between the two homozygotes MM and NN.)

There are men in the world today taller than our hypothetical MM, and others shorter than our hypothetical NN, but the suggested range of height would nevertheless be impressive, if human psychology remained the same, for stature has always been considered a character of utmost importance. There can be few of my readers who have not experienced the emotion which results from looking up at a taller person, or looking down to a shorter person. Probably we could afford to let this case rest entirely on the testimony of tall female readers of this book who have found themselves at parties and other gatherings obliged to dance with men shorter than themselves. Eisenhower (6a) recorded the indignation of Marshal Zhukov over the reports that he was shorter than his wife.

We shall here assume that there would be no sex differences in stature in our imaginary people, for although sex is known to affect the expression in the individual of a number of autosomal genes (4), it does not affect blood group genes.

Passing to the Rh series of genes, we shall restrict ourselves, since the actual situation is rather complex, to supposing that the Rh negative gene would in this case act as a dominant, producing an eye structure similar to what is called the Mongolian (or epicanthic) eye fold. Individuals homozygous for the Rh positive gene would have European type eyes.

Imaginary Races

Remembering that these various assumptions are purely imaginary, let us consider what sort of race classification would have grown up as travelers from "civilized" countries gradually explored the rest of the world and finally tried to summarize and systematize their observations.

There can be hardly any doubt that the situation would have been considered very striking and, from the point of view of physical anthropologists who were writing fifty years ago, very satisfactory. In western Europe people varying in skin color from brown to dark brown would predominate. (The darker brown would be uncommon.) In Asia and related regions individuals of a rather dark yellow color would be the common type, with a certain mixture of brown and dark brown. The frequency of very dark individuals would be at its height somewhere in central Asia. There would be good evidence (see Ch. IV) that the yellow skin color found occasionally in Europeans had been brought by direct migration from Asia. There would be a fairly high incidence of very dark brown individuals in certain parts of Africa.

The lightest colored skins would be found in the various races of western Europe and certain parts of central Europe, in the East Indies, in the Australian aborigines, and in certain tribes of North American and South American Indians.

All of the Indian tribes of both of the Americas would agree in being considerably taller than the average for the rest of the world, while the aboriginal inhabitants of Australia would agree in being distinctly shorter than the average. These differences would probably be considered very marked. (Serological characters of the blood, if differences were eventually discovered, would probably be found to vary so much with climate and environment that they would probably be considered useless for purposes of racial classification.)

One of the most notable observations would be that only in Europe and in the white inhabitants of America who are of European stock would the Mongoloid eye fold be observed to any extent. It would therefore be considered quite proper to mark off the European race as being absolutely distinct from all the other races of the world because of this striking morphological characteristic. The Basques would have a higher incidence of the eye fold than any known people. Figure 36 shows the racial categories which would be defined on the basis of the genes we have been discussing, provided they had the effects we have just supposed.

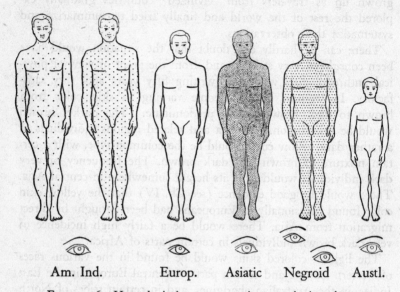

Am. Ind.   Europ.   Asiatic   Negroid   Austl.

FIGURE 36. *Hypothetical races, assuming certain imaginary visible external effects of blood group genes (see text). Relative stature as shown. Skin color is indicated by various degrees of stippling, and presence or absence of Mongoloid eye fold by sketches below.*

It would be observed (see above) that in the various great "racial" groups the skin color was not absolutely uniform. Nor would stature be found to be absolutely uniform within the groups in different parts of the world. In Asia and Europe, for instance, we should find that the majority of the inhabitants were of medium height, but that a certain number, of the order of 25 per cent of the total, would be rather tall, and a certain number, also about 25 per cent, would be rather short. "Clines" in stature would be found in Australia and up through the Pacific islands. Also, when the laws of heredity of these characteristics were investigated, it would be found that two individuals of medium height did not necessarily produce children who all grew up to a similar height. Instead, it would be possible for them to produce tall or short children, in addition to children of medium stature. This situation might be considered somewhat perplexing, but could easily be explained once the hereditary mechanism of the characteristic had been ascertained.

It would also be found that light brown individuals might result from a mating of dark brown parents. The genetic analysis would not prove too difficult to carry out (contrary to the situation which actually prevails in regard to skin color in the world today).

In the actual world we know, the skin color of individuals is influenced at least temporarily by exposure to the sun, and this, in turn, may be related to their occupation. Also there can be hardly any doubt that stature is importantly influenced by diet. We should therefore remind ourselves that in our hypothetical world, where we have given the serological genes the role of affecting skin color and stature, the climate, environment, occupation, and diet might also exert their influence and thus possibly complicate the genetic analysis. Let us oversimplify once more and suppose that this did not happen.

Hypothetical Classifications

Given the hypothetical situation which we have just outlined, it may hardly be doubted that physical anthropologists would not have hesitated to classify mankind more or less as follows: 1) The European race, characterized by relatively light color and the presence of the Mongolian eye fold; 2) the Asiatic race, characterized by the predominance of yellow individuals, not having the epicanthic fold, but of about the same average stature as the European race; 3) the primitive American race, characterized in general by tall stature, no epicanthic fold, but varying from tribe to tribe in its skin color, which would range from brown to light brown; 4) the aboriginal Australian race, a relatively light colored people, but practically pygmies in stature; they would have no epicanthic fold; and 5) an African race, possibly characteristic of the equatorial regions of

Africa, dark but with somewhat lighter skin than typical Asiatics, and having the epicanthic fold to a less extent than Europeans.

The European and Asiatic races would be imperfectly separated, but would be connected by a series of clines or intermediates in central Europe and Russia. This would be easily explained, however, as the result of repeated Asiatic invasions and migrations which had taken place in prehistoric and early historic times. The light color of certain individuals in southeastern Africa would be somewhat more difficult to explain, but the answer to all of these questions might depend a good deal on the region in which anthropologists in our hypothetical world supposed mankind to have originated.

Two other questions would come up which would be not quite so easy to answer as the above: (a) why the aborigines of the American continent should be so tall, and (b) why the Australian aborigines should be so short. Archaeological evidence would indicate that the people who migrated to America came across the Bering Strait region and were, on the whole, of medium height. In the early days of physical anthropology, in our hypothetical world, a good deal of loose speculation as to the effect of climate on stature would have been indulged in. As the science of anthropology advanced further, however, such explanations would be frowned upon, for the anthropologists would begin to insist that the only valid characters for racial classification are those which are non-adaptive and which are not affected by the environment. Investigations designed to test this point would probably not be found to detect any marked selective advantage or disadvantage characterizing either the A, B, M, or N genes (p. 150).

The possession of the Mongolian eye fold by the Europeans and their North American descendants would be somewhat of a puzzle also. One would be obliged to suppose that it was the result either of mutations or of early mixtures of the European groups with some early *non-sapiens* or *sapiens* type of man (p. 152).

The hypothetical distribution of morphological characteristics which would result from the imaginary effects of the blood grouping genes, which we have made up pretty much at random, would give each continent, on the whole, a clear-cut characteristic racial picture. Intergradations would be relatively infrequent, and it would be fairly easy to classify by inspection groups of individuals as coming from Europe, Asia, Africa, or Australia.

Back to Reality

The foregoing paragraphs are not meant to be a jest, but are intended to illuminate the contrast in our attitude toward visible, physical characteristics such as skin color and stature, and our attitude toward the invisible serological characteristics of the blood. If the blood grouping genes known at present really had the effects we have imagined, and if it were known how they were inherited, they would undoubtedly be considered highly satisfactory for racial classification. The average person is so impressed with skin color that he would doubtless be entirely satisfied of the importance of the pigmentation distinctions created by the A, B, O series of genes; and the hypothetical effect of the M and N genes on stature would be considered proof that these genes were of great importance in racial classification since they affected the characteristics of the skeleton (p. 21).

We now leave the dream world we have just created, and try to face the apparently less exciting facts of the real world. There is no evidence that skeletal characteristics are more stable, in an evolutionary sense, than other inherited characters. The blood group genes do not affect, so far as we know, the skin color, or the stature, or structure of the eye fold. Instead, they control the production of certain chemical substances in the blood. Since we have seen, however (in Ch. II), that in fundamental importance to the organism, probably all genes are nearly equivalent, there is no reason why the blood group genes should not be just as important for purposes of racial classification as if they had in reality the hypothetical effects we have ascribed to them above. It is in fact rather puzzling that blood group genes have not been more often used for classification.

Why Were Genes Neglected?

The genes which could be most useful to us in anthropology are, in the present state of our knowledge, the blood group genes. But they have not been used much by the average physical anthropologist in recent years. There are a number of reasons for this. 1) Physical anthropologists have preferred when possible to deal with skeletal material. This preference is partly due to the pious hope that characters of the skeleton, since it represents the harder and more permanent part of the human frame, will, therefore, on the whole be more permanent and less subject to modification in the course of evolution (14). There is no reason for believing that this actually is the case, however, and actually many of the mutations observed to occur frequently in Drosophila affect the skeleton, which in this species is on the outside. The chief reason for depending upon skeletons, of course, is their relative availability, especially for the study of ancient man. Although it has been possible to discover the blood groups of people who lived as long as 5000 years ago (5), we cannot expect to push such investigation much farther back than this, and as to the color of the skin, the artistic ability, the musical sense of early man or his capacity for adapting to a social group, we shall always be pretty much in the dark.

Most of the material available for the study of early man is skeletal, and a scientific study of this material certainly has its value. It is not the place of genetics to discourage the exploration of another field of science, but rather to offer checks on the hypotheses and assumptions which are used to examine and order that material. Most of the tie-up between archaeology and physical anthropology depends on the skeleton, and this is an important tie-up. Genetics can never replace the study of fossil remains, from the morphological standpoint, in human or other paleontology. But it can do much towards the proper conceptualization of that study (24).

The geneticists have long realized the advantage of a classification based on known genes, and Dobzhansky (6), one of our leading workers in the field of genetics, has stated clearly his own opinion that the study of geographic variation of a single human gene series, such as that which determines the blood groups, is capable of giving more information about the nature of races than could decades of mensuration and computing of racial averages. He does not deny, however, that the methods used by anthropologists in the past have some usefulness; he only insists that the limitations to these methods be understood.

2) The second reason for the lack of interest in blood groups for

classification was that the genetic variation from race to race was discovered only after other methods of anthropological classification had already been introduced and had enjoyed extensive use. Scientists, like other people, are conservative. 3) Many physical anthropologists, even today, do not understand the science of genetics well enough to appreciate the advantages which characteristics such as blood groups offer, and so have preferred to base their classification on traditional measurements, and on statistical averages determined from these. 4) A fourth reason was that the first advocates of blood group studies (16, 25), in their enthusiasm, claimed too much for their methods, and the physical anthropologists of today are still somewhat influenced by the reaction which resulted from the inevitable disappointment. 5) The fifth and perhaps most important reason is that the study of blood group frequencies very often does not confirm ideas about race which have already been developed on the basis of metrical and other observations, and the resulting classifications in many cases cut entirely across the traditional categories. Figure 25 showed how classifications according to blood group frequency can be entirely independent from that which results from classification based on the cephalic index or on skin pigmentation (p. 172). 6) It is unfortunately true that one of the pioneers of the use of blood groups in anthropological classification (11) was partly responsible for diminishing the confidence in the method by proposing a "biochemical index" $I = \dfrac{A + AB}{B + AB}$ for use in racial classification. It was early pointed out that this index, since it took no account of the amount of group O in a population, could not tell the whole story, but in spite of this it is still sometimes referred to. Its use restricted still further the information which serology could offer anthropologists, and this was already rather limited (see below).

An increasing knowledge of human genetics offers us a new method of classification which may be of more fundamental importance than the old one, and we cannot, just because its implications are startling, reject it. We must ascertain what the facts are, define physical races as the gene frequencies show them to be, or, if the data force us to such a conclusion, declare that the term "race" has no physical meaning.

Racial Classification by Blood Groups

Ottenberg (16) attempted one of the earliest racial classifications based on blood groups. There were available at that time data on only one set of genes, the O, A, B blood groups, and consequently the result was not an adequate classification of races by modern standards (one criterion is not enough, p. 193). Ottenberg's races were six: 1) European; 2) Intermediate — Arabs, Turks, Russians, etc.; 3) Hunan — Japan, South China, Hungary, Roumanian Jews; 4) Hindu-Manchu — Korea, North China, Gipsies, Hindus; 5) Afro-South Asiatic — Negroes, Madagascans, Malayans; 6) Pacifico-American Indians — Indians, Australians, Filipinos, Icelanders. Snyder (25) made the Australians a separate race from the Pacific race.

It will be apparent to any student of anthropology that this classification makes some very strange bedfellows. Ethnic groups which can be related only in the remote way we are all related to each other are included in the same "race." It is not surprising that anthropologists took one look at this list, shuddered, and said, in effect, "No thanks; I'll take vanilla."

A glance at the maps of gene frequencies (Figs. 33a and 33b) will show that the O, A, B frequencies can be nearly the same in different parts of the world, in ethnic groups which can be only distantly related. As examples we may consider the data shown in Table 31 (19).

A more recent attempt to use serological characters in anthropology is found in a book by Lahovary (12). This author makes some use of the M and N genes, and occasionally other blood factors, in addition to the classical O, A, B groups, and he distinguishes the following races: 1) European (Nordics and Alpines of Europe and the Near East); 2) Mediterranean; 3) Mongolian (Central Asia and Eurasia); 4) African (Blacks); 5) Indonesian; 6) American Indian; 7) Oceanic, including the Japanese; 8) Australian (a sub-variety of the Oceanic).

Lahovary was aware that a racial classification based merely on the O, A, B groups would in many cases give results which would not fit well with older ideas about race. He did not wish to abandon

TABLE 31

Similar Blood Group Distributions in Different
Peoples

People	Place	Percentage of Groups				Frequency of Gene		
		O	A	B	AB	p	q	r
Eskimo	Labrador and Baffin Island	46.5	53.5	0	0	.318	0	.682
Aborigines	W. Australia	48.1	51.9	0	0	.306	0	.694
Chinese	Canton	45.9	22.8	25.2	6.1	.154	.168	.678
Katangas	S. Belgian Congo	45.6	22.2	24.2	8.0	.156	.169	.675
Russians	Kazan	41.9	27.3	23.3	7.5	.194	.169	.648

the older points of view, however, so he attempted a compromise. In some cases he made use of information about the M, N types, and occasionally other blood factors, to help separate populations not clearly distinguished by A and B. In other cases, where populations probably not closely related proved to have about the same frequencies for A and B, he postulated that the A or B in one of these populations was "of different intensity." It is not too clear what this means, and it is not true that the A or B antigens differ in any detectable way from population to population (except for the different proportions of the subgroups, A_1 and A_2, of the A antigen). The idea probably goes back to the speculations of Hirszfeld (10) about an "evolution" of the A and B antigens from O, and this in turn is largely based on the old idea, now disproved, that American Indians belong only to group O (p. 330).

The classifications of Lahovary do not violate ordinary anthropological notions so much as those of Ottenberg, but at the same time it must be admitted that Ottenberg, somewhat like Dixon in the metrical field (p. 194), showed more courage in following his premises to their inevitable conclusions. Lahovary hedges at numerous points.

Most of Lahovary's book is restricted to a consideration of the races of Europe, where there are found, it is true, certain well-marked gradients or clines (p. 170) in the gene frequencies of A and B. This enabled him to make subdivisions at practically any point, and thus devise "serological races" which did not agree too badly with European races as defined on morphological, pigmentation, and linguistic grounds. But a glance at Figure 25 will show that a classification based on the B gene, for instance, will never agree well with one based on the cranial index or on skin color. In other words, Lahovary failed to realize that the characters by which we define races are independent of each other, and we must not expect a classification by one character to agree with another very closely, even in Europe, where the present populations are to a large extent traceable back to a few sources, and even these could not have been too different. It does not seem, therefore, that Lahovary has made a very great advance in methods of classifying races, in spite of his espousal of the genetic method, which in his case amounts mainly to the use of the classical A, B, O blood groups.

We have already implied that a valid and sensible classification of human races, based on genetic data, is possible. Suppose we show the same audacity as Ottenberg, but make use of the great amount of data which accumulated since. What sort of racial categories shall we be led to create, and will they be utterly different from the older ideas which were based on morphology and physical appearance?

Wiener (26) has proposed the following racial classification, based largely on the O, A, B and the Rh factors:

Caucasoid group — highest incidence of the Rh negative gene, relatively high incidence of genes for Rh_1 and A_2, moderate frequencies of other blood group genes.

Negroid group—highest incidence of gene Rh°, moderate frequency of the Rh negative gene, high relative incidence of genes A_2 and the rare intermediate A and Rh genes.

Mongoloid group — virtual absence of Rh negative gene and gene A_2, highest incidence of the rare gene Rh^z.

Wiener's classification, as first enunciated, distinguished only three races, and it seems likely from past experience that we shall find it convenient to divide the human species into rather more than three races (recall that the number of races to be recognized in a species may be to a large extent arbitrary). However, it must be admitted that this classification makes much more "sense" than those just referred to. But by making more use of M, N data, we can improve it still further. Wiener in fact attempted this (28) and as a result subdivided his Mongoloid group into an Asiatic sub-group, a Pacific Island and Australian group, and a group including the American Indians and Eskimos.

From what has been said already, and particularly from our hypothetical example (p. 253) in which we allowed certain blood grouping genes to be supposed to have effects on morphological and other physical characteristics of man, it is obvious that we could, if we liked, find ample justification for classifying men into a larger number of different races on the basis of blood groups. The races which would result from such a classification, however, would coincide only in part with the races of man as they have previously been delineated by anthropologists, and in some cases would appear even to be inconsistent with the known history of the people. The American Indian, for instance, known to be derived by direct descent largely or at least partly from Mongoloid ancestors emigrating from the Asiatic mainland, would have to be placed in a quite different race on the basis of blood groups. This only serves to emphasize the meaning which is being given the term "race" in this book. Serological factors are almost the only human characteristics of which we know the exact mechanism of inheritance, and it has been shown above that only the use of characters inherited in a known manner will satisfy our criteria for a satisfactory classification of races. The very idea of racial differentiation implies that geographically isolated groups, although ultimately *of the same origin,* may eventually come to differ, and we have explained the mechanisms by which such differentiation can be brought about. Therefore, there is no reason why the Mongoloid appearance of many American Indians should in itself prevent our placing them in a racial category different from that of contemporary Asiatics. Aside from blood groups, we do not know what proportion of Mongoloid genes they really have, for we have not solved the problems of how many genes co-operate to produce the "Mongoloid" appearance.

The Races Defined Here

The present author has suggested (3) the following tentative racial classification based on gene frequencies. It differs only slightly from Wiener's.

1. Early European group (hypothetical) — Possessing the highest incidence (over 30%) of the Rh negative type (15) (gene frequency of $rh > 0.6$) and probably no group B. A relatively high incidence of the gene Rh_1 and A_2. Gene N possibly somewhat higher than in present-day Europeans. Represented today by their modern descendants, the Basques.

2. European (Caucasoid) group — Possessing the next highest incidence of rh (the Rh negative gene) (see Table 29), and relatively high incidence of the genes Rh_1 and A_2, with moderate frequencies of other blood group genes. "Normal" frequencies of M and N, i.e., $M = $ ca. 30%, $MN = $ ca. 49%, $N = $ ca. 21%. (The italicized symbols stand for the genes, as opposed to the groups.)

3. African (Negroid) group — Possessing a tremendously high incidence of the gene Rh°, a moderate frequency of rh, relatively high incidence of genes A_2 and the rare intermediate (27) A ($A_{1,2}$, etc.) and Rh genes, rather high incidence of gene B. Probably normal M and N.

4. Asiatic (Mongoloid) group — Possessing high frequencies of genes A_1 and B, and the highest known incidence of the rare gene Rh^z, but little if any of the genes A_2 and rh (the Rh negative gene). Normal M and N. (It is possible that the inhabitants of India [see Tables 29 and 31] will prove to belong to an Asiatic subrace, or even a separate race, serologically, but information is still sadly lacking.)

5. American Indian group — Possessing varying (sometimes high, sometimes zero) incidence of gene A_1, no A_2, and probably no B or rh. Low incidence of gene N. Possessing Rh^z.

6. Australoid group — Possessing high incidence of gene A_1, no A_2, no rh, high incidence of gene N (and consequently a low incidence of gene M). Possessing Rh^z.

Table 32 shows the world's distribution of these races.

TABLE 32

Approximate Gene Frequencies in the Six Genetically Defined Races

Gene	1 Early European	2 European (Caucasian)	3 African (Negroid)	4 Asiatic (Mongoloid)	5 American	6 Australian
$A(p)$ $(A_2 + A_1)$ Ratio	ca.0.25	0.2–0.3	0.1–0.2	0.15–0.4	0–0.6	0.1–0.6
A_2/A_1*	>0.5?	0.1–0.3	ca.0.4	0	0	0
$B(q)$	<0.01?	0.05–0.20	0.05–0.25	0.1–0.3	0	0
$N(n)$	>0.5?	0.3–0.5	ca.0.5	0.4–0.5	0.1–0.2	0.8–1.0
Rh neg.(r)	>0.5?	0.4	ca.0.25	0	0	0
Rh° $(R°)$	<0.1?	ca.0.1	ca.0.6	ca.0.1	ca.0.01	ca.0.01
ptc †	ca.0.5	0.55–0.7	ca.0.45	0	0	0
non-secreting ‡	?	ca.0.5	>0.6	0?	0?	?
Other genes §	?	rh'	$A_{1,\,2}$	Rh^z	Rh^z	Rh^z

* For convenience in calculation, the ratio of the two subgroups, A_2 and A_1, and not the ratio of the gene frequencies, p_2/p_1, is given.

† The recessive gene for *not* tasting phenyl-thio-carbamide.

‡ The recessive gene for *not* secreting water soluble blood group substances into the gastric juice, saliva, etc.

§ Other genes the frequency of which seems to be higher in this population than in other races.

Such a classification corresponds well, omitting the inevitable intermediates, *with geography*.

In addition to the blood group genes, the frequencies of two other genes, neither strictly serological, help us in making our new racial distinctions. These are the genes for tasting PTC and related compounds (17), and the "secreting gene" (18, 20). The information we possess about the world distribution of these genes is not very great, but it will be seen that some at least of our new races differ in respect to the incidence of these genes. Further study should add many such new genes to our list, and enable us to subdivide our present races. We do not propose to make a racial analysis of all the various populations of the world at the present time, however, but, having indicated the general method, leave the more detailed application of it to future students, who will find more adequate and more precise data at their disposal.

General Considerations

Our six genetically determined races certainly conform in a broad way to geography (Fig. 37). Striking differences in certain gene frequencies mark off the inhabitants of the various continents. This is not surprising, since we have seen above that the evolutionary mechanisms which can produce racial differentiation are unlikely to do so unless we have at least a certain degree of geographic isolation (p. 158). Genetic interchange between the inhabitants of the different continents was probably, during the days of prehistory, relatively minor.

It must not be thought that the divisions between our genetic races will be absolutely sharp, any more than is the difference between races which are characterized by any other method. Isolation has not been absolute enough for that. Also, we must recall that although isolated groups originally alike may diverge from each other in regard to a number of characteristics, there is no law which says that they *must* diverge, especially in regard to characters having only slight adaptive value. In any case, migration and mixture have been going on, at a greater or less rate, throughout most of human history as we now attempt to reconstruct it.

To consider some special difficulties, it will be noted that our scheme of six genetic races makes no provision for a Pacific race, unlike some of the earlier schemes. The reason for this is that the Pacific peoples do not agree in exhibiting any distinctive combination of frequencies of the genes which we have thus far identified. The aborigines of certain islands near Australia show M and N frequencies similar to the Australians (Fig. 23) and are thus intermediate in this respect. However, they mostly have considerable amounts of the gene *B,* and we have seen that this is not a characteristic of the Australians. Also, the M frequencies of the Pacific peoples gradually rise to the European-Asiatic norm as we travel northward and westward (Fig. 35). These Pacific peoples do not

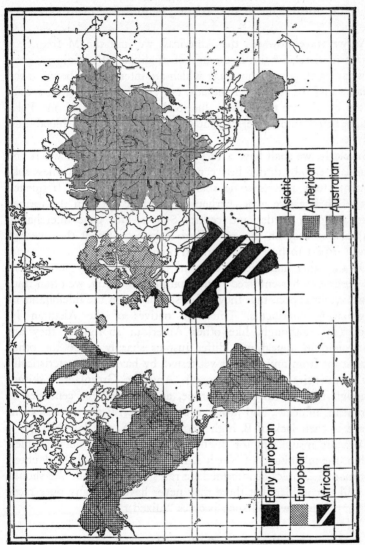

FIGURE 37. *World distribution of six genetically defined races.*

Early European

European

African

Asiatic

American

Australian

have gene frequencies constant enough for us to lump them with either the Australians or the Asiatics, or to define them as a separate race.

As we travel towards the Americas, we find the M frequency begins to rise, and the frequency of B drops off rapidly to zero, thus giving us populations (23) which are intermediate between the Asiatics and the American Indians. Nevertheless, there is no special reason to suppose that this is due to the introduction of any Polynesian blood into America, and/or American Indian blood into Polynesia.

Similarly, we shall have a very hard time deciding just where the boundary is to be drawn between European and Asiatic, unless subsequent study reveals some sharp discontinuity in the frequency of the Rh negative gene, perhaps somewhere between the former German-Polish border and central Siberia. But gene interchange has been so easy on the great Euro-Asiatic continent that we can hardly expect to find a sharp racial boundary.

On the other hand, if we examine populations in regions where the geography has enforced rather complete isolation, we often find, as we might expect, that they differ sharply from the inhabitants of neighboring continents. Thus the natives of the Aleutian Islands (13), although, like other American aborigines, they are Mongoloid in appearance, differ just as sharply as do the other Americans from any Asiatics yet tested, by having characteristically low frequencies of N (Table 25). And the Greenland Eskimo, although not too far from Europe, and exposed for centuries to European influence, also prove to be characteristically American in regard to their lack of B, high frequency of A, and low N (7).

Data are insufficient for discussion of other transitional peoples, such as the inhabitants of North Africa, but it can hardly be doubted that many examples of intermediate races will be found. We should do well to consider that there may never have been any pure races (p. 192), before we call such peoples "mixed races."

Similarity to Older Classifications

It will be noted that our proposed racial classification, although it is based upon gene frequencies, as we decided a valid classification must be (p. 27), does not really differ in any very startling way, in so far as the ultimate categories are concerned, from some of the older classifications based on skin color, hair form, etc. Far from discouraging us, this should be a sign that our new methods are not doing so badly. For, in spite of all protestations that they were considering race and not geography, most writers on anthropology have generally tried to set up classifications that made sense geographically. For this reason they emphasized often in the course of a single work various things at various times: sometimes skin color, sometimes head form, sometimes something else. Consequently they always reached, except when some bold worker like Dixon (p. 194) took the bit in his teeth and ran past all warning signals, a final goal of human races distributed roughly according to geography and common descent. All we have done is to show that the same thing can be accomplished more simply, and without so many inconsistencies in the application of our method, by considering gene frequencies.

Advantages of the Gene Method

But it must not be thought that the use of the genetic method has merely served to confirm what was already known. This method has advantages which we have already pointed out (p. 27) and which we may go over briefly again.

1) The method of gene frequencies is completely objective (subject to the qualification that our decision as to what boundary between frequencies is to separate two races remains always a man-made and arbitrary decision); 2) the gene method is quantitative rather than qualitative, so the observed frequencies give us some idea of how much different races differ from each other, and the consequences of race mixture can be accurately predicted (p. 111).

As an example of point 2), we may mention the Australian aborigines and the Ainu. Both of these peoples have been called by some authors "basic white" (11a). However, in the present state of our knowledge of the inheritance of skin color (p. 310), we cannot state how much the very dark skin of the Australian marks him off from the European. But a glance at his blood group frequencies tells us at once that he is pretty similar in regard to the original absence of B, but different in regard to M and Rh negative. It will be seen (p. 152) that we can probably account for the acquisition of the Rh negative gene by the Europeans by the hypothesis of mixture, and the peculiar M frequencies of the Australian by random genetic drift (p. 154). Thus it is not impossible to see a common origin for these diverse peoples, although they have by this time differentiated into separate races.

In regard to the Ainu, we find a frequency of B which suggests considerable Mongoloid mixture, but the M frequency is closer to that of Europeans. Random genetic drift has apparently not affected the M of the Ainu much. The B observed (ca. 30–40 per cent) is, however, so tremendously high that we cannot consider the Ainu, in spite of his light skin color, to be as closely related to Europeans as are the Australian aborigines (unless, of course, we consider it probable that random genetic drift or repeated mutation has raised the B frequency). It seems more plausible to suppose that the darker skin of the Australian has been acquired since his arrival in Australia, probably by the action of natural selection.

Racial Superiority

The genetic classification of races is more objective, and better founded scientifically, than older classifications. The differences we find between races are inherited in a known manner, not influenced by environment, and thus pretty fundamental. But the new criteria differ from some older criteria in an important respect. In certain parts of the world, an individual will be considered "inferior" if he has, for instance, a dark skin, but in no part of the world does the possession of a blood group A gene, or even an Rh negative gene, exclude him from the best society. There are no prejudices against genes. And since we have absolutely no reason to think that the possession or lack of any of the genes we have considered here confers on its possessor any advantage as a potential contributor to the advance of cultures and civilizations, there is no reason that any prejudice should exist. We have already pointed out — p. 10 — that there are actually no grounds, other than prejudices and emotions, for objecting to a dark skin, but it is not very easy to convince certain individuals of this (9).

References for Chapter IX

1. Birdsell, J. B., personal communication (1940).
2. Boas, F., *Anthropology and Modern Life*. W. W. Norton & Co., New York, 1928.
3. Boyd, W. C., *Quar. Rev. Biol.*, in press (1949).
4. Boyd, W. C., and L. G. Boyd, *Ann. Eug.*, 8, 46–51 (1937).
5. Boyd, W. C., and L. G. Boyd, *J. Imm.*, 32, 307–319 (1937).
6. Dobzhansky, Th., *Trans. N. Y. Acad. Sci.*, Ser. II, 4, 115–133 (1942).
6a. Eisenhower, D. W., *Crusade in Europe*. Doubleday and Co., Garden City, New York, 1948.
7. Fabricius-Hansen, V., *J. Imm.*, 36, 523–530 (1939).
8. Fischer, E., *Die Rehobother Bastards*. Verlag von Gustav Fischer, Jena, 1913.
9. Gates, R. R., *Population, 1*, no. 2, 25–36 (1934).
10. Hirszfeld, L., *Les Groupes Sanguins*. Masson et Cie, Paris, 1938.
11. Hirszfeld, L., and H. Hirszfeld, *Lancet, 197*, II, 675–679 (1919).
11a. Hooton, E. A., *Up from the Ape*, Macmillan Co., N. Y., 1946.
12. Lahovary, N., *Les Peuples Européens*. La Baconnière, Neuchâtel, 1946.
13. Laughlin, W. S., in press (1949).
14. Morant, G. M., *J. Roy. Anthrop. Inst.*, 66, 43–55 (1936).
15. Mourant, A. E., *Nature, 160*, 505–506 (1947).
16. Ottenberg, R., *J. A. M. A.*, 84, 1393–1395 (1925).
17. Parr, L. W., *J. Heredity, 25*, 187–190 (1934).
18. Schiff, F., *A. J. P. A.*, 27, 255–262 (1940).
19. Schiff, F., and W. C. Boyd, *Blood Grouping Technic*. Interscience Publishers, Inc., New York, 1942.
20. Schiff, F., and H. Sasaki, *Z. Imm.*, 77, 129–139 (1932).
21. Shapiro, H. L., *Migration and Environment*. Oxford Univ. Press, London, New York, and Toronto, 1939.
22. Sheldon, W. H., et al., *The Varieties of Human Physique*. Harper & Bros., New York and London, 1940.
23. Simmons, R. T., and J. J. Graydon, *Med. J. Australia*, 577–581, May 10, 1947.
24. Simpson, G. G., *Tempo and Mode in Evolution*. Columbia Univ. Press, New York, 1944.
25. Snyder, L. H., *Human Biol.*, 2, 128–133 (1930).
26. Wiener, A. S., *Am. J. Clin. Path.*, 16, 477–497 (1946).
27. Wiener, A. S., *Blood Groups and Transfusion*. Charles C Thomas, Springfield, 1943.
28. Wiener, A. S., *A. J. P. A.*, 6, 236–237 (1948).

CHAPTER X Other Human Genes

Water, water, everywhere,
Nor any drop to drink.
— COLERIDGE: *The Rime of the Ancient Mariner*

SINCE there is no particular reason to think that the blood grouping characteristics are inherently superior to, or differ in their essential importance from other physical characteristics, the reader may well have begun to feel that it is high time we began an examination of other inherited human traits to find out whether other human genes are known whose study will aid us in developing and amplifying the classification already presented.

Features of a Useful Character

We may recapitulate with a few general considerations as to what sort of characteristics seem likely to be of anthropological value. For a characteristic to be of most use to us as physical anthropologists, concerned with the classification of men, it must be (a) genetically determined — that is, it must not simply be an effect of the environment as is the loss of an arm or a leg due to an accident of war or industry, but must be hereditary. We should be reasonably certain that it is determined by a definite pair (or pairs) of genes or by a known series of alleles. It is also necessary (b) that the characteristic should not be too infrequent or too frequent in the populations that we examine since otherwise its usefulness for purposes of classification will be slight. For, if a gene is extremely rare and only a few individuals exhibit its effects there will always be some difficulty in deciding that the different examples of this condition are due to the same gene exactly and not to other genes having similar or nearly identical effects. Furthermore, in order to determine the gene frequency of a rare characteristic, and such determinations are always our aim in population studies, it will be necessary to examine an excessively large number of individuals. On the other hand, if the gene is too common, nearly all individuals will be alike in respect to the characteristic it determines and consequently it also will be of little use, the second situation being, in fact, simply an inversion of the first. Consequently we shall not be interested in classifying our subjects according to whether or not they are albinos or hemophiliacs, but on the other hand we shall not bother to note whether they were born with a mouth, two eyes, and five fingers.

Results to Date

The mechanisms of the heredity of such common characteristics as stature, the pigmentation of skin, hair, and eye, the shape of the head and face, are still imperfectly understood; in part, perhaps, because of their complexity, but in part, it cannot be doubted, because studies of them have thus far been made by so few investigators, and these students have often abandoned the problem after a few halfhearted attempts. The blood group characteristics were discovered by Dr. Landsteiner while he was making observations on the compatibility of mixtures of various human bloods, as a purely academic piece of research. The approximate mechanism of their inheritance was discovered only after studies of the blood groups in human families had been made by a comparatively large number of physicians and scientists, and even then it remained for a mathematician, who was especially interested in human genetics (2), to formulate the correct hypothesis, more than ten years later. Further differences such as M, N, and Rh (28, 29) were discovered in experiments designed to analyze the antigenic constitution of blood types and the reaction of blood grouping factors when blood containing them was injected into animals. Knowing this background we should not be surprised to learn that the gene difference which is probably next in value to blood groups in anthropological classification (although, as already indicated, it is not quite certain that a single gene pair is involved), "tasting" versus "non-tasting," was really discovered in what is essentially an accidental way.

Taste for PTC

About eighteen years ago Dr. A. L. Fox had occasion to prepare
a quantity of phenyl-thio-carbamide (usually abbreviated PTC) (17).
As he was placing this compound in a bottle some of it was dispersed into the air as dust. Thereupon another occupant of the
laboratory complained of the bitter taste of the dust. This surprised

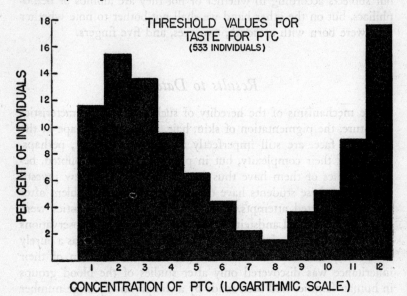

FIGURE 38. *Frequencies of various taste thresholds for
phenyl-thio-carbamide (after Hartmann).*

Fox, who being much closer to the scene of operations had of course
inhaled more of the dust, but had perceived no taste. He was so
positive that the stuff was tasteless that he went so far as to taste
some of the crystals directly, finding them as tasteless as chalk.
Nevertheless the other chemist was convinced the substance was
bitter and was confirmed in this impression when he in turn tasted
the crystals and found them to be intensely bitter. Naturally a lively
argument arose. In an attempt to settle it, the two chemists called
in various other laboratory workers, friends and other people with

whom they could establish contact. It was supposed that the verdict of these people would establish beyond question which of the two chemists was peculiar in his taste reaction. To their surprise, however, it did no such thing. Some people declared the substance was tasteless and some again found it bitter. The latter were in the majority. The investigators could not find any clear relationship between ability to taste PTC and age, race, or sex.

Geneticists (4, 41, 42) studied the problem of the inheritance of this taste ability and came to the conclusion that the lack of ability to taste PTC and related compounds is inherited as a simple Mendelian recessive. Thus originated the discovery of what may be another human gene pair which we may represent as T and t, T representing the "tasting gene" and t representing the "non-tasting" gene (25, 42, 43).

If different people are examined for their ability to taste phenyl-thio-carbamide it is found that there is nearly always a relatively sharp difference in taste thresholds between those who can taste fairly low concentrations and those who either are entirely unable to taste the substance or can taste it only in the strongest concentrations (see Fig. 38).

Table 33 shows some of the data which have been obtained in classifying individuals into tasters and non-tasters for phenyl-thio-carbamide. It will be observed that well-marked geographical differences exist. Certain groups of people, such as the American Indians, seem to consist of nearly 100 per cent tasters, while in other ethnic groups, as in Wales, large numbers of non-tasters, amounting in some cases to more than 50 per cent of the total, may be found.

It has been suggested that the ability to taste is determined by a single Mendelian gene pair, with the tasting gene (T) being dominant over the non-tasting gene (t). An analysis similar to that outlined in App. XIII–1 for a gene pair is given by Blakeslee (4) and Hogben (25). If this theory is true, however, there must be some difference in the penetrance (p. 77) of the gene in the two sexes, for the percentage of tasters in a good many populations has been found to be definitely higher in women than in men (5).

Although thousands of persons have been tested with phenyl-thio-carbamide, it still seems that, although perhaps the majority of individuals inherit the factor as an all-or-none characteristic, the

TABLE 33

Percentage of "Tasters" in Different Localities (5, 7, 8)

Place	No. Tested		Percentage of Tasters		Ratio Female/Male Tasters
	Male	Female	Male	Female	
Dublin	21	199	54.3	75.6	1.41
	24	374	59.1	72.7	1.23
Wales	125	112	44.7	74.3	1.66
Zagorsk (USSR)	197	289	57.8	67.2	1.16
Kharkov (USSR)	52	109	67.3	63.3	0.94
Tiflis (all) (USSR)	216	239	72.3	80.8	1.12
Tiflis (USSR)					
(West Georgians)	110	108	75.5	80.6	1.07
(East Georgians)	60	61	66.7	82.0	1.23
Cairo (all)	310	259	77.3	78.7	1.02
Cairo					
(Copts)	59	51	71.3	76.5	1.07
(Mohammedans)	251	208	78.6	79.3	1.01
Assiut (all)	229	251	74.3	78.1	1.05
Assiut					
(Copts)	182	199	73.1	76.4	1.05
(Mohammedans)	47	52	78.7	84.7	1.08
San Sebastián (all)	54	118	76.0	71.2	0.94
San Sebastián					
(Basques)	29	69	82.7	71.0	0.86
(Non-Basques)	25	49	68.0	71.5	1.05
Boarij					
(Syrians)	61	58	60.6	75.9	1.25
Meshghara, Syria					
(Christians)	82	14	69.5	71.4	1.03
(Moslems)	115	56	79.1	89.3	1.13
Beyrouth and Ghazir					
(Armenians)	147	164	72.8	77.4	1.06
Baghdad					
(Christians)	46	14	80.4	50.0	0.62
(Moslems)	217	105	69.6	72.4	1.04
(Jews)	55	113	80.0	84.1	1.05
Ramah, N. M.	121	148	98.0	98.4	1.00

See also Gates (19), Strandskov (45), and Parr (33).

gene displaying simple dominance, certain families show peculiarities, and individuals of an intermediate degree of ability to taste are
found (5). Some of these individuals can apparently taste the substance, but to them it does not have the immediate and intense bitter
taste which the rest of us tasters perceive. For them the taste is somewhat hard to characterize and is not particularly objectionable.
Either another gene must be involved or a modifying gene acting
on the originally postulated Mendelian pair exists. It is to be re-
gretted, therefore, that writers such as Hogben (25) offer the family
data on tasting as conclusive evidence that a human characteristic
which is definitely due to the presence or absence of a single Mendelian gene has been added to the list of those already found
serologically. Even in Hogben's presentation, for instance, the non-
taster $\times$ non-taster matings, which by hypothesis should produce
only non-tasters, are shown as producing five tasters. Neither Hogben nor Snyder (42), from whom the data were taken, offers any
explanation of this.

It will be noticed that the results for the tasting gene parallel in
general what has already been observed for the Rh negative and
A_2 genes, that is, that the European populations tend to differ rather
strikingly from Mongoloid populations. In both cases there is insufficient information about the Africans.

It was a matter of considerable interest, of course, to find what
the taste reactions of the anthropoid apes would be, and this question was investigated by Fisher, Ford, and Huxley in 1939 (6).
They found that the chimpanzees in the London zoo showed definite differences in taste threshold for phenyl-thio-carbamide, just
as do human beings; and since these differences seemed to be consistent and peculiar to the individual, we are doubtless justified in
supposing that they are inherited, since it is hard to see how they
could be the result of conditioning. It is the opinion of Fisher, Ford,
and Huxley that their observations suggest that our ancestors, which
we have in common with those of the anthropoids, may have possessed both the T and the t genes, have passed them on to us, and
that the heterozygote may enjoy some selective advantage over either
of the homozygotes, since otherwise, in the long period of time that
has elapsed, selection, or genetic drift, or both, would probably have
eliminated one of the genes from the species. As to the nature of this

selective advantage, no suggestion was made. It probably has no direct connection with the ability to taste phenyl-thio-carbamide, which in any case was synthesized only a relatively short time ago. But the genes which control the ability to taste this substance may at the same time affect other and more important aspects of the physiology of man. We do not as yet know what these aspects are.* A selective advantage for the heterozygote, as opposed to both homozygotes, has been shown convincingly for certain characters of Drosophila by Dobzhansky and Spassky (14). Perhaps this phenomenon occurs elsewhere and it may help to explain the survival of many of the seemingly neutral (or even disadvantageous) genes which seem to have persisted for a long time in a species. Dobzhansky, however, believes that such phenomena are more often the consequence of a balance of mutation rates than a consequence of any selective advantage of the heterozygote.

It has been found that rats differ considerably in their threshold for tasting PTC, practically as much, in fact, as do human beings, an observation which might lend some support to the suggestion put forward by Fisher, Ford, and Huxley, since rats are even further down in the evolutionary scale than are anthropoids. Phenyl-thio-carbamide is not toxic in the minute amounts required for determining taste threshold in man (cf. 26), but in any considerable quantity it is toxic (35), and the "non-tasting" rats were sometimes killed by eating meals of food containing it. A related substance, α-naphthol-thio-carbamide, abbreviated ANTU, was subsequently developed for use as a rodent poison. It seems to be especially effective against the Norway rat.

---

* It may be remarked that phenyl thio-carbamide probably owes its bitter taste to chemical groupings similar to some found in thiouracil. This last substance, together with some of its derivatives, has been used as an antagonist to the hormone of the thyroid gland in certain clinical instances. It might be that homozygous tasters are unduly sensitive to some of the anti-thyroid substances which occur in certain foods such as cabbage and turnips, for at least one of these substances is also chemically somewhat similar (1a). The homozygous non-tasters might be unduly insensitive, which might easily be a disadvantage in regions poor in iodine. Thus the heterozygotes might possess a better endocrine balance. An association between diabetes and "taste-blindness" has been suggested (45a). In some such way it is possible to imagine that either the tasting or the non-tasting gene might have evolutionary importance. Experiments designed to test these ideas are now in progress.

Secreting Gene

Another and somewhat remarkable gene difference which has been found in man is related to the blood groups but is not, in itself, a blood-grouping factor. This is the secreting gene (39, 40). It was discovered fairly early that the blood group antigens A and B were generally present in the saliva and (as we know now) in almost all of the body tissues of an individual if they were present in his red blood cells (i.e., a group B individual would have the B substance in his saliva and gastric juice, a group A person would have A, an AB both, and a group O person neither). The use of proper reagents enabled the rule to be extended to the group O substance also (37). But in some cases the group substance could not be demonstrated in saliva or body fluids, or was present in very small amounts, and Schiff (39) suggested that the presence or absence of the blood group substance in the saliva was determined by a special gene, which he designated as S (for secretor); the non-secreting gene was designated as s, and S was supposed to be the dominant member of the pair. Such a theory explains well the families which have thus far been studied, as illustrated in Table 34.

TABLE 34

Inheritance of "Secreting" Factor (48)

Mating	Number of Families	Children	
		S	s
S × S	105	241	33
S × s	62	103	67
s × s	18	0	42

Later Schiff was able to demonstrate that there were differences in the incidence of the secreting gene in different ethnic groups, as is illustrated in Table 35.

Unfortunately, determining whether an individual belongs to the secreting or to the non-secreting group is rather a tedious process, especially in the case of individuals of group O. Therefore, Schiff's

TABLE 35

Frequency of Secretors and Non-secretors in Various Racial Groups

Series	Place	Reference	Number Tested	Per Cent Secretors	Per Cent Non-secretors	Gene Frequency for Secretor (S)	Gene Frequency for Non-secretor (s)
Negroes	New York	(38)	178	61.2	38.8	0.38	0.62
Danes	Copenhagen	(24)	263	74.0	26.0	0.49	0.51
Japanese	Japan		424	75.7	24.3	0.51	0.49
Germans	Berlin	(38)	363	78.0	22.0	0.53	0.47
Poles	Poland		88	79.4	21.6	0.54	0.46
Whites	New York	(38)	74	82.4	17.6	0.58	0.42
Finns	Helsinki	(34)	196	86.3	13.7	0.63	0.37
American Indians	New Mexico	(9)	69	98.5	1.5	0.88	0.12
American Indians	Utah	(32)	79	100.0	0	1.00	0

results have not been extended much, and no adequate survey of racial differences in the frequency of this human gene has yet been obtained. When such information is available to us, however, it may prove fully as interesting and important as that available in connection with any other genetically controlled human characteristic.

Mid-digital Hair

Danforth (12) suggested that complete absence of hair on the middle segment of the fingers is a simple recessive trait in man, and there can be no doubt that the condition is inherited. Danforth reported a study of 80 families with 178 children. Bernstein and Burks (3) extended Danforth's study, but concluded that more than a simple Mendelian pair of genes were involved. They offered the hypothesis of five multiple alleles, D_0, D_1, D_2, D_3, D_4 (listed in order of increasing dominance) where the subscripts correspond to the number of fingers having mid-digital hair. Individuals of the genotype $D_0 D_0$ would have no mid-digital hair.

TABLE 36

Incidence of Mid-digital Hair in Various Populations
(6, 7, 8)

Population	Place	Number Examined		Per Cent with Mid-digital Hair	
		Males	Females	Males	Females
Russians					
Georgians	n. Moscow	116	115	64.6	45.3
(West)	Tiflis	119	124	49.6	43.5
Georgians					
(East)	Tiflis	62	71	56.4	33.8
Russians	Kharkov	58	112	56.9	50.9
Egyptians					
(Copts)	Cairo	55	52	65.5	46.2
(Moslems)	Cairo	228	203	45.6	36.4
(Copts)	Assiut	202	215	52.5	53.0
(Moslems)	Assiut	50	53	68.0	28.3
Basques	San Sebastian	25	53	64.0	73.6
Syrians					
(Moslems)	Boarij	68	61	77.9	55.7
(Christians)	Meshghara	90	16	68.9	50.0
(Moslems)	Meshghara	129	66	58.1	54.5
Armenians	Beyrouth and Ghazir	165	172	62.4	61.6
Arabs					
(Moslems)	Baghdad	233	132	67.4	50.7
(Christians)	Baghdad	48	14	64.6	50.7
Jews	Baghdad	69	136	71.0	59.6

There are probably racial differences in the incidence of mid-digital hair. The principal studies are shown in Table 36.

The extent of the racial variation, at least in these studies, would seem to be less than that shown by certain other hereditary characteristics.

Other Genes

We now come to the question of the inheritance of eye color. It has long been believed that bright blue eyes are inherited as a definite Mendelian recessive, although the inheritance of the other varieties of eye pigmentation is still somewhat obscure. For a recent although not definitive study of the question, the reader is referred to a paper by Brues (10). However, according to Gates (18), blue eyes which are inherited as a dominant have been observed, and this means that up to the present, at any rate, we are debarred from interpreting most of the material which has been obtained on eye pigmentation in terms of gene frequencies. This material suffers from the added disadvantage that a large number of different systems of recording the degree of pigmentation and other characteristics of the iris have been used by different workers, making it difficult to compare and correlate different series of studies. For typical systems of recording eye color, the reader is referred to Martin's *Augenfarben Tafeln* (31), Riddell (36), Brues (10), Tocher (47), and Boyd and Boyd (6). The difference between them is considerable and none can be regarded as completely adequate. Examples of racial variation in eye color will be found in Chapter XI, Table 39.

The first suggestion as to the mode of inheritance of a character is of course that it is determined by the presence of one gene of a Mendelian pair, and this idea has been proposed in connection with a large number of human traits. Nevertheless, it has seldom been found to explain all the facts, and the above short list practically exhausts the series of human characteristics which would be potentially useful to us and which can still with any plausibility be explained on the basis of a pair of genes or even a series of allelomorphs. It is true that such a mechanism has been *proposed* for a number of other characteristics. For instance, Wiener, Zieve, and Fries (49) have suggested the hypothesis that allergy is inherited as a simple Mendelian pair. They represent the genes making for allergy as H and the normal non-allergic gene by h. It is thought that the homozygous HH individual always develops allergy, usually before puberty, whereas the heterozygous Hh person may or may not develop allergy, and if he does is likely to develop it only after the age of puberty. The data analyzed by Wiener, Zieve, and Fries agree well with this hypothesis, but the whole subject of allergy is far too complex for us to state with confidence that the exact mode of inheritance of all its varieties is yet understood.

That there is a hereditary factor in allergy can scarcely be doubted. Even in cases of food allergies, where the subject may not know that he suffers from allergy, the hereditary factor may operate (21, 11). Unfortunately we cannot be sure that the inheritance is due to the action of a simple Mendelian pair of genes.

No matter how many genes may prove to be involved in the inheritance of allergies, however, it seems likely that racial differences in the incidence of some at least of these genes exist. Thus in Italy there is a disease known as favism, which is caused by eating the horse bean (*Vicia faba*) or by inhaling its pollen. The symptoms indicate a hemolytic effect on the red blood cells, leading to chills, vomiting, jaundice, and hemoglobinuria, sometimes with enlargement of the liver and spleen. Racial differences in susceptibility to favism probably exist, for it seems to be limited in Europe to peoples of the Mediterranean "race." The horse bean (called there the broad bean) is commonly eaten in England, but the population is not affected by it. In the United States (where, however, the general population does not know or eat the horse bean), descendants of Italian families sometimes get the disease (30).*

For rare human genes special methods of genetic analysis have been devised, and some of them will be discussed in the Appendix on statistical methods (p. 437).

The inheritance of baldness (a character whose expression is affected by sex) may be fairly simple, and racial differences in the frequencies of the genes involved probably exist.

Harris (22) examined a series of 900 Englishmen, and concluded that the hypothesis that premature (by "premature" in this case we mean before the age of forty-two) baldness is inherited discretely and distinctly from late baldness, and that it is inherited as a simple Mendelian dominant, would fit the observations. Further studies will of course be needed to make sure that the inheritance is as simple as this.

There can be little doubt that there are marked racial differences

---

* For the benefit of specialists in allergy, it may be mentioned that it is possible that the effects of the horse bean *might* be due not to a real allergy, but to a direct action of certain proteins of this bean which have the property of combining with human and other red cells. The racial differences then might be due to differences in absorption of these proteins into the circulation. But this is pure speculation at present.

in the incidence of premature baldness in man. Harris found 120 out of 900 Englishmen had gone bald prematurely, or in other words 13.3 per cent. In a series of more than 150 Navaho Indian males examined (44), not a single prematurely bald male was found. Other data suggest also that racial differences exist, but further studies along this line (and also further studies of the genetic mechanism) will be needed before we can make much use of the trait as a physical anthropological characteristic.

The well-known difference between the incidence of baldness in men and in women has been explained by Hamilton (20) on the hypothesis that the hereditary tendency to baldness will manifest itself only in the presence of an adequate level of male sex hormone in the body. Although women produce some male hormone, the same levels are seldom reached as in men.

There remain a large number of human characteristics which are pretty certainly inherited in Mendelian fashion (1, 19). Their inheritance has been established by the careful study of pedigrees of affected families. A number of abnormal conditions of the eye are inherited — see summary in (19). Unfortunately, all or nearly all of the rest of these characteristics occur so rarely that their value for anthropological classification is almost zero. To establish gene frequencies it would be necessary to study an impracticably large number of individuals and in many cases the sample afforded by an entire small population or tribe would be insufficient to prevent a decided effect due to random genetic drift (p. 154), so that relatively meaningless variations from place to place in the incidence of a character would be found and in the usual population sample we might even fail to encounter a single person exhibiting the trait.

A case which is perhaps somewhat on the borderline is color blindness, apparently usually a sex linked characteristic which occurs in white males with a frequency of something like 5–8 per cent. It is supposed to be transmitted by a recessive gene located on the X chromosome, and it is displayed by females only rarely, i.e., when both of their X chromosomes contain the gene. Consequently gene frequencies must in practice be estimated entirely by the study of the approximately 5 per cent of males who display the characteristic. The mechanism of inheritance just outlined fits a number of pedigrees of color blindness, but a survey of the literature on color blindness (19) seems to indicate that at least six types exist. They are called protanopia (P), deuteranopia (D), protanomalia (PA), deuteranomalia (DA), extreme protanomalia (EPA), and extreme deuteranomalia (EDA). Their supposed dominance relations are given by Gates (19) in his *Human Genetics*. Other complications, such as incomplete dominance, also come into

TABLE 37

Per Cent of Color Blindness in Males in Certain Ethnic Groups

Ethnic Group	Number of Persons Tested	Per Cent of Color-blind Males
Eskimo	125	0.8
Melanesians (New Guinea)		1
Navaho Indians	535♂	1.1
Japanese		3
Chukchi (Eastern Siberia)		3
Bechuanal (S. Africa)	407♂	3.4
American Negroes	2019♂	3.9
Egyptians		5
Lapps		6
Chinese	1164♂	6.9
White Americans	795♂	8.4
Europeans	3734	8.04

the picture. Also it is not always easy to be sure what type of color blindness a given individual really has (19). Therefore we are not able at the present time to make much use of the (still fragmentary) studies on the incidence of color blindness for purposes of anthropological classification. Kroeber (27) and Gates (19) have summarized what is known about the incidence of red-green color blindness in males of various "races." (See Table 37.) No startling conclusions emerge from an examination of these data.

A hereditary lack of normal pigmentation in skin, hair, and eyes, known as albinism, occurs in man, and is often inherited as a simple autosomal recessive, although some pedigrees suggest a somewhat more complicated mechanism (19). Its incidence in European races is only about 1 in 10,000, so it is far too rare to be of any anthropological use. Furthermore the data on the incidence in other populations are most unsatisfactory.

Next on the list, perhaps, come certain abnormalities known as inborn errors of metabolism, in which the metabolism of some substance in the body differs from that in the normal, or some substance is excreted by the individual, which is not usually found, or found only in traces in the excreta of normal individuals. For instance *cystinurea,* a condition in which the amino acid cystine appears in the urine, is inherited as a rare recessive in man (46). Alkaptonuria, a condition in which alkapton, probably a derivative of the amino acid tyrosine, occurs in the urine, is similarly inherited (19). Similar abnormalities have been found in animals also. A classical example of this is furnished by the dog. Nitrogenous compounds of the purine group (things like caffein, for example) are oxidized in most dogs to the compound which is known as allantoin. In the Dalmatian coach dog, however, they are oxidized incompletely, only so far as the compound known as uric acid, which happens to be also the stage which is reached in the purine metabolism of man. The condition is inherited, but the canine species differs in this case from man in displaying both conditions, and therefore two "races."

A number of other such abnormalities of metabolism exist. Many of them have been shown to be inherited in a definite Mendelian fashion; thus the presence of a five carbon sugar (pentose) is a definitely hereditary, but excessively rare, condition in man (15). Its rarity means that it is for our purposes merely a physiological curiosity and of no value for purposes of classification. Some investigators (Lasker), for example, thought that the cases of pentosuria in the world could be traced back to a single family, and thus ultimately to a single individual. This mutation has "spread" but has not become more frequent (p. 114).

Materials for Further Study

At intervals in the course of human history, and especially in the last few centuries, during which there has been a scientific study of nature and of man, a good deal of information has been accumulated about human inheritance and recently two large books, consisting each of two volumes, have been written on the subject (1, 19). It might therefore have been supposed that the preparation of the present chapter would have been a very easy matter, since abundant material lies ready at hand. The blood group genes should be only the hors d'oeuvres of a rich repast now ready to serve. Alas, this is not the case. If we examine attentively the two large works on human inheritance referred to, the first published by Baur, Fischer, and Lenz (1), the second by Professor Gates (19), we discover that in reality we have very little exact knowledge of human heredity. It is true that a large number of abnormal conditions are known to be inherited in man, and they have been investigated, more or less casually, mostly by physicians; but few, if any, of these characteristics are determined by a known genetic mechanism in a known way. The authors have compiled whatever material was available to them and, whether or not final analysis of the mechanics of the inheritance of human traits has been worked out in a given case, they have simply presented us with the evidence so far as it goes. This often is not far. For, up to the present time, very little money has been made available for research in human genetics, and such meager information as we have comes from the efforts of people who found themselves interested in the subject and seized what small opportunity they could to make observations which they thought would be of some value. Furthermore, analysis of genetic traits in man is not as easy as it is with animals, for with animals one can almost always make trial breedings to test the truth or falsehood of a hypothesis, but in man it must be tested by the accumulation of sufficient family material to have statistical validity. The *identification* of hereditary human traits has been carried out in many cases, but the analysis of the exact genetic mechanism has usually not been completed because it required more time and money than the investigator could afford to devote to what was essentially only a hobby.

Thus the story of the study of human heredity is largely a story of brave beginnings which have not yet achieved the final stages of complete scientific proof. In the book by Gates, for instance, in addition to the blood groups, there are discussed such subjects as Eye Color, Hair Color, Color Blindness, Hereditary Variations and

Abnormalities of the Eye, Hereditary Variations and Abnormalities of the Ear, Albinism, Abnormalities and Diseases of the Skin, Hair, Nails and Teeth, Anatomical Abnormalities of the Hands, Feet and Limbs, Anomalies of the Skeleton and of the Bone Structure, Metabolic Defects and Derangements, Hemophilia and Related Hereditary Conditions, Other Inherited Diseases and Abnormalities of the Blood System, Allergy, Hereditary Syndromes, Inherited Abnormalities of the Alimentary Canal, Various Sexual and Intersexual Conditions, Twins and Twinning, Inherited Muscular and Neuro-Muscular Abnormalities, Hereditary Variations, Defects and Diseases of the Nervous System, Mental Defects, Mental Ability, Cancer, Constitution and Body-Build, Congenital Abnormalities, Stature and Size, and Anthropological Characters. After examination of all the evidence we are obliged to say that investigations into the families of persons possessing these characteristics have not in any case been sufficient to establish the exact mechanism of inheritance, with the exception of the few characters we have already discussed, and of certain rare abnormalities such as (possibly) polydactyly, and even here proof is lacking that the gene determining the polydactyly of one family is the same as that which determines polydactyly in another. The requisite cross-matings have, of course, never been carried out.

So, aside from a few rare abnormalities which from their very nature can never be of much use to us in anthropology, we must regretfully admit that the students of human heredity have so far not carried out a thoroughgoing job of identification of human genetic mechanisms, save in the case of the blood groups. It is not too difficult to understand why this should be true. Financial rewards for such work are almost nonexistent, and a knowledge of human heredity is a kind of knowledge which at present commands little respect. It is important to know how to manufacture plutonium, but nobody cares how your Great-uncle George got that extra toe. A knowledge of the exact mechanism of blood group reactions proved to be of importance in saving the lives of patients in hospitals, therefore one can understand why this branch of the subject flourished while many other budding investigations never reached full flower.

Some idea of possible methods by which a correct analysis of other human hereditary traits may be attained in the future will be given in Chapter XIII. By the use of these and other methods, the human geneticist of the future, it cannot be doubted, will provide us with much valuable material bearing on questions of race.

REFERENCES FOR CHAPTER X

1a. Astwood, E. B., M. A. Greer, and M. G. Ettlinger, *Jour. Biol. Chem., 181,* 121–130 (1949).

1. Baur, E., E. Fischer, and F. Lenz, *Menschliche Erblichkeitslehre.* J. F. Lehmanns Verlag, München, 1927.

2. Bernstein, F., *Z. f. ind. Abst.-und Vererbl., 37,* 237–270 (1925).

3. Bernstein, M. M., and B. S. Burks, *J. Heredity, 33,* 45–53 (1942).

4. Blakeslee, A. F., *Proc. Nat. Acad. Sci., 18,* 120–130 (1932).

5. Boyd, W. C., and L. G. Boyd, *Ann. Eug., 8,* 46–51 (1937).

6. Boyd, W. C., and L. G. Boyd, *A. J. P. A., 23,* 49–70 (1937).

7. Boyd, W. C., and L. G. Boyd, *Human Biol., 13,* 398–404 (1941).

8. Boyd, W. C., and L. G. Boyd, *A. J. P. A., 28,* 319–330 (1941).

9. Boyd, W. C., and L. G. Boyd, *A. J. P. A., 7,* 569–574 (1949).

10. Brues, A. M., *A. J. P. A., 4,* 1–36 (1946).

11. Coca, A. F., *Familial Nonreagenic Food Allergy.* Charles C. Thomas, Springfield, 1943.

12. Danforth, C. H., *A. J. P. A., 4,* 189–204 (1921).

14. Dobzhansky, Th., and B. Spassky, *Genetics, 29,* 270–290 (1944).

15. Enklewitz, M., and M. Lasker, *Am. J. Med. Sci., 186,* 539–548 (1933).

16. Fisher, R. A., E. B. Ford, and J. S. Huxley, *Nature, 144,* 750–751 (1939).

17. Fox, A. L., *Proc. Nat. Acad. Sci., 18,* 115–120 (1932).

18. Gates, R. R., *Brit. Med. J.* (I), 921 (1938).

19. Gates, R. R., *Human Genetics.* Macmillan Co., New York, 1946.

20. Hamilton, J. B., *Am. J. Anat., 71,* 451–480 (1942).

21. Hanhart, E., *Deut. med. Wochens., 63,* 1753–1756 (1937).

22. Harris, H., *Ann. Eug., 13,* 172–181 (1946).

23. Hartmann, G., *Ann. Eug., 9,* 123–135 (1939).

24. Hartmann, G., *Det Kgl. Danske Videnskabernes Selskab. Biologiske Meddelelser, 16,* No. 2 (1941).

25. Hogben, L., *An Introduction to Mathematical Genetics.* W. W. Norton & Co., New York, 1946.

26. Hutt, F. B., *J. Heredity, 38,* 377–378 (1947).

27. Kroeber, A. L., *Anthropology.* Harcourt, Brace & Co., New York, 1948.

28. Landsteiner, K., and P. Levine, *J. E. M., 47,* 757–775 (1928).

29. Landsteiner, K., and A. S. Wiener, *Proc. Soc. Exp. Biol. & Med., 43,* 223–224 (1940).

30. Luisada, A., *Medicine, 20,* 229–250 (1941).

31. Martin, R., *Augenfarbentafeln.* Lehrbuch der Anthropologie G. Fischer, Jena, 1928.

32. Matson, G. A., and C. L. Piper, *A. J. P. A., 5,* 357–368 (1947).

33. Parr, L. W., *J. Heredity, 25,* 187–190 (1934).

34. Putkonen, T., *Acta Soc. Med. Fenn.* "Duodecim" Ser. A, *14,* Fasc. 2 (1930).

35. Richter, C. P., and K. H. Clisby, *Arch. Path., 33,* 46–57 (1942).

36. Riddell, W. J. B., *Ann. Eug., 2,* 245–259 (1942).

37. Schiff, F., *Z. Imm. u. Exper. Therap., 82,* 302–310 (1934).

38. Schiff, F., *A. J. P. A., 27,* 255–262 (1940).

39. Schiff, F., and H. Sasaki, *Klin. Woch., 11,* 1426–1429 (1932).

40. Schiff, F., and H. Sasaki, *Z. f. Immu. u. Exper. Therap., 77,* 129–139 (1932).

41. Snyder, L. H., *Science, 74,* 151–152 (1931).

42. Snyder, L. H., *Ohio J. Sci., 32,* 436–440 (1932).

43. Snyder, L. H., *The Principles of Heredity.* D. C. Heath & Co., Boston, 3rd Ed., 1946.

44. Spuhler, J. N., personal communication (1949).

45. Strandskov, H. H., *Sci. Monthly, 52,* 203–215 (1941).

45a. Terry, M. C., and G. Segall, *J. Hered., 38,* 135–137 (1947).

46. Thin, R., *Edinburgh Med. J., 36,* 490–492 (1929).

47. Tocher, J. F., *Biometrika, 6,* 129–235 (1908).

48. Wiener, A. S., *Blood Groups and Transfusion.* Charles C Thomas, Springfield, 1943.

49. Wiener, A. S., I. Zieve, and J. H. Fries, *Ann. Eug., 7,* 141–162 (1936).

CHAPTER XI

Incompletely Analyzed Genetic Characteristics

And makes us rather bear those ills we have
Than fly to others that we know not of?
Thus conscience does make cowards of us all . . .
SHAKESPEARE — *Hamlet, Prince of Denmark*

By incompletely analyzed characteristics, we mean characteristics which have not been studied sufficiently so that the exact genetic mechanism by which they are inherited is known, even though it may be believed or even well established that they are definitely hereditary in character.

Stature

For a long time stature has been considered an anthropological characteristic, and of course it is. If we examine races which are sufficiently different, we may find statistically significant differences in average stature, or even (in a few cases) a difference in stature so great that there is no overlapping. An example of this is given by Morant (39) from a study of the stature of 98 Congo Pygmies (Fig. 39), 109 Japanese from the Kaga province, and 105 Dinkas. An absolute separation was found between the ranges of stature of the Pygmies and the Dinkas. The tallest member of the Pygmies was shorter than the shortest of the Dinkas, although, as Morant points out (39), it is probable that with larger samples the distribution might overlap to some extent. However, a mixed series made by taking 100 Pygmies and 100 Dinkas would very definitely give a bimodal character of distribution, that is a distribution showing two means instead of one (Fig. 40). Both series (the Pygmies and the Dinkas) overlap the range of stature found in the 109 Japanese men studied in the Kaga province. The distribution would, however, obviously still be bimodal if the Japanese and the Pygmies or the Japanese and the Dinkas were lumped together. Therefore,

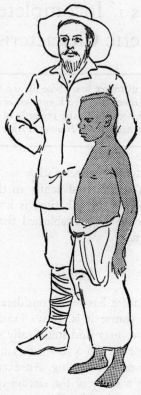

FIGURE 39. *Drawing showing a Pygmy beside a European of normal stature.*

on the basis of statistical evidence, we are justified in considering the average stature of these groups as different.

Stature is far from an ideal character to use in human classifications, for it varies, even within the same population, from one individual to the other, there is a definite sex difference, and in all probability one's final height is determined not only by heredity but

also by environment (p. 89). In connection with this latter possibility, we must keep in mind the fact that many peoples seem to
be gradually increasing in height, and that there is evidence that
this increase has been going on for a long time in Europe (30).
This may be connected with improved nutrition, but we might recall also that there is a general evolutionary principle that organisms of a phylum tend to increase in size as evolution goes on (53).

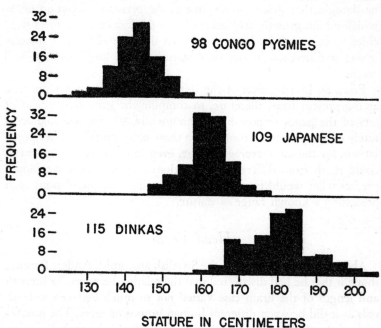

FIGURE 40. *Distribution of stature in Pygmies, Japanese,
and Dinkas.*

Knowing little or nothing of how the characters are inherited,
we cannot assess quantitatively the difference (in terms of gene
frequencies) between two populations. We may measure the phenotypes, it is true, but since some genes produce much greater morphological difference than do others, and since their final product
— the adult organism — depends in so many cases on the environment, mere records of the phenotypic frequencies which result from

the action of unknown combinations of unknown numbers of genes will tell us little.

We do not know how many genes are involved in the inheritance of stature, and we do not know exactly how they operate. The total height of a man is made up by the combined lengths of the head, neck, trunk, and legs. Davenport (13) in his study of the inheritance of stature found some correlation between some of these variables; he thought that shortness was due to the presence of certain genes which inhibit growth, and believed that the factors for tallness were chiefly recessive. It is also probable that the time of onset of puberty makes a difference in the final stature which an individual will reach.

From an investigation of the stature of a group we are not able at the present time, therefore, to compute the gene frequencies of any of the genes responsible. Consequently, we are not able accurately to compare these results with those obtained from other populations, for the same average stature, even in the same environment, could result from different combinations of genes; also, we cannot predict what would be the result of crossing two populations each possessing a known range of stature.

Head Form

About a hundred years ago the Swedish anatomist, Anders Retzius, thought that he had discovered that the relation between the breadth and length of the brain case varied not so much between individuals as it did between different human groups or races. The proportions of the skull can be expressed numerically as the cephalic index, which is the breadth of the skull expressed as a percentage of the length. The cranial index is computed from the measurements of a skull; the cephalic index from those of a living head. The difference is usually slight. Some skulls are long and narrow and are called *dolichocephalic*. Other skulls are short and broad and are called *brachycephalic*. It is common to call skulls dolichocephalic if the index breadth/length, expressed as percentage, is below 75. We call them brachycephalic if it is over 80. Skull forms between these limits are called *mesocephalic*. Measurements of head form offer the advantage that the cephalic index seems to remain almost constant after infancy; the characteristic head form is established early in life, and therefore the cephalic index measurement could be applied to the children in a population as well as to the adults. There are cradle effects, which are perhaps usually temporary, but it is now recognized that certain forms of hard cradle produce a flattening of the occiput; and thus make the individual more brachycephalic than he would naturally be (20).

The two authors chiefly responsible for the use of the cephalic index in the establishment and definition of subdivisions of the white race were Deniker (16) and Ripley (48). The fair long-headed whites were called Nordics by Deniker, and Ripley gave the dark, roundheaded whites the name Alpine. But a French sociologist, de Lapouge (34), a German journalist, Ammon (2), and a German dentist, Röse (49), completed these characterizations by postulating, in addition, certain correlated psychic qualities. Ammon said: "The long heads [dolichocephalics] of German descent represent the bearers of higher spiritual life, the occupants of dominant positions, to which they are destined by nature, the innate defenders of the fatherland and the social order. Their whole character predetermines them to aristocracy. From purely scientific interests, to which the longheads are driven by their desire for knowledge and to which they devote all the impetus of their character, the round heads keep more aloof. Their inclination to the democratic theory of equality is due to the fact that they themselves do not exceed mediocrity and feel nothing but an aversion, if not hatred, against grandness which they cannot understand."

Weidenreich (57) points out that Ammon and Röse tried to prove that even in the same racial group the good and bad qualities — judged by their advancement in their respective careers — were correlated with higher or lower skull indices. Röse measured the heads of university people, soldiers, employees of big industrial corporations, business leaders, clerks and laborers and summarized his results in the *ex cathedra* sentence (49): "The higher the position and the greater the salary, the longer are the heads." More recently writers in Nazi Germany speculated on the color of the souls of the different white races. Günther (25) reported that the soul of the Dinaric race seemed to be a dark green. Günther was awarded the Goethe medal for art and science in 1941. Without further examination of the results of Röse and Günther, we may dismiss them as belonging to that mystical Teutonic school of anthropology which passed out of existence, we hope forever, with the end of World War II.

The claim that the Northern and Middle European longheads and roundheads represented two completely different races was first advanced by the Swedish anatomist, G. Retzius (46), and by C. M. Fürst (22). Finding that a high percentage of the modern population of Sweden was longheaded and of fair complexion, they identified the long Neolithic skulls studied by them with the Nordics and identified the round skulls as those of an alien population, probably with a dark complexion, which had migrated to Sweden from the East in increasing numbers as time went on. The mesocephalic skulls were regarded as hybrids of the longheads and the roundheads.

The identifications were based almost exclusively upon comparison of the brain cases, but to a certain extent also on metrical characters of the face, although in the case of the roundheaded Neolithic people the facial parts were mostly fragmentary and not distinct enough for much use to be made of them. It was assumed that the occurrence and distribution of these two "races" as they were found in Sweden was typical of all Northern and Middle Europe.

Archaeologists found that in Germany and Switzerland in Neolithic and early historic times, the majority of the skulls were dolichocephalic, with only a limited number of brachycephalics. But in later times the proportions became completely reversed (p. 302), so that today the overwhelming majority of the population in both countries is brachycephalic with a minority of dolichocephalics (Fig. 41). The latest and most careful anthropometric measurements in Europe show that the central European population is *not* dolichocephalic but brachycephalic to a pronounced degree. If, as was once postulated, the desirable qualities in the European racial stock belonged to the longheads and the undesirable ones to the roundheads, the European population now would be in a rather bad way.

For many years it was considered that the dolichocephalics had been replaced by brachycephalics solely as the result of Asiatic immigration, although the other observed facts did not seem to

agree with such an enormous migration as would have been necessary. Nevertheless, for many years, the substitution by immigration
theory was rather generally accepted, and it was assumed that the

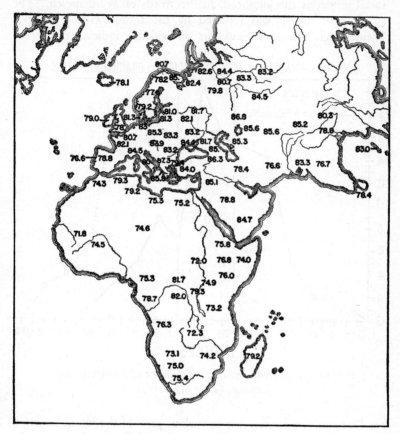

FIGURE 41. *Cranial index in Eurasia and Africa (after Gerhardt).*

brachycephalic skulls had belonged to Asiatic individuals with dark
skin and hair who had migrated into Europe in early historic times.
Weidenreich pointed out that to escape from this embarrassing
dilemma there was only one way open, which was to consider that
the roundheads were not derived entirely from foreign Asiatic

elements which had come in from outside, but had been derived by modification from people who were originally longheaded, and therefore the roundhead could be considered as having the same racial origin as the longhead. In the words of Weidenreich, "The substitution theory was replaced by the transformation theory." Weidenreich offered various bits of evidence indicating that the

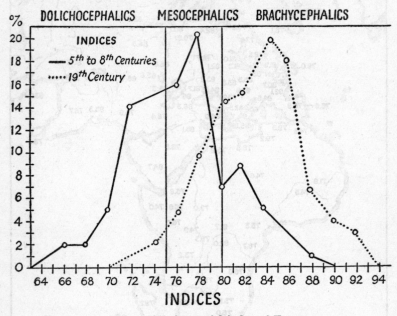

FIGURE 42. *Recent shift in cranial index of European populations (after Schwerz).*

head form of the human race in various parts of the world has been changing from dolichocephaly to brachycephaly and is apparently still changing today. This is illustrated in Figure 42 (56). Weidenreich does not offer any evolutionary cause for this transformation but if we examine the list of possible evolutionary forces cited in Chapter V I think we can conclude that the most likely force is selection, although at certain times and in certain places other agencies may also have operated.

Today many recognize (11, 29, 56, 57) that a definite process of brachycephalization has been going on in Europe, probably aided by other factors in addition to whatever influx of genes immigrants from Asia may have carried; and it is no longer necessary to suppose that the early brachycephalics were all dark skinned and dark haired. For all we know, they may have had hair which was fair or dark, perhaps ranging from flaxen and platinum to dark blond.

It is not hard to see why early anthropologists picked upon the skull as a means of racial classification. The skull is exceedingly durable, so that it is often found in a fair state of preservation when the rest of the body, including the remainder of the skeleton, has disappeared. Also the skull, by its conformation, offers the opportunity of making numerous measurements with a fairly high degree of precision, whether or not we know what these measurements mean. The characteristics of the skull were selected, not because there was any proof that they were uniquely fitted to distinguish one race from another, but simply because there were a lot of skulls in various burial places and (eventually) in most museums. Also the fact that the skull contains the brain, the seat of intelligence, may have helped convince early anthropologists that the skull would be of more value in distinguishing the ethnic origin and innate abilities of different sorts of men than would other parts of the body. Actually there is little evidence which indicates that this is true.

Are Skulls the Key?

Even if we grant that, after all, human skulls must tell us *something* about their former owners, we must keep in mind certain elementary fallacies which have clouded the logic of some of our predecessors. Weidenreich (57) points out that skulls cannot really be separated sharply into three classes — dolichocephalic, mesocephalic, and brachycephalic. A separation *is* made, but it is entirely arbitrary, and actually each of these categories runs into the other without any break. We can therefore set up any arbitrary limits we like which enable us to decide what we wish to consider a medium head, a longhead, or a roundhead. The mechanism of inheritance of skull form, although skull shape must be at least partially determined by heredity, has never been completely worked out. It seems certain, however (3), that skull form is determined by a number of different genes, and therefore we cannot treat brachycephaly and dolichocephaly as if they were the result of a single Mendelian pair of genes. Authors who have attempted to do so have obtained conflicting results; some have found brachycephaly dominant to dolichocephaly, but others could not confirm this. It has been found that inherited or constitutional factors, such as the gene for polydactyly (26), may influence the shape of the head. Godin (24) believed that in the majority of cases the shape of the child's head was determined by that of the mother. Baur, Fischer, and Lenz (3) have pointed out that identical cephalic indices might result from quite different conformations of various cranial bones which in turn might be due to entirely different genes. Some authors seem to have confused the increase in incidence of brachycephaly in Europe in historic times with proof that brachycephaly is determined by a dominant gene. Similar proposals have been made for the New World. To one of the exhibits in the Mesa Verde Museum in Colorado is attached a legend which reads: "The Pueblo Indians appear to have been the direct descendants of the Basket Makers. Although the shape of the skull was radically different this is believed to have resulted from two causes.

"(1) [Effects of a hard cradle.]

"(2) Natural dominance of round headedness over long headedness. Because of this trait the round-headed Basket Makers, even though in the minority, would cause the heads gradually to broaden as they inter-married with the long-headed members of the tribe."

Again the insidious idea of genophagy comes out! This passage could never have been written by anybody familiar with the concepts of genetic equilibrium (Ch. IV).

Craniometry

It is now pretty well recognized that from the measurement of the cephalic index alone it is impossible to distinguish different races. If a number of measurements are made on the skull it is possible to make some distinctions, as is shown in Table 38, but it will be noticed that even when a large number of measurements are made, the distinction is not absolute and a number of characteristics

TABLE 38 (From 33)

Distinguishing Races by Skull Characters

Character	Caucasoid (white)			Mongoloid (yellow)	Negroid (black)
	Nordic (North European)	Alpine (Central European)	Mediterranean (S. European)		
Skull length	Long	Short	Long	Short	Long
Skull breadth	Narrow	Broad	Narrow	Broad	Narrow
Skull height	High	High	Moderately high	Middle	Low
Sagittal contour	Rounded	Arched	Rounded	Arched	Flat
Face breadth	Narrow	Wide	Narrow	Very wide	Narrow
Face height	High	High	Moderately high	High	Low
Orbital opening	Angular	Rounded	Angular	Rounded	Rectangular
Nasal opening	Narrow	Moderately wide	Narrow	Narrow	Wide
Lower nasal margin	Sharp	Sharp	Sharp	Sharp	"Troughed" or "guttered"
Facial profile	Straight	Straight	Straight	Straight	Downward slant
Palate shape	Narrow	Moderately wide	Narrow	Moderately wide	Wide
General impression	Massive, rugged, elongate, ovoid	Large, moderately rugged, rounded	Small, smooth, elongate, pentagonoid to ovoid	Large, smooth, rounded	Massive, smooth, elongate, constricted oval

must be determined, none of which is known to be inherited in a Mendelian manner. Krogman believes that it should be possible to distinguish basic divisions of mankind, such as white from yellow, yellow from black, and white from black, with a reasonable degree of accuracy. However, Howells (29) is content to assert merely that the trained eye can generally spot the narrow, poorly filled skull of the Australian aborigine with its large brows and small chin, or the wide face and peculiar high-pitched cranium of the Eskimo, or the long, straight face of the European. He admits that Negroes, American Indians, and Mongoloids are generally hard to distinguish. The uncertain genetic basis of skull form and the possible effects of the environment upon them has been recognized by Coon (11), who states: "We must also remember that the men who conquered the cold lived under new and rigorous climatic and dietary conditions and that these conditions must have exerted a strong influence upon the more plastic elements of their bodily form. Therefore metrical or morphological differences in physical type which appear during the course of the millennia, may imply in some instances a response to environment rather than a diversity of origin."

The shape of the head has been found to be influenced by environmental factors such as vitamin lack (21, 41), use of hard cradles, etc. The studies of Boas (5) on the effect of environment on head form have already been mentioned. His conclusions were criticized by Morant and Samson (40), although in his reply (6) Boas convinces us that many of their criticisms were not to be taken too seriously.

In a more recent study which will be much harder to "debunk," Shapiro (50) found that there were real and impressive changes in the cephalic index in the Japanese in Hawaii after only one generation. His studies indicated that the male Hawaiian-born showed a difference in cephalic index from the male immigrant of 2.60, which is more than 6 times the standard error (this term is defined in Appendix A).

Shapiro also found significant changes in at least 21 different measurements, including weight, length of the lower arm, length of the hand, total leg length, chest width, total face length, trunk height, and so forth. He concluded that it was necessary to recognize the dynamic, plastic character of the human organism and, by logical extension, the plastic character of human populations.

Nasal Index

The nasal index (breadth of the nose × 100, divided by the height of the nose) (37) has long been used as one of the means of distinguishing races. It is probably a highly adaptive character (15, 55), however, and its mode of inheritance is still far from clear (23).

Hair Form

The form of human hair has long attracted the attention of observers, and Pruner-Bey (45) states that Greek authors constantly used words denoting different hair form when writing about different peoples. However, the variations in hair form visible to the naked eye are rather hard to describe or record with precision, so it was felt by many that a great advance had been made when Pruner-Bey (45) in a paper read before the Anthropological Society of Paris in 1863 reported the results of the microscopic study of transverse sections of human hair. This worker thought that he had detected significant racial differences in the shape of the cross section of the hairs, and a correlation between this and the hair form as we see it with the naked eye. He stated that the flatter the hair the more it curls, and the rounder the hair, the more stiff and smooth it will be. On one end of the scale he placed the Negroes and Papuans, and on the other the Polynesians, Japanese, and American Indians. Many intergradations between the two extremes were thought to exist. Pruner-Bey went so far as to say, "A single hair, presenting the average form characteristic of the race, might serve to define it."

Unfortunately Pruner-Bey worked with very small samples, and evidently did not appreciate either the variation from one individual to another within the same race, or the individual variations in the separate hairs of the same person. Few today would be so optimistic about the use of hair form in racial classification, although it is still used (27) to some extent. Also the difficulty of obtaining satisfactory microscopic sections of hairs for measurement is much greater than would have been supposed, and this severely limits the usefulness of the method.

But as usual, the most serious limitation is our lack of understanding of the heredity of the character. No doubt it is largely determined by genes, but we still must ask what genes, and how many? Are these genes dominant, neutral, or recessive? The mechanism of inheritance of hair form has been studied by Keers (31), the Davenports (14), and Bean (4), but the analysis is still far from complete. It is therefore impossible to compare different populations quantitatively for this characteristic. Woolly hair has been observed to arise as a mutation in families of Caucasian descent, and in such cases seems to act as a simple dominant. It would therefore be increased rapidly in incidence by the action of natural selection (Chap. VII) in an environment in which it offered an advantage. Perhaps under certain conditions kinky hair does offer a selective advantage.

Pigmentation

Skin color has been used for purposes of racial classification for a very long time; nevertheless the exact manner in which it is inherited is still in doubt (3, 23). Skin color is due mainly to the presence of the black pigment melanin in greater or less concentrations, the yellow pigment carotene, and the red blood in the superficial capillaries (18, 28). The production and deposition of melanin in the skin is influenced partly by hormones of the adrenal cortex, and to a considerable extent by exposure to light, particularly light of certain wave lengths. The only accurate way of recording skin color is the spectrophotometric method, which was used by Edwards and Duntley (19). (See Fig. 43.)

In view of these facts, it is hardly to be supposed that the inheritance of total skin color can be extremely simple, and the studies which have been made up to the present have not as yet revealed the hereditary mechanism. The most extensive work was done by Davenport (12), who, having studied chiefly the varying blackness of different skins, proposed the relatively simple theory that skin color is controlled by two pairs of cumulative factors. If we follow Davenport (12) and denote the genes producing heavy deposits of melanin as G and F, expressing the alleles which produce only slight deposits as *g* and *f*, we have the possible combinations shown in Figure 44. From this it would be predicted that a mating of black and white would always produce mulattoes of quite uniform skin color. Mating among such mulattoes could theoretically sometimes produce children darker than either parent (children obtaining *G*

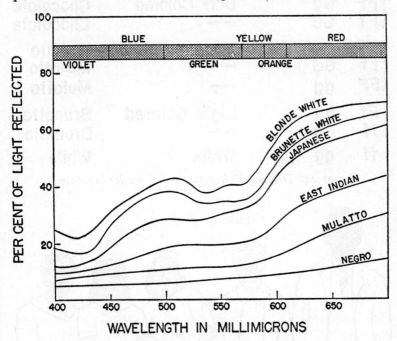

FIGURE 43. *Photospectrometric analysis of the skin color of various races (after Edwards and Duntley).*

from one parent and *F* from another). Relatively simple cases of segregation for skin color have in fact been sometimes observed in South Africa (23). But in other mixed populations authenticated cases are practically non-existent (54). Probably more than two gene pairs are usually involved. Results of a typical American Negro mating are shown in Figure 45.

Davenport did not think he had found any clear-cut cases of "throwbacks" in mixed marriages in which the parents were apparently white. The inhabitants of Jamaica, where this study was

Genotype		Skin Color According To	
		Davenport	Glass
FF	GG	Black	Black
FF	Gg	Dark Colored	Chocolate
Ff	GG	—	Chocolate
Ff	Gg	Medium Colored	Mulatto
ff	GG	—	Mulatto
FF	gg	—	Mulatto
Ff	gg	Light Colored	Brunette
ff	Gg	—	Brunette
ff	gg	White	White

FIGURE 44. *Davenport's hypothesis of skin color inheritance.*

FIGURE 45. *Skin color in a typical American Negro family.*

chiefly carried out, agreed that the idea of such throwbacks was probably a myth. Davenport also points out the possibility that illegitimacy might explain supposed reversions to a much darker skin color; from his genetic hypothesis he did not think genetic reversion could actually occur at all frequently. Davenport found no evidence that there was any correlation between skin color and hair form in later generations derived from Negro-white crosses. Thus the two "Negroid" traits are inherited independently, as would be expected.

Eye Color

It is one of the oldest observations that the color of the iris differs in populations in different parts of the world, and physical anthropologists have usually recorded the eye color of the populations studied by them. The records have varied from mere verbal descriptions of the eyes (47), or numerical estimation on some arbitrary scale of the degree of pigmentation (7, 47), to matching of the eyes examined as nearly as possible to a graded series of artificial eyes (37). Color photography has been used also. All of these methods suffer from some disadvantages, but at the same time all serve to provide some record of the iris pigmentation of the population examined. As an example of the results of recording the eye color of various populations in a very simple, although doubtless very crude, fashion, we offer in Table 39 a summary of eye color studies on various European and Near Eastern populations, where considerable variation is found. In studies on Negroes or American Indians the lighter grades of eye color are seldom encountered.

One of the questions which is desirable to answer, of course, is the mechanism of inheritance of human eye color. If this were known, studies of gene frequencies in various populations might enable us to make quantitative comparisons. However, the exact mechanism by which human eye color is inherited has not yet been worked out, and it is obviously rather complex. Certain facts are known or at least suspected. There is a sex difference in eye color. Color often darkens with age; and women of a given age tend to have darker eyes than men of the same age in many populations; for instance, Riddell (47), studying eye color in Glasgow, estimated that a woman there had, on the average, an eye color that of a male about twenty-nine years older. It is also believed that pure blue eyes

TABLE 39 (From 7, 8, 9)

Frequency in Per Cent of Eye Pigmentation

Place	Number Tested		Per Cent Having Eye Pigmentation of Grade *			
			1	2	3	4
Irish (Dublin)	Males	24	50.0	12.5	29.2	8.3
	Females	360	34.7	27.5	30.6	7.2
Wales (N. Towns)	Males	102	40.2	21.6	35.3	2.9
	Females	88	28.4	29.5	33.0	9.1
Russia (Zagorsk,	Males	197	32.5	37.1	22.8	7.6
N. Moscow)	Females	290	32.4	37.9	24.5	5.2
Russia (Kharkov)	Males	65	15.4	43.1	29.2	12.3
	Females	120	28.3	28.3	34.2	9.2
Russia (Tiflis)						
(West Georgians)	Males	121	7.4	12.4	47.1	33.1
	Females	124	4.0	15.3	50.0	30.7
(East Georgians)	Males	63	0	17.5	55.5	27.0
	Females	71	1.4	8.5	45.1	45.0
Egypt (Cairo)	Males	52	0	7.7	28.8	63.5
Copts	Females	53	1.9	0	13.2	84.9
Muslims	Males	264	0.8	5.3	15.1	78.8
	Females	217	0.5	2.8	14.7	82.0
Egypt (Assiut)	Males	192	0	1.5	25.0	73.5
Copts	Females	199	0	1.5	23.1	75.4
Muslims	Males	43	0	0	29.4	70.6
	Females	48	2.1	2.1	18.8	77.0
Spain (San Sebastián)						
Basque	Males	25	8.0	20.0	60.0	12.0
	Females	53	17.0	20.7	58.5	3.8
Non-Basques	Males	17	11.8	5.9	76.4	5.9
	Females	45	0	15.6	62.2	22.2
Syria (Boarij)						
Muslims	Males	68	7.4	13.2	75.0	4.4
	Females	60	10.0	20.0	68.3	1.7
Syria (Meshghara)						
Christians	Males	89	4.5	16.8	74.2	4.5
	Females	17	5.9	11.8	64.7	17.6
Muslims	Males	142	10.6	13.4	69.7	6.3
	Females	67	4.5	9.0	76.1	10.4
Beyrouth and Ghazir						
(Armenians)	Males	142	2.1	12.7	77.5	7.7
	Females	155	6.5	8.4	70.3	14.8
Baghdad						
(Christians)	Males	48	2.1	4.2	62.5	31.2
	Females	15	6.7	0	53.3	40.0
(Muslims)	Males	236	0.8	4.2	61.9	33.1
	Females	136	0	3.7	41.2	55.2
(Jews)	Males	60	5.0	5.0	31.7	58.3
	Females	132	2.3	3.0	21.2	73.5

* Eye pigmentation is given in four arbitrary grades, grade 4 being the darkest.

are recessive to darker eyes, an analogy with what is known about the tendency of the darker degrees of pigmentation to be dominant in animals, and this belief has often been stated as a demonstrated fact; nevertheless, it is far from being proved beyond a doubt. The inheritance of other degrees of pigmentation is still obscure, although certain tentative theories have been proposed (p. 286). The change in color with age, and the sex difference in pigmentation, are alone sufficient to render an exact genetic analysis difficult. The difficulties of recording eye color in an unequivocal and reproducible manner further complicate the subject.

Eye color furnishes a good example of the undeveloped state of human genetics. Few anthropological studies meet less opposition than an examination of the eyes to determine their color, and many workers have made such examinations in the course of their investigations. What seems to be needed is a study of a sufficient number of families in the light of definite, although tentative, theories about the hereditary mechanism. Then, as the first crude hypotheses are disproved, more refined ones can be introduced and the method of classification altered accordingly, if such alteration seems to be needed. Eventually the moment will come when it is realized that the newest theory accounts satisfactorily for all the known facts. If this time should come in the near future, eye color classification will at once move far up towards the head of the list of characters useful for anthropological classification.

The Mongolian Spot

The so-called Mongolian or sacral spot is a black-and-blue mark found on the lower part of the back of infants and young children of all, probably, of the racial groups in which the skin has much pigmentation (3, 23). It is thus not specifically a Mongolian characteristic, but is observed not only among Koreans, Chinese, Japanese, Eskimo and American Indians, but also often among Negroes, Spaniards, Portuguese, the peoples of the Malay Peninsula and in Polynesians. It seems to be found sometimes in the "white" races. Perrier (44) ascribes its incidence in European children to the great Asiatic invasions of Attila in the fifth century, of Genghis Khan in the twelfth, and of Tamerlane in the fourteenth. This compares in an interesting way with Candela's theory of the introduction of blood group gene B into Europe (see p. 116). A theory of inheritance of the sacral spot, based on two pairs of genes, has been formulated by Larsen and Godfrey (35). It accounts for the results observed in their study of 473 children from various mixed matings. Gates (23), however, believes that large-scale observations of many races and racial crosses will be required to make the genetics of the character fully understood.

The Epicanthic Eye Fold

The peculiarity of the eyelid of certain Mongoloids, causing the so-called "slant eyes," and covering the eyelashes, seems to be hereditary, although it is undoubtedly more frequent in children — at least in many Mongoloid populations — than in the older adults. In most European populations the Mongolian epicanthic eye fold is almost completely absent, as in Germany and Italy. Nevertheless, a considerable frequency of blood group gene *B,* which presumably came from Asiatics who originally possessed the epicanthic fold, is present. In these populations genes for the epicanthic eye fold are therefore presumably present, unless they have been eliminated by selection, and since we have no reason to think this character is a disadvantageous one, it is not likely that they have. Since the epicanthic eye fold is so seldom seen in Europe, we must conclude either that it is due to a recessive gene, and only manifests itself in the homozygote, or that it is the result of the interaction of a number of independent genes, which have got independently assorted in the dilute (from the Mongoloid point of view) populations of Europe. The latter alternative is perhaps the more probable.

General Summary

A great many more pages could be written on the difficulties of genetic analysis of morphological and other characteristics which have been previously used or proposed for purposes of racial classification. We have not, for instance, discussed hair color. It is pointed out by Mather (38) that the biometrical studies made in man by Galton, Pearson, and their associates have disclosed a wealth of variation suggestive of a polygenetic interpretation of the inheritance of many common characteristics. If a number of genes are involved in determining a characteristic and if, in addition, as often happens with morphological characteristics, the environment may also have an effect, the difficulties of exact genetic analysis become extremely great, especially in man, where one cannot perform breeding experiments at will but must examine the consequences of marriages and unions voluntarily or incidentally contracted. Without exact genetic analysis we are not in a position to state how much one group differs from another group.

As an example of the complexity which may possibly be encountered when a genetic analysis of morphological characters is eventually attempted, it may be instructive to take an actual case. Alvord (1) undertook the analysis of two unrelated families, both of which displayed in some of their members syndactyly (skeletal fusions between phalanges in hands and feet) or zygodactyly (webbed digits), or both. Six generations including more than 350 "direct line" descendants of one of the families were studied. It was concluded that, although the trait has ordinarily been assumed to be transmitted as a simple autosomal dominant, the mechanism of inheritance is actually much more complex. Alvord concluded that there were probably numerous "modifying factors" operating, some apparently influenced by sex, and that the mechanism of inheritance of the abnormality was not necessarily the same in the two families. In addition, rather marked differences in the expression of the gene (or genes) were found, so that some phenotypically normal members could transmit zygodactyly or syndactyly or both, and polydactyly could be transmitted through an individual who was non-polydactyl but zygodactyl, and so on, suggesting that the different manifestations are essentially interchangeable, and may possibly result from variable effects on the development of the phalanges in different individuals.

This difference in "expressivity" of what *may be* the same main gene illustrates one of the difficulties which may be encountered when we try to reduce the results of any of the customary morphological or biometrical observations to a genetic basis. Also Alvord suggested that a number of *different* genes may affect the developing digits in a similar or even an identical fashion. Considering the relatively extensive family material studied in this instance, and the striking nature of the characteristic being studied, it is a lesson in caution to realize that the author did not presume to offer anything like a complete genetic analysis of this undoubtedly hereditary physical characteristic. Nevertheless, until this has been done, as Alvord fully realized, the results of studies on different families cannot be strictly compared, and thus the character would not be of much anthropological value, even if it were frequent enough in any ethnic groups known to us, which it is not.

Although the attempts which have been made thus far to analyze hereditary characteristics of man have almost invariably revealed a situation which is complex and difficult to reduce to a clear statement about the action or interaction of several genes in various environments, this need not always be the case. On the contrary, it might well be that thoroughgoing attempts to discover the genetic basis for some of the bodily traits which we could use for classification would uncover some fairly simple examples of gene action. No proved example from human genetics can be offered, but there are examples in some of the lower forms, and we have no reason to suppose that analogous situations could not exist in man.

A good example is furnished by hereditary obesity in the mouse (17), of which one kind is caused by one particular gene (which happens to produce yellow coat color also). General bodily obesity in man might well prove a genetically complex trait, and doubtless there are a number of other hereditary types of obesity in mice. In this particular instance, however, the gene is detectable by the yellow coat color which it produces even in the heterozygous condition.

It was found that the possession merely of the "yellow" gene (or whatever portion of the particular chromosome which has been identified as this gene) caused marked obesity. The physiological mechanism seemed to be a slight increase of appetite, a slightly reduced activity, and a considerably greater efficiency of food utilization. That somewhat analogous genes affecting body weight in man exist can hardly be doubted; the only uncertainty is whether any such *simple* situation can be found. In the meantime, however, anthropologists should continue to take a hopeful view of the possibility of identifying characteristics which are caused in man by the possession of a single gene. Characteristics which seem to vary in frequency in different ethnic groups exposed to the same environment should furnish the greatest temptation to the genetically minded physical anthropologist.

The "somatotypes" of Sheldon (52), although established arbitrarily and apparently with little thought of what genetic mechanism determines them, furnish examples of human physical characteristics which the physical anthropologist of the future might attempt to analyze genetically. As a preliminary to this, of course, we should want a survey of the types of physique in various races.

If we had any known example of a common characteristic which definitely rendered an individual superior or inferior to all of his fellows, and which was known to be inherited, it would obviously be imperative to work out the genetics of this characteristic, and this has been done in some cases.* The present evidence, however, does not suggest that any existing human race differs materially, on the average, from any other human race in regard to any such important characteristic as intelligence, adaptability, or ability to survive in various climates with suitable artificial aids. It is true that human intelligence seems to (and probably does) vary enormously from one individual to another, but similar variations are apparently found in all the races with which we are acquainted. Such studies as have been made in some cases suggested that the incidence of inherited mental defect is lower in the "uncivilized" races than in the "civilized" peoples (23). Individuals of genius have arisen from all sorts of racial origins, but as yet we know little or nothing of the genetics of the inheritance of "genius," which is almost certain to prove a fairly complex matter.

Without genetic analysis of a characteristic, there is always the possibility that two groups of men exhibiting about the same visible or external characteristics may nevertheless differ genetically a good deal, for, as has already been pointed out, different genes may sometimes produce practically the same end effect (1). A good example of this is furnished by the several different mechanisms by which suppression of the eruption of the upper lateral incisors is ef-

---

* *Phenylpyruvic amentia* (43), *mongolian idiocy* (36, 42), and *other characters* (see 23).

fected (51). Drawing conclusions as to racial affinities from the study of similar characteristics not inherited in the same manner, or for that matter, similar characteristics the mode of whose inheritance is not known, can be very misleading in physical anthropology. The experiment of Dixon (p. 194) again furnishes us with a good example of this.

As a possible guide to further work, let us end with a summary of the supposed genetic relationships of factors determining certain morphological characteristics. The indicated conclusions are of course to the highest degree tentative and hypothetical. All of the characters listed belong in the category of the incompletely analyzed hereditary characteristics.

TABLE 40

Mendelian Characteristics in Man (10)

Dominant	Recessive
Skin, Hair, Nails, Teeth	
Black skin (two genes, incomplete dominance)	"White" skin
Piebald (skin and hair spotted with white)	Self color
White forelock	Self color
Dark hair (several genes)	Light hair
Non-red hair	Red hair
Dark skin (several genes)	White skin
Freckles	No freckles
Pigmented skin, hair, eyes	Albino
Curly hair (hybrid, wavy)	Straight hair
Woolly hair (Negroid type; several genes)	Straight hair
Woolly hair (Caucasoid type)	Non-woolly hair
Abundant body hair	Little body hair
Normal	Hairless (Hypotrichosis)
Hairlessness (congenital hypotrichosis)	Normal
Early baldness (dominant in male)	Normal
Scaly skin (Ichthyosis)	Normal
Thickened skin (Tylosis)	Normal
Absent teeth (various types)	Normal
Defective dentin (opalescent teeth)	Normal
Free ear lobes	Adherent ear lobes

TABLE 40 (*Continued*)

Mendelian Characteristics in Man (10)

Dominant	Recessive
Eyes	
Brown	Blue or gray
Hazel or green	Blue or gray
Pigmented iris	Albino
"Mongolian fold"	No fold
Drooping eyelids (Ptosis)	Normal
Nearsightedness (Myopia) (curvature of cornea too great)	Normal
Normal	Nearsightedness
Farsightedness (Hyperopia) (short eyeball)	Normal
Astigmatism (cornea not spherical)	Normal
Cataract (opaque lens)	Normal
Glaucoma (excessive pressure in eyeball)	Normal
Skeleton and Muscles	
Short stature (several genes)	Tall stature
Dwarfism (Achondroplasia)	Normal
Midget (Ateliosis) (two genes?)	Normal
Short broad skull (several genes)	Long narrow skull
Extra digits (Polydactyly)	Normal
Short digits (Brachydactyly)	Normal
Split hand ("lobster claw")	Normal
Hare lip and cleft palate (also a recessive?)	Normal
Rupture, susceptibility to	Normal
Absent long palmar muscle	Normal
Circulatory and Respiratory Systems	
Hemolytic jaundice	Normal
Nosebleed and blood cysts (Telangiectases)	Normal
Varicose veins and hemorrhoids	Normal
Hereditary dropsy (Edema)	Normal
High blood pressure (Hypertension)	Normal
Allergy	Normal
Resistance to tuberculosis	Susceptibility to T.B.
Excretory System	
Polycystic kidney	Normal
Diabetes insipidus	Normal

TABLE 40 (*Continued*)

Mendelian Characteristics in Man (10)

Dominant	Recessive
Endocrine Glands	
Diabetes mellitus	Normal
Digestive System	
Normal	Pyloric stenosis
Ulcers (mode of inheritance uncertain)	
Enlarged colon (Hirschsprung's disease)	Normal
Reproductive System	
Hypospadias	Normal
Cancers and Other Malignant Tumors	
Normal	Xeroderma pigmentosum
von Recklinghausen's disease	Normal
Cancer of the stomach (?)	Normal
Normal	Retinal glioma
Nervous System	
Tasters	Non-tasters
Normal	Congenital deafness
Auditory nerve atrophy	Normal
Otosclerosis	Normal
Normal (mild type dominant)	Muscular atrophy
Normal	Spinal ataxia
Paralysis agitans	Normal
Huntington's chorea	Normal
Normal (mild type dominant)	Feeble-mindedness
Normal	Amaurotic idiocy
Normal	Schizophrenia
Manic-depressive psychoses	Normal

Special Talents (*Dominance Uncertain*)
Musical ability
Ability in drawing, painting, sculpture
Mathematical ability

REFERENCES FOR CHAPTER XI

1. Alvord, R. M., *J. Heredity, 38*, 49–53 (1947).
2. Ammon, O., *Die Natürliche Auslese beim Menschen.* Verlag von Gustav Fischer, Jena, 1893.
3. Baur, E., E. Fischer, and F. Lenz, *Menschliche Erblichkeitslehre.* J. F. Lehmanns Verlag, München, 1927.
4. Bean, R. B., *Am. Nat., 45,* 524–536 (1911).
5. Boas, F., *Race, Language and Culture.* Macmillan Co., New York, 1940.
6. Boas, F., *Am. Anthrop., 42,* 183–189 (1940).
7. Boyd, W. C., and L. G. Boyd, *A.J.P.A., 23,* 49–70 (1937).
8. Boyd, W. C., and L. G. Boyd, *Human Biol., 13,* 398–404 (1941).
9. Boyd, W. C., and L. G. Boyd, *A. J. P. A., 28,* 319–330 (1941).
10. Colin, E. C., *Elements of Genetics.* Blakiston Co., Philadelphia, 1946.
11. Coon, C. S., *The Races of Europe.* Macmillan Co., New York, 1939.
12. Davenport, C. B., Carnegie Inst. Wash. Pub. No. 188, 1–106 (1913).
13. Davenport, C. B., *Genetics, 2,* 313–389 (1917).
14. Davenport, G. C., and C. B. Davenport, *Am. Nat., 42,* 341–349 (1908).
15. Davies, A., *J. Roy. Anthrop. Inst., 62,* 337–359 (1932).
16. Deniker, J., *Les races et les peuples de la terre.* Paris, 1900.
17. Dickie, M. M., and G. W. Wooley, *J. Heredity, 37,* 365–368 (1946).
18. Dummett, C. O., *J. Dental Res., 25,* 421–432 (1946).
19. Edwards, E. A., and S. Q. Duntley, *Am. J. Anat., 65,* 1–33 (1939).
20. Ehrich, R. W., and C. S. Coon, *A. J. P. A., 6,* 181–186 (1948).
21. Fischer, E., cited by Baur, Fischer, and Lenz, 1924.
22. Fürst, C. M., *K. svensk. vetensk. handl. Stockholm, 49,* 1–77 (1912).
23. Gates, R. R., *Human Genetics.* Macmillan Co., New York, 1946.
24. Godin, P., *Bull. Soc. Pediat. Paris, 30,* 274–277 (1932).
25. Günther, H., *Rassenkunde des deutschen Volkes,* München, 1922.
26. Günther, H. F. K., cited by Baur, Fischer, and Lenz, 1930.
27. Haddon, A. C., *The Races of Man.* Macmillan Co., New York, 1925.
28. Hooton, E. A., *Up from the Ape.* Macmillan Co., New York, 1946.
29. Howells, W. W., *Mankind So Far.* Doubleday, Doran & Co., Inc., Garden City, New York, 1944.
30. Huntington, E., *The Mainsprings of Civilization.* John Wiley & Sons, Inc., New York, 1945.
31. Keers, W., *Arch. f. Rass.-Biol., 27,* 362–389 (1934).
32. Krogman, W. M., *Eugenical News, 21,* 139–146 (1936).
33. Krogman, W. M., *F. B. I. Law Enforc. Bull., 8,* No. 8, 1–29 (1939).
34. Lapouge, G. V. De, *L'aryen, son rôle social.* Paris, 1899.
35. Larsen, N. R., and L. S. Godfrey, *A. J. P. A., 10,* 253–274 (1927).
36. Macklin, M. T., *Am. J. Med. Sci., 178,* 315–337 (1929).

37. Martin, R., *Lehrbuch der Anthropologie*. Verlag von Gustav Fischer, Jena, 1928.

38. Mather, K., *Biol. Rev., 18,* 32–64 (1943).

39. Morant, G. M., *Biometrika, 31,* 72–98 (1939).

40. Morant, G. M., and O. Samson, *Biometrika, 28,* 1–31 (1936).

41. Neubauer, cited by Baur, Fischer, and Lenz, 1925.

42. Penrose, L. S., *J. Genetics, 27,* 219–224 (1933).

43. Penrose, L. S., *Lancet, 229,* 192–194 (1935).

44. Perrier, H., *Rev. Méd. de la Suisse Romande, 46,* 252–253 (1925).

45. Pruner-Bey, *Anthrop. Rev., 2,* 1–23 (1864).

46. Retzius, G., *Crania suecica antiqua*. Stockholm, 1900.

47. Riddell, W. J. B., *Ann. Eug., 2,* 245–259 (1942).

48. Ripley, W. Z., *The Races of Europe; A Sociological Study*. D. Appleton & Co., New York, 1899.

49. Röse, C., *Arch. Rassen-u. Ges.-Biol., 2,* 689–798; *3,* 42–134 (1905, 1906).

50. Shapiro, H. L., *Migration and Environment*. Oxford Univ. Press, London, New York, and Toronto, 1939.

51. Schultz, A. H., *Human Biol., 6,* 627–631 (1934).

52. Sheldon, W. H., *et al., The Varieties of Human Physique*. Harper & Bros., New York, and London, 1940.

53. Simpson, G. G., *Tempo and Mode in Evolution,* Columbia Univ. Press, New York, 1944.

54. Stern, C., *J. Heredity, 38,* 233–234 (1947).

55. Thomson, A., and L. H. D. Buxton, *J. Roy. Anthrop. Inst., 53,* 92–122 (1923).

56. Weidenreich, F., *Southwest. J. Anthrop., 1,* 1–54 (1945).

57. Weidenreich, F., *Apes, Giants, and Man*. Univ. Chicago Press, Chicago, 1946.

CHAPTER XII **Man's Past**

> What song the Syrens sang, or what name Achilles assumed
> when he hid himself among women, although puzzling ques-
> tions, are not beyond all conjecture.
>   —SIR THOMAS BROWNE, "Hydriotaphia"

SINCE we are concerned, as anthropologists, with the evolution
of man (p. 131), we must now inquire: How much can we learn
of the history of human races, using "race" in the genetic sense?
What methods are at our disposal in attempting to answer the
question?

Materials Available

The materials available to us are of two classes: a) observations
on the present geographical distribution of human races and the
genetic traits we have used in defining them, and b), information
which may be obtained from an examination of ancient human
remains, particularly skeletons. From the first sort of information
we may attempt to reconstruct the geographical distribution of races
in the past, making certain assumptions about the mechanisms
which have been responsible for bringing about the present distributions. From the second sort of information we may try to ascertain some at least of the racial features of skeletons and other
remains which are found at various parts of the earth's surface.

Neither of these procedures is new, and neither differs in any
essential way from the procedures of those physical anthropologists
who relied on purely morphological criteria.

It is altogether likely that the most important means for reconstructing early human history will always be method a), inference
of past distributions from the present situation. In this respect we

can greatly amplify the work of the morphologists, because the characters we detect are clear-cut, "all or none" factors inherited in a known manner. Our speculations, guided by the laws of heredity and evolution (Chs. II and V) can be much more precise and in all probability better founded. In our reconstructions of past situations, we can take into account the number of genes contributed by various populations, and avoid errors which might result from careless assumptions that physical characters can spread in the same way cultural characteristics can. Also, we are not completely debarred from obtaining some information about ancient remains (p. 247).

Scarcity of Fossil Remains

Any idea that human prehistory can be reconstructed from an examination of fossil remains is an *ignis fatuus*. There aren't enough fossil bones.

Let us consider the fossil remains of the horse, the course of whose evolution is pretty well understood. We are in possession of a relatively large number of skeletal remains of this animal, representing various stages of evolution. And yet the material we have is a pathetically small fraction of what once existed in the form of living animals. Using conservative figures for the numbers of individuals and generations, it has been calculated that if all the horses that have ever lived, from *Hyracotherium* (*Eohippus*) to *Equus,* were to form a parade 75 miles wide and walk steadily, as close together as possible, at a speed of 6 miles per hour, they would require 90 years to pass the reviewing stand (20).

Or, to put it another way, a pile of photographs, one of each horse, on paper of the thickness on which this book is printed, would be about *10 million miles high*. No one knows how many thousands of fossilized specimens have reached museums, but certainly not over one horse in several million has survived the hazards of burial, fossilization, solution in rock, removal by erosion, and failure to be discovered. For other groups, such as early Tertiary primates, in which we are more interested here, the museum expectation is destined to be much lower, perhaps of the order of one chance in 10^{10} or 10^{15} (20). To the non-mathematical reader, we can only remark that these are very small chances indeed, very much less than the chance that he will some day be struck by lightning.

The remains of early man are much scarcer than those of early horses. Therefore, we cannot expect to find a complete line of fossils connecting the present-day races of man with their original ancestors. Naturally, if it were possible, we should like to trace the descent of man back without a break to the earliest primates. But the situation at present seems to be so unsatisfactory that we cannot definitely assert that we have found skeletons older than 25,000 years of *any* of the ancestors of any of the human races which now live in the various parts of the earth. It is true that certain anthropologists (32) have thought that they detected a Chinese flavor in some of the ancient skulls found in the caves near Peking, but others (18, 25) utterly disagree with this. Dobzhansky (8) says, "Whether the Peking and Java men were specifically, or only racially, distinct from the Neanderthalians, is an open question." The general picture which emerges is that *Homo sapiens* as a stock is a good deal older than was suggested until recently, and Neanderthal man may, or may not be, as old. And as we shall see, there is evidence that some mixing may have occurred between the two variants.

The Size of Human Populations

We appreciate the special difficulties of trying to fill in the gaps in the record of human ancestry when we realize that there is every reason to believe that until fairly recently, geologically speaking, man was a relatively rare animal. Some years ago, Pearl and Gould (26), in a very interesting essay on world population growth, discussed several hypotheses as to the numbers of men existing in the past. They came to the conclusion that in all probability the numbers of human beings in the whole world remained on the whole below the level of 425 million until about the year 1630, and although they realized that the existing skeletal remains are inadequate to enable us to make certain that populations larger than their "base line" of 425 million might not possibly have existed in the past, they considered it unlikely. After the year 1630 a sharp increase in the world's population began, which has continued until the present time. This phenomenon was explained by Pearl and Gould as being due partly to the new discoveries of relatively uninhabited areas of the earth, and the development of new discoveries and new ideas which made it possible for man to exploit, much more effectively than he had known how to do before, the natural resources which were inherent in the earth on which he lived. Increasing facility of communication and transportation accelerated the tempo of trade; and what is often called the *Industrial Revolution* in Europe also played its part without doubt, making it possible for many more human beings to exist than had ever existed before.

Gordon Childe (6) is of the opinion that a similar, but of course much less marked, increase in the world's population took place after the last glacial period, when a food-producing economy was established for the first time. It was only when man ceased to be a food gatherer and became a food producer that his numbers could increase on a new scale. Therefore, it is possible that there have been two periods of marked acceleration in world population growth, one in the Neolithic period, which of course never led to populations much larger than the hypothetical 425 million of Pearl, and probably did not equal it, and the enormous increase in the last 300 years which is so out of proportion to what had occurred before that an analogous increase, if observed in the population numbers of a parasite or a micro-organism might be, as Pearl points out, referred to as an epidemic.

The device of living in cities was probably also an important factor. We may distinguish, therefore, three great revolutions each of which resulted in a human world population greater than that which went before:

1. Neolithic — about 8000 B.C.
2. Urban — about 3000 B.C.
3. Industrial — about 1800 A.D.

It is therefore not surprising that human skeletal remains of very early times have not been found in the abundance which could be desired, since men at that time were scarce.

Probable "Polyphyletic" Origin of Man

We can probably never be certain about the place and the time of the origin of *Homo sapiens,* but Dobzhansky is of the opinion that probably mankind did not originate in any one single place. Howells (19) believes that mankind probably originated as early as the Miocene. The place or places of origin are thought by Howells to include possibly Asia or Africa, with perhaps a slight edge in favor of Asia. Dobzhansky (8) has brought strong arguments to bear against the idea which is occasionally brought forward (14) for a polyphyletic origin of man from orang-like, gorilla-like, and chimpanzee-like ancestors. He points out that the orang, gorilla, and chimpanzee as we know them today are unquestionably separate species, apparently completely isolated reproductively. It is therefore highly unlikely that such full species could converge to such an extent that the human races derived from them would show no reproductive isolation at all. It is generally agreed (Gates excepted) that the present races of man form a single species. The *possibility* of intermixture always seems to have existed and there is evidence that it frequently occurred. Therefore Dobzhansky (8) agrees with Weidenreich (33) that several known fossil hominids are the actual ancestors of living mankind, but he does not think it necessary to assume that each fossil type became transformed into a separate human race. According to Dobzhansky, the contributions of the ancestral type to the general pool of genes which the species possesses have been broken up and recombined by the process of reproduction, and also probably acted upon by the forces of natural selection before they became incorporated into the modern racial groups. Thus we all share in our mixed hominid ancestry.

There is no reason to suppose that any of the hominid populations was homogeneous, serologically or otherwise. We know nothing about the blood groups of Neanderthal man, but it seems entirely possible that, if mixture with *H. sapiens* occurred, new serological characteristics not originally possessed by *Homo sapiens* might have been introduced by mixture with *Homo neanderthalensis, Homo solensis* and perhaps other subspecies. In a way we thus are more inclined to reconsider the polyphyletic theory of the origin of the human race, a theory which was for a long time abandoned but which in the light of new discoveries seems not entirely impossible.

Any resemblances which may be found between the skeletons of primitive hominids and the modern human inhabitants of the same region have been assumed by various workers to indicate the descent of the modern group from the primitive hominids in question. Dobzhansky points out, however, that such resemblances can be accounted for in other ways. In different parts of the world the environment might have differed so that in some places the process of selection favored the development in the inhabitants of certain morphological characteristics, while in other parts of the world other characteristics would be favored. So the resemblance between the ancient skeletons and the modern inhabitants might be due to a similar evolutionary agency having acted on both for a sufficient length of time. Dobzhansky does allow, however, for the possibility that some of these resemblances might be due to the fact that some of the original primitive inhabitants of various regions were mixed with and had their genes incorporated with the gene pool of the modern inhabitants, who may largely be the descendants of the invaders.

We must, therefore, start our consideration of the racial history of mankind with a question: Was or was not early man more homogeneous than present-day man taken as a whole? There seem to be two main possibilities: if mankind originated mostly at one place and at one time and from one ancestor (or set of ancestors), then it is a possibility that early man was relatively homogeneous and that different individual members of the race resembled each other closely. If on the other hand modern man, as some anthropologists believe (7, 8, 33), is the result of the fusion of various hominid groups at different times and places, then early man may well have been fully as diverse as present-day *Homo sapiens*. Schultz (30) found a relatively high variability in the gibbons he studied, suggesting perhaps that the second of the above possibilities is the more likely.

Early Human Races

Let us now return to the procedure which at the beginning of this chapter seemed to offer the best approach to the racial history of man, namely a survey of present-day races, and their probable geographical origin. Since racial characters can, and obviously do, evolve independently of each other, we shall do well to consider each character of our "racial constellation" separately. This procedure has the further merit that it enables us to consider separately characteristics which have different values, for the characteristics about whose distribution we know the most will have on the whole the greatest value for reconstructing early racial history.

Let us begin with the blood groups, because, as we have already shown, far more is known about the distribution of the blood groups in various parts of the world than about any other human characteristic, and we know the exact genetic mechanism by which the blood groups are inherited and shall therefore be in a position to talk about genes and not merely about phenotypic physical characteristics determined in a manner as yet unknown. Later, of course, we may want to examine some of the other human physical characteristics.

The origin of the present human races will be cleared up if we can account for the origin of the differences in frequencies of various genes which we now observe.

The A, B, O System

The chief characteristics of the blood group distribution in the human race have already been outlined in Chapter VIII.

The blood group factors A and B, or at any rate factors closely resembling them, are possessed by various of the anthropoids (p. 334). There is therefore no difficulty in supposing that earliest man started with the possession of the O, A, and B genes. It is difficult to tell the proportion in which these existed. There are four mechanisms which we should consider as possibly having been operative (see Chapter V) in bringing about the present geographical differences. These mechanisms are: 1) mutation, 2) selection, 3) genetic drift or "isolation," and 4) mixture, either between races which had acquired different gene frequencies by the action of one or more of the above agencies, or between species which had been different for a very long time. The latter would imply what is termed a polyphyletic origin of the human race as we now have it.

American Indians, Mutations

When the first observations were made on the blood groups of the North American Indians it was found that group B was extremely rare and that group A seemed to occur mostly in tribes where there was considerable possibility of European mixture. The frequency of the gene *A* in the Indians examined in these early investigations was generally found to be less than in the modern populations of Western Europe, and consequently less than that in the white population of the United States. Since it was pretty well agreed that the American Indian had come to this continent from Asia at no very remote time, it was suggested that the stocks which were the ancestors of the American Indian had left Asia *before the blood groups A and B had originated* and that after this time the A and B genes had originated in Asia as mutations (12, 13, 31). Although it was never precisely stated in so many words, it is obvious (39) that many proponents of this mutation concept of the origin of blood groups had in mind merely the concept of a single mutation for A and a single mutation for B, each occurring some place in the Old World. The fact that such misunderstanding of the evolutionary powers of mutation alone should have been possible shows how little genetic principles were comprehended at that time by writers dealing with human evolution. Some authors even went so far as to localize the hypothetical mutation for B as having occurred in Asia and the mutation for A in Europe, since B is less frequent in Europe than in Asia.

It has already been shown above (Ch. V) how untenable is the idea that a single mutation (unaided by other agencies) could appreciably alter the genetic frequency of a hereditary factor in a population, and after this began to be realized, scientists who still maintained that the blood groups must have originated as mutations suggested that an increased frequency of mutation (13) had occurred in Asia and Europe, after the American Indians had left for this continent, and had continued long enough to lead ultimately to the production of the relatively high frequencies of these genes which are now present in many parts of the Old World, especially in Asia.

However, it was found (23) that blood group A, in certain North American Indian tribes, was actually much more frequent than in any part of Asia and much more frequent than in the white population of North America. Tests showed that the highest frequencies in these tribes occurred not among groups of mixed blood but among those whose pedigrees were the purest, the obviously hybridized groups having less. It therefore became immediately obvious that the blood group A, at least, had been brought to America by the American Indians themselves, or by their ancestors. European mixture could never have produced the very high frequencies found. However, the conservatism of science at certain times is so great that obviously necessary corrections in hypotheses are not made until long after the discoveries which make them necessary have been reported. It was several years before it was generally recognized that there is absolutely no need to suppose that the A in the American Indians was introduced by white mixture or that the A in Asia and Europe arose as a mutation, although this shift in point of view was indicated by the evidence available by 1926.

Even if we consider the Indians who have only moderate amounts of A, it can be shown by calculation that the hypothesis of mixture with the "white race" to explain the presence of A in the North American Indians who possess it is a very unlikely one, since it would lead us to expect that the Indians should also possess a good deal more group B than they actually do, since the frequency of the B gene in most European populations is real and finite, even though lower than that of A. This problem can be treated statistically (2). Table 41 shows that the hypothesis of mixture is extremely unlikely in most cases.

As opposed to the very real presence of large amounts of group A in certain American Indian tribes, however, there seems to be a definite absence of group B in nearly all American aborigines not known to possess European blood. Until recently there were two notable exceptions to this statement. Golden (15) reported a considerable percentage of group B in the Caraja Indians in Brazil, and Rahm (28) reported that 30 out of 33 Yahgans (or Yámanas) which he tested in Tierra del Fuego belong to group B. The Yahgans have since been retested by Lipschütz (22) (cf. 29) with the result that in pure Yahgans, no group B was found at all. Rahm is now in-

TABLE 41 (Condensed from 2)

Blood Groups of American Indians

Item	Tribe	Place	Number Tested	O	A	B	AB	P_g	W_o	Ex	P_o
1	Blackfeet	Gleichen, Alberta	123	15.5	83.7	0	0.8	>0.10	100	A	<10^{-6}
2	Blackfeet p	Montana	115	23.5	76.5	0	0	1.00	100	A	<10^{-6}
3	Blackfeet p	Blackfeet Agency, Montana	107	22.4	76.7	0	0.9a	>0.10	100	A	<10^{-6}
4	Blackfeet p	Browning, Montana	103	24.3	74.8	0	1.0	>0.10	100	A	<10^{-6}
5	Bloods p	Alberta, Canada	24	16.7	83.3	0	0	1.00	100	A	0.00047
6	Bloods	Browning, Montana	69	17.4	81.2	0	1.4a	>0.10	100	A	<10^{-6}
7	Bloods	Cardston, Alberta	105	19.1	80.0	0	0.9	>0.10	100	A	<10^{-6}
8	Navaho	N. Mexico	622	69.1	30.6	0.2	0	>0.10	53	A	<10^{-6}
9	Piegan	Brocket, Alberta	42	19.1	80.9	0	0	1.00	100	A	0.000012
10	Maya?	Yucatán	738	76.5	16.7	5.4	1.4b	0.23	44	B	<10^{-6}

Explanation of symbols used in Table 41: Results are arranged, under each main heading, alphabetically according to tribes. The symbols O, A, B, and AB refer to the percentage of these groups found in the population. P_g represents the probability that the observed frequencies could represent a random sample from a population having some values of $p + q + r = 1$ (i.e., genetically obeying Bernstein's theory). W_o represents the "optimal per cent of white mixture" calculated (Appendix A) so as to give values agreeing optimally with the observed for the group in question. Ex is the "element in excess" in the observed, as opposed to the calculated figures. P_o is the "optimal probability" or the chance that the difference between the observed and calculated frequencies is due to random sampling, p signifies pure, or "said to be pure," a signifies that the per cents were calculated by me from the original data, b signifies pure, or "said to be pure." Results in italics are results which can be seen, by inspection or by calculation, to be very clined to think that possibly the serum he used in doing the tests had gone bad in the rather long interval which elapsed from the time it was sent from Germany to the time when he reached the Yahgans and was able to test their blood (4). Therefore there remains only the group B reported by Golden in Brazil and the finding of some group B in Peruvian mummies (5) to indicate that there was ever any appreciable amount of group B at all in this continent until the arrival of the white man. And in the case of the mummies, it is perhaps still a possibility that the material tested was not really from individuals who died before European contact became possible.

It would be possible, of course, to abandon the idea of mutation as an explanation for the present A in Asia and Europe, but to retain it as an explanation for the presence of B, since group B does seem to be absent from the American Indian with the two possible exceptions just mentioned. It is also absent from many of the peoples of the Pacific Islands and from the Australian aborigines with the exception of the natives of the extreme northern coastal fringe, which has been infiltrated in recent centuries by Melanesian elements. This suggestion would involve our assuming that at one time there was a greatly increased rate of mutation from O to B or A to B (or both) in Asia, without any such increase occurring on this continent. Furthermore, the short time that the North American Indians have been on this continent requires that we assume, on this hypothesis, a rate of mutation among the Asiatics higher than any which has been observed in studies on Drosophila or rodents or other experimental animals (3). There is, however, still another fact which should dissuade us from hastily accepting the mutation point of view: factors wholly or substantially indistinguishable from A and B are present in the other anthropoids (35). Table 42 shows what is known about the A and B blood groups of various primates and it will be seen that A and B are by no means unknown in primate species other than man.

Substances closely related to the A and B blood group substances of man are present in other members of the animal kingdom. The blood group A substance is particularly widespread. It has been found possible to isolate from animal sources A- and B-like substances in fairly pure form, which are used in treating universal donor

TABLE 42

The Occurrence of Blood Factors O, A, and B in Man and Other Primates

Organism	Blood Factors
Lemurs	B°
Tarsii	?
Platyrrhina	B°; A*, B*
Cercopithecidae	A*, B*
Gibbons	A, B
Orangs	A, B; A*, B*
Chimpanzees	A, O; A*
Gorillas	A*, B*
Existing human races	A, B, O

The symbols A°, B° indicate A-like and B-like antigens in the red cells, reacting with human anti-A and anti-B agglutinins; A* and B* indicate A-like and B-like antigens found in the tissues and secretions.

This table is based on work by Landsteiner (35) and Wiener, Candela and Goss.

blood (group O) before using it for transfusion. The present raw materials are hog stomach for the A substance, and horse stomach for the B-like substances (37). Therefore, far from being something new and peculiar to the human race, the A and B substances seem to be old and respected elements of our phylogeny. They may have been modified somewhat in the course of evolution just as other human characteristics have, but they seem hardly to be any more novel, in the true sense of the word, than does the spinal column.

If the A and B genes had actually been recent mutations in human history, so recent that this was the reason the American Indians did not possess them, one would have expected that the B gene, which was supposed by the mutationist school to be the most recent in origin, would also have been late in reaching other regions removed by distance from Asia. In particular, if, as one author somewhat rashly supposed, the origin of the B gene was somewhat later than the beginning of the Christian Era, one would expect that the old Egyptian mummies, some of them antedating the beginning of the

Christian era by several thousand years, would not exhibit any trace of the B characteristics. However, when a technique capable of detecting A and B substances in mummified tissue was developed (5) it was found that A and B were sometimes present even in the oldest material which could be examined, notably in some predynastic Egyptian mummies more than 5000 years old. There therefore seem to be a number of persuasive reasons why we should not assume that the A and B genes originated as recent mutations, and a number of reasons for supposing that they are part of our common heritage from our early anthropoid ancestors.

Action of Selection

When we come to the second agency which might have modified blood group frequencies in the world, namely, natural selection, we shall be obliged to return, on the whole, a verdict of not proved. It is very difficult to establish that a character has no selective advantage, whatever, and, as Fisher has shown mathematically (10), selective advantages which seem at first sight very small may nevertheless be quite sufficient to bring about evolutionary modification of the characteristics of a species.

We may tentatively suggest that *if* selection does act on the blood group characteristics, there is some reason to think that B is somewhat favored over O and A, since the present distribution of blood group frequencies suggests that the frequency of the B characteristic has increased markedly in Asia and Europe within fairly recent times geologically, or even within historical times (3). However, this increase could probably be accounted for by other factors, and is no more than a slight indication that some advantage might inhere in the possession of the blood group B. For example, we have reason to believe that the ancestors of the American Indians and of the Polynesians must have come from some part of the Pacific Coast of the Asiatic mainland, at no very remote time. Indians and Polynesians are notable for their lack of B, yet the present populations of the Asiatic coast show considerable B. Also a map of the Southern Pacific region, if we plot on it the frequencies of gene *B,* suggests a gradient from north to south, implying possibly a migration pressure of B genes in this direction. The evidence is rather clear (1, 36) that B was introduced only into the northern part of Australia, and that in fairly recent times.

Migration

Haldane (16) believes that we are justified in supposing that "Neolithic Europe was occupied by peoples of a blood group distribution not unlike that of American tribes, that is to say with B rare or absent (q small or zero) whilst the frequencies of O and A (and therefore the values of r and p) were variable. . . ." [*] He supposes further that "the areas with high p were however rather irregularly distributed. There was probably one around the Baltic, and another in the Iberian peninsula. . . . This primitive European population has been diluted by immigration from the east of peoples in whom q was higher and r lower, whilst p lay (in most cases at least) within the European range."

This picture is consistent with the idea that earliest man probably possessed a blood group distribution not far different from that of present-day Asiatics or Negroes, say $p = 0.25$, $q = 0.15$, $r = 0.60$, but that isolation early produced groups devoid of gene B. After a possible small dribble of people with some B, such groups without B later entered America, probably in more than one wave, and isolation in the new environment was favored to such a degree that still further differentiation took place, giving some tribes with much A, some with a moderate amount, and some, possibly, with none. In Central Asia, and in Africa, groups with about the normal frequencies would seem to have remained. All this may be supposed to have taken place some time before or during the Pleistocene.

Then followed a great numerical increase of the populations in Asia, and to some extent in Africa. These spilled over somewhat into Europe, modifying the blood group distribution there, and leaving the east-to-west gradient of q seen on the map. To a certain extent, doubtless, the A possessors retreated, to "refuge areas," before the advance of the B possessors, whom we may perhaps suppose to have been more advanced in the arts of war, hunting, and/or agriculture. The Asiatic B possessors did not penetrate, in

[*] The symbols p, q, and r stand for the frequencies (p. 226) of the genes A, B, and O respectively.

this last advance, to Australia or the New World, though they did reach, for instance, New Guinea.

Four possible stages in the hypothetical distribution of early man and the blood groups are shown in Figure 46.

The intervals between the stages are supposed to be very long. Changes from one stage to the other need not have been simultaneous; in particular, events in America may have been even later than other changes shown in stage IV. Man is shown losing B before entering the New World, but it is equally possible that this happened after he reached America.

Random Genetic Drift

The third factor which we must consider as possibly operating to bring about the present blood group distribution in the world is the factor of isolation, or random genetic drift as it has been termed by Sewall Wright (38). In small populations it would be quite possible for a blood group gene, especially one that was not very common to begin with, to disappear entirely by accident, without any action whatever of natural selection (p. 154).

In fact this may be the most probable explanation of the present world distribution of the A, B, O blood groups. We find that the American Indians and the Australian aborigines, together with most of the Polynesian populations, apparently possess little if any group B, while group B is widely distributed throughout Africa, Asia, and the Melanesian populations of the Pacific. We do not know how many individuals were represented in the (presumably) several successive migrations from Asia to the New World, but the numbers might well have been small, and in such cases there would have been a good opportunity for the relatively rare blood group gene B to be lost by random sampling — that is, by mere failure to be reproduced in the new population, either in Asia or the New World, and the same argument could apply to Australia and the Polynesians (see p. 171).

The chief objection to this line of argument seems to be the fact that we have to suppose that genetic drift eliminated the gene B in several different human populations: the American Indians reaching the New World, the Polynesians, the Australian aborigines, and

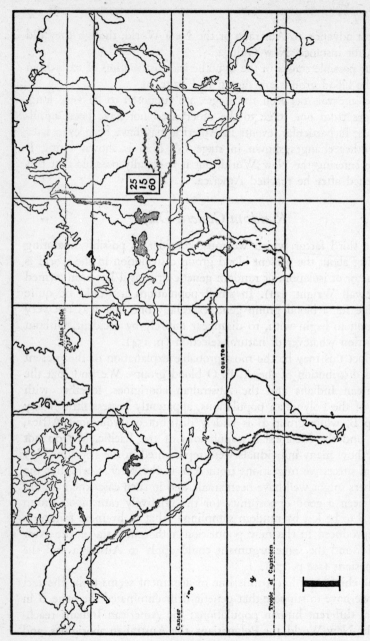

FIGURE 46a. *Hypothetical migrations of early man leading to present blood group distributions. Hypothetical original Asiatic population.*

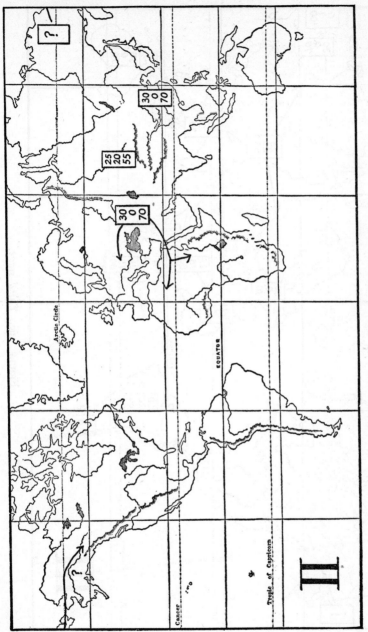

FIGURE 46b. *Second stage of migration.*

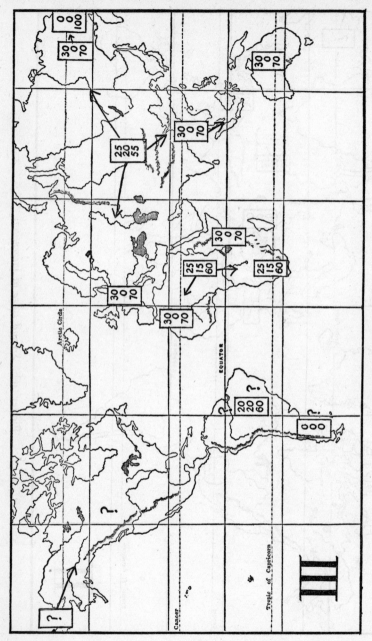

FIGURE 46c. Third stage.

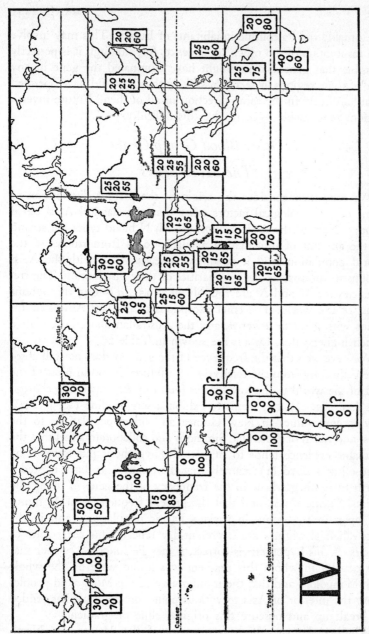

FIGURE 46d. *Fourth stage (preceding present situation) (after Schiff and Boyd).*

presumably the Paleolithic inhabitants of Europe. This may involve the assumption of too much coincidence, for, although it is perfectly possible that genetic drift might have eliminated the gene in any one of these regions, it seems less likely that it would have operated simultaneously in the same direction in all of them. Future investigations may enable us to resolve this difficulty.

Other Blood Group Genes
The M, N Series

We may now consider the origin of the present distribution of some of the serological factors other than the classical A, B blood groups. Next to the A, B groups, the M, N blood types are second in the amount of information available to us from studies of the world population, and it is somewhat easier than with the A, B groups to summarize the peculiarities of their distribution. The frequencies for M and N are roughly $m = 0.55$, $n = 0.45$ throughout most of the world. The chief exceptions to this are American Indians with a much lower n, and the Australian aborigines, with a much higher value. Details are shown in Table 25.

We have seen that the frequency of the gene M does not fall absolutely abruptly from the relatively high figures found in most of the rest of the world to the low figures found in the Australian aborigines (see Fig. 23), but seems to exhibit a sort of cline (see p. 233), having low values in New Guinea and other populations to the west and north of Australia. Simmons and collaborators feel that the available evidence tends to support the hypothesis put forward by Birdsell and Boyd (1): namely that there may once have existed a north to south gradient in the frequency of the gene M along the Asiatic Pacific Coast, and that the present frequencies of M found in Japan in the Ainu, in various Pacific populations, and in the Australian aborigines are a present-day relic of this early state of affairs. If this hypothesis is correct, it may be supposed further that the peoples in whom this gradient was found were on the whole non-Mongoloid and that the immigration of the Mongoloid peoples from the interior of Asia to various points on the coast has tended to break up and obscure this original cline or gradient.

Whether the very high frequencies of the M gene in North

America are simply a reflection of the original gradient seems some-what doubtful, since the American Indians are at least partly Mon-goloid in most other characteristics. Although some of the high M frequency could be explained on this basis, we should also have to resort to the hypothesis of random genetic variation to account for the extensive loss of N genes in a population evidently largely derived from the Asiatic Mongols who probably possessed plenty of N. It should be noted that, although American Indians vary a good deal in their O and A frequencies, a fact which might be explained by random genetic variation, they are fairly homogeneous for M and N, although the Navaho show distinctly less N than do most others.

The fact that we have found it needful to invoke the hypothesis of genetic drift to account for the characteristics of the American Indian in regard to both the A, B groups and the M and N blood types might suggest that the American continent was originally populated by numbers of people which were effectively so small, genetically, that the phenomenon of "random genetic drift," which we know is most effective in small isolated populations, operated fairly often. If this is a true picture of early man in America, then the large migrations envisaged by certain writers of the past become less probable. Of course, it will be understood that we cannot now distinguish between a large population which leaves Asia and arrives in the New World, only to find its numbers reduced almost to zero by disease or privation, and a small population which leaves Asia and arrives essentially intact.

Investigation of the M gene in anthropoids has revealed facts which are somewhat surprising. Reagents which were all equally good for detecting the M gene in man often showed striking differ-ences in their reaction with various primate bloods. This was par-ticularly true with the blood of the rhesus monkey. Landsteiner and Wiener (21) concluded that *all* individuals of the species of Chimpanzees possessed genes for both M-like and N-like antigens, so that the entire hereditary mechanism of the M and N factors in these animals was different from what it is in man. We are quite unable to state at what stage the human race acquired the present system of two allelomorphic genes M and N, determining three types — M, N, and MN.

The Rh Series

In addition to the A, B blood groups and the M and N blood types, considerable information is now available on the world distribution of the Rh or rhesus blood types (see Table 29) and their subtypes. Not enough information has accumulated for us to attempt much of a reconstruction of early situations, however.

The problem of accounting for the presence of the Rh negative genes in peoples of European stock, in the face of its almost complete absence in the rest of the world, was at first quite a puzzle. It has been proposed by Hogben (17) and by Wiener (34) (see p. 151) that the action of the disease which sometimes results from Rh incompatibility would tend to eliminate the Rh negative gene if its frequency were below a certain value (0.50). Above this value, the presence of the disease would tend to eliminate the Rh positive genes. Thus we should have a position of unstable equilibrium when a population possessed the gene frequencies $Rh = 0.50$, $rh = 0.50$. Any departure from this state in either direction would lead to further departure in the same direction. The conclusions of Hogben have been challenged by a number of authors and R. A. Fisher (27) has stated that, in his opinion, it is far from certain that the existence of a disease which results in the death of certain types of children which can be produced by a given mating will necessarily mean that this mating will produce, on the average, fewer children than do unaffected matings. He points out that there is a strong tendency to compensate for the loss of children who die at birth or in infancy by having a larger number of births, so that the total family may be as large as, or larger than, one in which the Rh blood types of the parents were completely compatible. If it were not for these arguments, it would be easy to suppose that the Rh negative gene had originally existed in all the human race, but that in the population of Asia, where natural selection may be supposed to act more severely than it does on the present-day population of Europe, the disadvantageous Rh negative gene had been eliminated. Until recently, this was about the only plausible theory as to why peoples of European stock differ in Rh frequencies from all the other peoples of the world who have been examined. Mixture with some other geographically isolated subspecies of man, such as Neander-thal man, might explain the situation if we were sure that Nean-derthal man had been predominantly Rh negative and that peoples of European stock possess more Neanderthal genes than do the peoples of Asia. Neither of these possibilities, however, was more than speculation. Wiener (34) pointed out in a paper published in 1942 that ". . . if one assumes the existence of populations in the past (and possibly still surviving at the present time) consisting almost exclusively of Rh-negative individuals, then from crosses with other populations consisting largely of Rh positive persons . . . a hybrid population could result. . . ." Wiener offered no sugges-tion as to what that high Rh negative population might prove to be.

The situation was altered almost overnight by the discovery (9, 24) that the Basques, a genetically isolated, non-Indo-European population of Europe, long thought to represent an early stratum of the colonists of Europe, possessed much more Rh negative (ca. 30 per cent) than do the other Europeans. It was at once suggested (24), and seems highly probable, that the average European, with his 13-15 per cent Rh negative, originally acquired it by mixture with an early European population of which the Basques are at present the only known living example.

Subgroups

Although peoples of European stock seem to differ serologically from the populations of all or nearly all the rest of the world, except possibly the African, in that they have the subgroup A_2 of the blood group A (see p. 236) and have a considerable amount of rh' and rh'' genes, when and in what manner they acquired these differ-ences is not easy to state. We do not at the present time know of any human (or even anthropoid) group with much more A_2, pro-portionally, than the average European. Perhaps A_2 has some selec-tive disadvantage, and under the conditions of stringent selection in Asia was eliminated, before the ancestors of the American Indians left for this continent. In paleolithic European man the gene, al-though possibly somewhat inferior to A_1, lingered on. But all this must be admitted to be in the highest degree conjectural.

Other Characteristics

We are unable to make a very good guess as to the time of origin of the Mongolian eye fold, since this is a characteristic which is not detectable in skeletal material, and it is evidently genetically complex, so not much can be inferred from present-day distributions. From its occurrence in American Indians we may suppose its origin to be before the time when the ancestors of the American Indians left Asia for the New World. Other genes, such as the one (if there is only one) conferring on its possessors the ability to taste phenyl-thio-carbamide, may be much more ancient and may possibly go back to the anthropoids or even earlier (11). Again, however, it is extremely difficult to guess when the present geographical differences in the distribution of the gene were set up.

Our earliest glimpse of the racial pre-history of mankind, therefore, does not go back much beyond the dawn of the earliest written history. We start with the assumption of a possibly already somewhat differentiated *sapiens* stock, sparsely scattered over considerable areas of Asia, and possibly also in Europe. We suppose that this stock possessed the O, A, and B blood groups, and somehow acquired the modern human mechanism of inheritance of M and N, possessed in an unknown quantity the gene for tasting phenyl-thio-carbamide and may or may not have possessed the Rh negative gene. This essentially primitive "white stock"* may have spread all through Asia, to Europe, and to the Japanese islands, where remnants of it are still found in the Ainu, and also down through Southern Asia to Australia and other regions. We have already shown there is reason to suppose that at this time or somewhat later a gradient from south to north in the frequency of the M gene existed, so that the northern population had more M than did the southern. After dispersal, this primitive white stock — in warmer climates — was probably acquiring a darker complexion, although

* These stocks are called basically "white" (p. 273) because on being crossed with white races the offspring suggest that not so many genes (or less dominant genes) for dark pigmentation were present in the dark (or black) ancestors as is the case with the African Negroes. Body hair and certain morphological features also help bolster up this conviction. Also the gene *r'* (*Cde*) is found in both Europeans and Australians.

retaining many of the primitive cranial characteristics we characterize as "white." The Australian aborigines would seem to be at least partially derived from the southern groups possessing a low frequency of M; later influences acting on small isolated populations may have caused the frequency to drop and possibly to reach zero in certain Australian tribes (1).

REFERENCES FOR CHAPTER XII

1. Birdsell, J. B., and W. C. Boyd, *A. J. P. A., 27,* 69–90 (1940).
2. Boyd, W. C., *A. J. P. A., 25,* 215–235 (1939).
3. Boyd, W. C., *A. J. P. A., 27,* 333–364 (1940).
4. Boyd, W. C., *A. J. P. A., 4,* 490 (1946).
5. Boyd, W. C., and L. G. Boyd, *J. Imm., 32,* 307–319 (1937).
6. Childe, V. G., *Man Makes Himself.* Watts & Co., London, 1936.
7. Coon, C. S., *The Races of Europe.* Macmillan Co., New York, 1939.
8. Dobzhansky, Th., *A. J. P. A., 2,* 251–265 (1944).
9. Etcheverry, M. A., *El Día Médica, 17,* 1237–1251 (1945).
10. Fisher, R. A., *The Genetical Theory of Natural Selection.* Clarendon Press, Oxford, 1930.
11. Fisher, R. A., E. B. Ford, and J. Huxley, *Nature, 144,* 750–751 (1939).
12. Gates, R. R., *A. J. P. A., 12,* 475–485 (1929).
13. Gates, R. R., *Genetica, 18,* 47–65 (1936).
14. Gates, R. R., *Human Ancestry.* Harvard Univ. Press, Cambridge, 1948.
15. Golden, G., *Lancet, 219,* II, 278–279 (1930).
16. Haldane, J. B. S., *Human Biol., 12,* 457–480 (1940).
17. Hogben, L., *Nature, 152,* 721–722 (1943).
18. Hooton, E. A., *Up from the Ape.* Macmillan Co., New York, 1946.
19. Howells, W., *Mankind So Far.* Doubleday, Doran & Co., Garden City, New York, 1944.
20. Jepson, G. L., *Trans. N. Y. Acad. Sci., 6,* II, 81–124 (1944).
21. Landsteiner, K., and A. S. Wiener, *J. Imm., 33,* 19–25 (1937).
22. Lipschütz, A., G. Mostny, and L. Robin, *A. J. P. A., 4,* 301–321 (1946).
23. Matson, G. A., and H. F. Schrader, *J. Imm., 25,* 155–163 (1933).
24. Mourant, A. E., *Nature, 160,* 505–506 (1947).
25. Murray, R. W., *Man's Unknown Ancestors.* Bruce Pub. Co., Milwaukee, 1943.
26. Pearl, R., and S. A. Gould, *Human Biol., 8,* 399–419 (1936).
27. Race, R. R., *Brit. Med. J., 2,* 165 (1944).
28. Rahm, G., *Invest. y Prog., 5,* 160–162 (1931).

29. Santiana, A., *Los Fueguinos; sus grupos sanguíneos*. Quito, Imp. de la Univ., 1946.
30. Schultz, A. H., *A. J. P. A., 2*, 1–129 (1944).
31. Snyder, L. H., *Blood Grouping in Relation to Clinical and Legal Medicine*. Williams & Wilkins Co., Baltimore, 1929.
32. Weidenreich, F., *Peking Nat. Hist. Bull., 13*, 161–174 (1939).
33. Weidenreich, F., *Apes, Giants, and Man*. Univ. Chicago Press, Chicago, 1946.
34. Wiener, A. S., *Science, 96*, 407–408 (1942).
35. Wiener, A. S., *Blood Groups and Transfusion*. Charles C Thomas, Springfield, 1943.
36. Wilson, H., J. J. Graydon, R. T. Simmons, and L. M. Bryce, *Med. J. Australia, 2*, 581–589 (1944).
37. Witebsky, E., N. C. Klendshoj, and C. McNeil, *Proc. Soc. Exp. Biol. & Med., 55*, 167–170 (1944).
38. Wright, S., *Am. Nat., 63*, 274–279 (1929).
39. Wyman, L. C., and W. C. Boyd, *Am. Anthrop., 37*, 181–200 (1935).

CHAPTER XIII

Man's Future

> Others mistrust and say, "But time escapes:
>   Live now or never!"
> He said, "What's time? leave Now for dogs and apes!
>   Man has Forever."
>   — BROWNING

The Future of Our Race Concepts

IT has been the purpose of this book to point the way towards an intelligent and profitable study of the physical characteristics of man, and if this purpose has been at all achieved, the reader will have gained the impression that such study is best accomplished chiefly by the investigation of the geographical distribution of known genes, and by attempts to discover the genes which determine other physical characteristics which vary in incidence in different human populations. What is now known is in all probability a mere fraction of the knowledge which the future will bring.

Making use of the rather meager data now available bearing on the few characters which are inherited in a known manner, genetic races of man have been distinguished (p. 268). These races correspond, in the degree to which they differ from each other, to the races which are delineated within the species of some of the lower organisms. Whether we consider the differences to be *important* or not is entirely up to us. Scientifically all we can state is that our races may perhaps continue to be convenient designations for different human geographical groups, but it is more likely that new discoveries will provide different, and still better, means for differentiating men into racial groups.

Merely because blood groups have been used as illustrations so often in the preceding chapters, we should not conclude that they will necessarily continue to offer any unique advantage for racial classification. Their special advantages at the present time consist in the fact that we know the way in which they are inherited, and we possess reagents which detect the results of the action of nearly every individual gene involved, a fact which greatly facilitates genetic analysis. The analysis of phenotypes into genotypes is not likely to be so easy with characteristics such as skin color (p. 310), although we of course cannot know what future research will bring forth in the way of new and rapid methods. Other characteristics, as yet incompletely studied, will probably eventually prove equally valuable. At the moment, we are forced to base our tentative conclusions upon what is really a very scanty knowledge of human genetics, which has been largely a by-product of the research of clinicians and other persons who are not primarily geneticists. Once any considerable number of persons trained in the methods of genetics turn their energies to the problem of analyzing the genetic basis of human characteristics, we may expect a mass of data to accumulate which will enable us to differentiate human races with much more exactness, and draw much more far-reaching conclusions as to their origin.

Finding the Genetic Basis of Traits

A few words should perhaps be said about the methods of discovering new genes. Some of these methods have already been discussed or included by implication in certain sections in the preceding chapters, but we may now attempt to be a little more explicit. It should be obvious to all readers that most of the human physical characters we are likely to want to study are complex, and therefore not determined by a single gene pair. We have discussed the inheritance of the color of the skin, and some of the hypotheses which have been offered to explain its inheritance. At least two pairs of genes were seen to be required (p. 310). A re-examination of Mendel's work (Ch. II) will give us an idea of how a genetic analysis might be expected to proceed.

As a first step, we shall choose some character in which individuals show a satisfactory degree of contrast. It will be simpler if we do not start with characters which are markedly influenced by sex, although this imposes a rather severe limitation on our work, since so many characters do vary with sex, and sex-influenced characters will sooner or later have to be studied, if our knowledge of human genetics is to be made at all complete. The next step is to examine the offspring of matings of parents who differ in regard to the feature we have chosen to study. It is always tempting to hope that the study will prove that the presence or absence of a single gene determines the character, and that we have thus located a new gene pair (which may or may not prove to be on one of the chromosomes which we have already identified as carrying genes for the various blood group antigens, or for the taste reaction for phenyl-thio-carbamide, etc.). Experience (cf. p. 313) teaches us, however, that the rosy expectation of finding each new character to be due to a single pair of alleles will not usually be fulfilled. Multiple genes or allelomorphs are very likely to be involved (p. 241). Differences in *penetrance* and *expressivity* may also be encountered (p. 77).

The individual children of the matings we study will probably exhibit the character under investigation to a greater or less extent, and various gradations between the extremes will be observed. Difficult problems of differentiation between phenotypes — a matter which often involves individual judgment — and of nomenclature for purposes of recording, etc., will arise. The important thing to look for is *segregation:* that is, a situation in which a certain character, or a certain factor contributing towards the possession of a character, appears in some of the offspring but is nearly or entirely lacking in the others. We may then *postulate* that this segregating character is determined by a single gene, but we cannot as a rule immediately be sure of this. Our postulate must be tested by the observation of still more families (see Appendix XIII–1).

It is at this point that the efforts of the would-be student of human genetics have often failed in the past. The preliminary studies have been gone through triumphantly, but the prospect of the dismal and probably financially unrewarding job of accumulating data, until each successive hypothesis of the hereditary mechanism has either been proved or disproved, has seemed too forbidding, and further work has been abandoned.

We cannot with justice state that lack of scientific vision or even lack of interest in human genetics has been entirely responsible for the present situation. The lack of information about human genetics is rather a by-product of our particular way of organizing (or not organizing) scientific inquiry, and of our way of recruiting new members to this particular branch of science (or for that matter to scientific work in general). Almost every young scientist is faced with the necessity of building up as soon as possible a scientific reputation, which he must have to enable him to get financial support for further scientific work or to get a hearing for the results of his later work and ideas; and more prosaically, to make it possible for him to secure a teaching or research position in order to support himself and his family. Few young researchers have been in a position to embark on a program of research which *might* not result in any scientific publication until they had put in twenty years or so of hard work. It is necessary to score small initial successes in order to be in line for a chance at the bigger successes, and even then the chance at the latter may come at a time when it is already too late in life for the investigator to do his best work. It is to be hoped that in the future a more liberal attitude towards basic research which does not promise immediate and spectacular results will prevail and that governments which can spend money like water during a war will be willing to support during peacetime a few promising scholars, for life if necessary, and not require immediate publications, and in particular that funds will be made available for the scientists who wish to study and analyze the very important subject of the genetics of human physique. There are signs that something of this sort may eventually come about in this country.

Hypothetical Illustration

It is not possible for any of us, sitting back perhaps in a comfortable armchair, to predict with certainty what the course of future research in human heredity will be. We may, however, consider a hypothetical illustration, which may possibly not be too far from typical of the problems which will arise. Let us suppose that a young student has decided to study the inheritance of the shape of the nose. His first task will be to classify the shape of the nose according to some system which seems sensible to him.

As an illustration of the sort of classification which a beginner might set up for noses, we may refer to the classification proposed in Martin's (27) magnificent textbook of morphological anthropology.

First Martin considers the *nasal index,* which is the ratio of the breadth of the nose to its length (these measurements are all made from well-defined specified points). This varies somewhat with sex, but not as much as might at first be feared. The nasal index varies considerably with race and Martin gives tables of its values for males, and occasionally for females, for various populations. More important, he calls attention to the fact that the nasal index does not by any means tell the whole story about a nose.

In the first place, some races (e.g. Bushmen) have very concave noses, and the appearance of the nose is lower and broader than the nasal index suggests. In the second place, the shape and position of the nostrils must be considered. Then Martin gives fifteen different ideal types of nasal profile, to one of which nearly any human nose would be similar. Also, he considers the depth of the nose (that is, the extent to which it protrudes from the face). Then the fleshy lobes of the nose (Nasenflügel) can vary. Obviously a good many kinds of noses are possible (Fig. 47).

The next task of the investigator, and one which strangely has only too often been ignored, is to find out, from a study of embryology and early development, how his classifications and his various types correspond with the actual facts of morphological development. Martin, in the work just referred to, gives this fundamental question, in the case of noses, scant attention. In most cases it can be confidently anticipated that a study of the embryology and growth of an organ will enable the original "exhaustive" classification, which may have seemed so impressive, but is actually often only superficial, to be amended, and a better and revised version, giving information of more fundamental importance, will then result.

Now the student has the problem of trying to find out how many genes, acting in what way, determine the shape of the nose. Also climatic and other environmental influences must be considered. For purposes of orientation, the student will examine a large number of families, and tentatively record certain characteristics, or certain developmental trends, which he thinks may be unit characters —

that is, brought about by the action of single genes. At first this will be to a large extent a matter of guesswork. As an example of one guess (but unfortunately one which is not likely to lead to further progress) we may mention that Fischer (13) has stated that

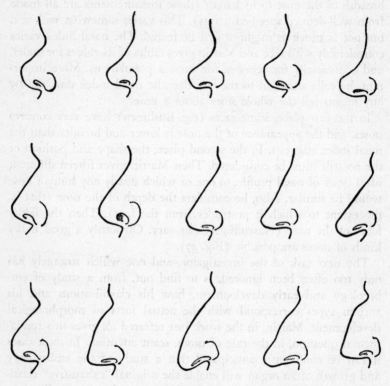

FIGURE 47. *Hypothetical scheme of nose classification (after Martin).*

in general the high European type of nose seems to be dominant over other types [cf. Whitney (41)], and Salaman (33) has supposed that the narrow Ashkenazic types of nose, and also the "North European" nose, are dominant over the more characteristic "Jewish" nose. It seems in the highest degree unlikely that any of these are unit characters, caused by the action of only one gene. The student will consider them, however, and either make a preliminary test of the proposed genetic mechanisms, or invent a more probable hypothesis for his first family surveys.

Let us suppose that our hypothetical student has a really analytical mind, and makes plausible guesses. Then there must come the period of accumulating sufficient data to prove or disprove each hypothesis, and of replacing discarded hypotheses by new ones. Let us suppose that the student is successful, and that he singles out one aspect of nasal development and shows that it is always due to the action of a certain gene, which he may label with any letter or combination of letters he chooses. This gene may prove to be dominant, recessive, or neutral. If it is a neutral gene it may manifest its action even in the presence of other allelomorphs of itself. If the gene is recessive, it will be covered up in persons who possess an allelomorphic gene which is dominant to it. A study of matings of people who both exhibit the recessive characteristic will usually show whether or not the character is in fact a single gene. Some of the mathematical aspects of such studies are dealt with in Appendix A.

Once a single gene is identified, the task of identifying others which are alleles or which have related effects becomes easier, but is by no means ended. The number of genes having an influence on the shape of the nose is probably fairly large, but possibly no more numerous than the series of genes (at least eight) which we know to operate in determining the Rh blood types. Analysis of the Rh factors was made easier, however, by the fact that the effect of these genes is usually manifested even in the presence of other genes of the series, and that specific chemical reagents (agglutinins) are available for detecting the end results, in the human red cells, produced by the action of these genes. In the study of the anatomical features of man more difficulty will doubtless be encountered. In particular it seems likely that in the case of genes affecting morphological factors the penetrance or expressivity (or both) may vary a good deal from gene to gene. By patient study, however, the complete story could almost certainly be worked out for any given physical character. The geographical distribution of the newly discovered genes could then be determined, and new refinements of existing racial categories could be introduced as a result.

Students who embark on such work will have to keep in mind

several possible pitfalls. If the characters are influenced by the sex of the individual, the investigators must not assume without further study that the gene is sex-linked (p. 68). If more than one gene is found to be involved, they must not assume immediately that these genes are alleles. They must not assume that a gene is dominant or recessive to any other gene until this is actually demonstrated by the study of family material. They must not assume that they have identified all the genes which influence noses until they can predict, in a satisfactory manner, from the parental (and possibly grandparental) types, the possible nasal structures of the offspring of all the families available to them. They must not assume that in different races the same gene must necessarily be involved in producing a character which superficially, at least, seems to be the same or that any gene identified must occur in other populations with the same frequency.

Another thing which the physical anthropologist of the future will keep in mind is the possible multiple effects of genes. For instance, there is no reason at all to deny the possibility that some of the "blood group" genes may have, in addition to their serological effects, other effects, as yet unknown to us, on the physiology and morphology of the individuals who possess them. No such effects have as yet been identified, and we cannot be sure that there are any. But until much more is known about human genetics than is known at present, the possibility always remains that one or more of the blood group genes may eventually be found to influence some other character such as the shape of some small facet of one of the 206 bones of the normal body, or the number of taste buds per square centimeter of the tongue, or the relative length of the little toe, or something equally unlikely. So far, relatively little search has been made for possible multiple effects of genes in man.*

We can hardly doubt that prolonged series of investigations of the sort suggested here, if carried out with perseverance and intelligence, would eventually make the whole riddle of human inheritance relatively clear. The numbers of individual genes involved in many cases may prove to be fewer than we might at present fear.

---

* The report of Grubb (15a) that the Lewis blood antigen and the "non-secreting" characteristic are apparently caused by the same gene may possibly be the first example of multiple effects of a human gene.

As a very crude example, we may mention that it is not entirely impossible that a fairly small number of genes are involved in the determination of facial features, for it is a common observation that strong segregation of these characteristics often occurs in families, so that, even in spite of sex differences, some children look very much like the father, and some very much like the mother. Or the facial type of one of the grandparents may emerge. If the physiognomy were determined, in each individual, by a large number of genes, on different chromosomes, many of these would get separated rather often in the process of reproduction, even in one generation. The result would be that we would more often observe an apparent blending of the parental features in all the children.

Our final goal is the determination of the main genes responsible for human physique and mental abilities, and their mode of operation and interaction. It would be especially important, as already stated, to identify which genes can influence human behavior, indirectly, as by affecting the endocrine glands, the sex organs, etc., or directly by affecting varieties of temperament, etc. We already know enough (3, 15, 38) to predict that genes must exist which largely control such things as musical ability, mathematical ability, and the high degrees of physical co-ordination necessary for outstanding performances in such games as tennis and polo. When more thorough genetic studies have been made, we shall then be in a position to classify men more accurately and minutely than is possible at present. We shall also be in a position to assess the relative abilities, in regard to any particular line of endeavor, of different persons or of different geographical groups. We have already suggested that the over-all differences of this sort between geographical groups are probably small; but we know that the differences between individuals of the same group are sometimes very great.

All of this knowledge which we hope may be discovered in the future will be of very great value to the cultural anthropologist and the sociologist. It should be of even greater value to parents and educators. Children who are known to be born without any genes for musical performance ability, for example, will be spared the ordeal of years of useless music lessons.

"Improving" the Human Stock

On the other hand, we must beware of painting for ourselves any rosy picture such as that which has been offered in the past by those who called themselves eugenists. The eugenists seemed to suppose that once our proper human destiny was sufficiently understood (and some of them seemed to take it for granted that this happy state of affairs had already been attained), it would be possible to begin to select for desirable genes in man, and to eliminate undesirable genes. Thus they thought to improve the human species. But before we decide that some human beings are better than others, we must ask ourselves, "Better for what?" The earth offers a large number of different types of physical environment, and the complex contemporaneous human cultures, or just the cultures of the Western World in which we live, offer a very large number of different outlets for different varieties of human ability. It is not easy to say with confidence that any of the varieties of ability are bad, and others are good, or that some are better than others. Was Sir Isaac Newton more valuable to the human race than Ludwig van Beethoven? This question cannot be answered scientifically because it is a silly question and has no meaning, and nearly all similar questions which involve the ideas of good and bad in human abilities are equally silly.

It is very easy to be too sure of how things would work out in a hypothetical case. In a primitive society, where ability to run, hunt, and fight seems to be demanded of all, it might be supposed that any inherited physical disability would act practically as a lethal, and no doubt selection against such traits is strong. However, the legends of the blind poet Homer, and the lame smith Hephaestos (39), and observations on "primitive" peoples of today, suggest that even in early times persons with major physical disabilities could still sometimes make valuable contributions to the society in which they lived, and be rewarded by being allowed to survive, at least. In our own time there have been many men and women who have made important intellectual contributions to our culture, in spite of serious physical handicaps. The names of Edison, Steinmetz, and Dostoevsky come to mind, and the list could be almost indefinitely extended.

There are a few human genes which it would undoubtedly be desirable to eliminate, if this could be done without causing more suffering in the process of elimination than their presence among us causes now. Genes causing congenital idiocy are perhaps among these. A number of other examples could be thought of, although it does not always prove as simple a problem as one might think (8).

The elimination of a dominant gene, in a society willing and able to undertake the project, would be fairly simple. Sterilization of all affected persons, or the voluntary avoidance of the production of offspring by them, would accomplish this in one generation. Unfortunately, most of the human genes known to be undesirable are recessive, and in such cases sterilization of the affected persons would act very slowly. Hogben (20) has pointed out that continued sterilization of all individuals affected by albinism would only reduce the incidence of the gene to half its present frequency in a period of time about equivalent to the entire Christian era. Any scheme to improve the human race which requires lengths of time of this order can thus be dismissed as chimerical. Long before the artificial selection had produced much effect, we could anticipate either that medical science would have discovered how to prevent the undesirable effects of the gene, as it has already in the case of diabetes, or that mankind, by indulging in some folly such as an atomic war (34), would have wiped out most of the populations which were thus trying to improve themselves.

For the time being, at least, we shall do much better to devote our energies to making better education available to those who already possess genes making them capable of benefiting from it, and to attempt to improve the mutual understanding and relationships of the various groups of men who at present consider themselves racially or culturally distinct.

In the meantime, further genetics-guided study, as outlined here, should eventually make possible a fairly complete and accurate classification of mankind into races. These races also will probably not differ very much in over-all innate abilities, and it is very interesting to ask ourselves: what will happen to these racial distinctions, and to the racial distinctions which have seemed to certain persons so important in the past?

The Future of Races

Racial doctrines and prejudices about race have been extremely prevalent in our time (19), and have even led to attempts to exterminate particular "races" in certain areas of the world. It is not too obvious what will happen in the future. If we are Utopians, of course, we may believe in some inevitable millennium, and if we are entirely pessimistic about the human species we may believe that its case is hopeless. As scientists we should not belong to either of these camps, but try to answer the question by an impartial examination of the available evidence. Will mankind continue to diverge into more and more distinct races, or will the forces of amalgamation produce a more and more homogeneous world population of *Homo sapiens?* Anything we say on this subject must necessarily be somewhat in the line of prophecy, and time, in the usual way, will determine whether it was correct or false. However, we have a few facts on which to base our predictions, although we may have to base some of them on less certain grounds than we do the others.

This book has been written after the end of a great war which was, in part at least, due to conflicts over racial issues, and which terminated in a way clearly indicating a definite possibility that organized civilization as we know it today may succeed in totally destroying itself. If this should happen but not render the planet uninhabitable, it would leave the human species to be perpetuated mostly by the populations of regions not reached by our modern weapons, including perhaps the aborigines of the Australian desert, and Eskimo and other inhabitants of the polar regions, and the natives of Central Africa. The genetic composition of future *Homo sapiens* might be greatly altered if this should happen. [In addition, undesirable mutations might result (28a) from the penetrating radiation released by atomic weapons.] It seems impossible at present to predict whether or not this (from our point of view) disastrous outcome will actually occur or not. It seems, however, to be more constructive to work on the assumption that it will somehow be avoided, although at the time of writing a method of avoiding it appears to be as yet unknown and unobtainable. Let us suppose, for the sake of argument, that organized civilization will avoid destroy-

ing itself by the use of atomic bombs, radioactive dust, bacteriological warfare, poison gas, or anything similar, and that the same
racial groups which we have at present will continue to contribute
to the racial picture in the future. What shall we predict to be the
outcome?

Relative Size of Populations

There is reason to think that technological advance will at least
roughly equalize the military power of the various nations, and
that this will be accomplished before any great change in the relative population numbers which at present exist has time to take
place. This would imply that the relative numbers of different races
in various parts of the world at the present time can serve as a rough
guide to the relative numbers of their descendants in the eventual
world population. If this is so, then the citizenship of the future
world state will be largely Asiatic by descent, with the Africans,
Americans, and Europeans coming in a very bad second indeed,
and the descendants of Icelanders, for example, being a minority so
small as hardly to be mentioned. (Not that there is any reason to
believe the population of Iceland inferior; this prediction is made
solely on the basis of present numbers.)

Also, we must take account of changes in birth rate. It is low
and declining in most European countries. In Eastern Europe, the
U.S.S.R., Turkey, Japan, Palestine, parts of North Africa, and certain Latin American countries the fertility is also declining, but the
decline in mortality has got ahead of the decline in fertility, and
this has meant very rapid population increase. Although it seems
certain that the population growth in these countries will eventually
slow down, their capacity for growth is still immense (5). The
population of the U.S.S.R. in 1970 might be as much as 70,000,000
more than it was in 1940. There is not convincing evidence from
history that a country in which a declining birth rate once sets in
ever reverses the trend and again begins rapidly to increase its numbers. It seems practically certain, therefore, that the great bulk of the
population of the world in the next few generations will be recruited
from Asia, Africa, and perhaps the Near East, certain islands of the
Pacific and Caribbean, and parts of Central and South America (5).

It is difficult to believe that this will be accomplished without a considerable degree of miscegenation, which may result in the long run in a type of *Homo sapiens* showing less difference between geographical groups than at present, especially in regard to some of the outward physical characteristics such as skin color and types of face and hair, since we must anticipate that it will be largely Asiatics and Africans who will be the main producers of the population of the new world. How straight versus kinky hair will make out is hard to predict in our present state of ignorance. Possibly at the time which we are attempting to visualize nobody will care.

In spite of the notable role in scientific research and technological development which has been played in recent times by the populations of Europe and more recently by those of North America, there is every reason to think that their ultimate role on the stage of history will be a minor one and the final composite *Homo sapiens* will on the whole not particularly resemble physically the present inhabitants of the Western World.

The conclusions of writers such as Burch and Pendell (6) that rapidly increasing populations can be induced to restrict their numbers by the use of contraceptive measures seem to be based on pure optimism. It is very difficult indeed to see how an uneducated Indian family is going to learn about contraception, and how it can afford the expense of contraceptive apparatus which costs a sum which equals a substantial fraction of their yearly food budget. It seems much more likely that population increase in the parts of the world where it is now greatest will continue at least for several generations (5).

Potential Contributors to the Probable Future World Population

Since we have no scientific reason to suppose that the Asiatic (7) is less capable of developing science and technology than the European, there is no reason to suppose that the world will suffer any cultural or technological decline as a result of the final adjustment of populations and population densities, which seems inevitable, and even desirable. The ultimate limit will probably be set mainly by the world capacity for food production (4, 5, 26).

It seems fairly obvious from current political events that so long as any relatively uninhabited areas remain in the world there will be pressure from peoples of the more densely populated areas to occupy them (29). It also seems true that as long as culturally un-developed areas exist, other more aggressive, and in their own opinion culturally more advanced, neighbors will wish to take over the administration of such areas. We cannot look forward to an era of permanent peace, therefore, until each area of the world's surface is inhabited to the proper degree by human beings. This degree will be determined largely by climate, soil productivity, and the ultimate standard of living (6) which the human race adopts.

No doubt British and American readers will hope that the stand-ard of living to be adopted will be similar to that which exists in their own countries. For this hope, however, our glimpse into the future of mankind offers little support. America is at the present time occupied by a fairly sparse population enjoying the highest standard of living in the world, mainly because other areas of the world where much denser populations exist have not yet developed the technological and scientific devices which would enable them to compete. However, in the Second World War many Americans must have realized that the supposedly backward Asiatic Japanese had essentially mastered many of the "secrets" of Western technol-ogy, all in the brief period of time since 1860.

There is every reason to think that the principles of science will within a generation or so penetrate to the most remote quarters of the globe, and nations composed of individuals with quite different standards of living will be able to construct atomic bombs, rocket weapons, and other devices which will enable them to compete, in war at least, with the at present technologically more advanced nations of European stock. From a long-range point of view there-fore, there is no doubt that the more numerous populations are destined to be the great replenishers of the human species in the future.

Nations existing at a very low living standard may nevertheless from time to time produce, and allow adequate education to, great men. Witness the great chemist, Mendeleev, arising from the back-ward Russian society of his day, and Buddha growing up in over-populated India.

We may ask ourselves, will natural selection, in the densely populated world of the future, play any great role in altering the frequency of any of the genes we have considered as bases of racial
classification? It is doubtful if there will be much effect due to this
agency. We have not been able to find that any of the blood groups
offer a marked selective advantage or disadvantage — with the probable exception of the Rh factor, and even there the opinion of experts
is still divided (31). The gene for tasting phenyl-thio-carbamide,
whatever its main purpose, teleologically speaking, may be, seems
to have existed for a long time before the development of *sapiens*
man. Head form may have some selective advantage but if so the
advantages are probably in the direction of brachycephaly. Skin
color, however, might offer varying advantages in different areas.
In the tropics it may be an advantage to have a darker skin color,
in the North possibly an advantage to be lighter, and it may be
that the permanent situation will adjust itself along some such lines
of distinction. This would leave a place in the sun, or more properly
speaking, *out of the sun,* for the so-called white race. They will be
allowed to inhabit the frozen North, the southern tip of South
America and Antarctica, while the darker-skinned members of the
race will probably monopolize the more tropical and even the temperate zones.

The future we predict for races therefore is that they will largely
cease to exist, and no harm will be done. Considering the difficulties
which racial doctrines have caused us in the past few decades, this
is hardly a dismal prospect, and is likely to offend only those who
still maintain irrational prejudices against the idea of racial mixture.

Rate of Race Mixture

An interesting study of the rate at which mixture between American Indian and white populations occurs has been published by
Cook (10). He finds, unsurprisingly, that the rate of mixture depends on cultural conditions rather than on the physical characteristics. He has computed that in California 100 years will suffice
to give complete mixture in the case of the cismontane Indians
studied by him but he supposes that in the case of the Great Basin
and Nevada Indians 500 years will be required. Both of these are

relatively small periods compared to the length of time mankind has existed and the great expanse of time which (we hope) still lies before the human species. But the final results of world tendencies towards race mixture will certainly not be achieved overnight, no matter how modern transport and the anticipated breaking down of racial prejudices may accelerate them.

The process of race crossing between Chinese and English and other mixtures has been studied by various workers (1, 14, 17, 21, 23, 24, 37). None of this work suggests that race mixture will not continue to occur, or that it is harmful in any way. That race mixture is not harmful, and may in fact be beneficial, is suggested by studies of Castle (9) and Haldane (16).

Probable Appearance of Future World Population

As to the characteristics of the future race or races which will emerge from miscegenation we may draw some fairly definite conclusions. In factors controlled by genes in a known manner the calculation is easy to make and we can see in Appendix IV–2 of this book (p. 416) how to do it. If an overwhelming number of Asiatics possessing about 30 per cent of blood group B mate with a relatively small number of North American Indians or white Europeans possessing relatively small amounts of blood group B (0–5 per cent) the offspring will have considerable amounts of blood group B, and the percentages of B in the hybrids will amount to 20 or 25 per cent or over. The same sort of calculation applies to the other genetic characteristics. The future world population will therefore consist mostly of individuals who can taste phenyl-thio-carbamide, who are very seldom Rh negative, etc. If we wish to speak also of the physical characteristics by which race was formerly defined, certain conclusions can still be drawn. From an early but thorough study of European-Hottentot mixture (12), Fischer concluded that dark hair and eyes, lighter skin color, tallness and an increased fronto-jugal index tended to predominate. European characteristics which tended to predominate in the offspring were apparently only those of skin color and stature.

In a study of Australian-white crosses Davenport (11) found that the shorter arm, shorter leg, and broader head of the white tended to predominate in the offspring but the narrower chest and shoulders, the dark hair and eyes of the Australian predominated. Straight hair tended to be dominant and we have accepted this preliminary generalization in our mention of the Mongolization of ancient Asiatic populations in Chapter XII. Skin color appeared to be intermediate. The reader will gather from such facts as Krogman's (22) listing tallness in man as dominant, whereas Davenport considered it a recessive, that much uncertainty about all these hereditary characteristics still remains (p. 298).

Considering these observations, and the relative numbers of the different modern races, we may perhaps surmise that the man of the future will be brachycephalic, perhaps about as tall as present-day inhabitants of Southern Europe, with dark brown eyes, a brown skin, and straight (or perhaps slightly wavy) hair. The population of the world, after the miscegenation which is here predicted, will be fairly uniform in appearance. We thus have reason to suppose that, whether or not we began with a heterogeneous species of *Homo sapiens,* we shall probably finish with a fairly homogeneous species at the end.

For the comfort of any who may feel depressed at the picture presented, we may point out the very definite evidence obtained by Wright (43) and others (cf. 15) that crossing of inbred families tends to improve the resulting offspring, and therefore may be expected to result in improvement of the human stock by reducing the possible undesirable effects of inbreeding. Crosses of different human strains are often (18) but not always (28, 40) more variable than either parental strain. Their offspring, particularly, may show considerable variation. Since the important advances of mankind have probably been largely due to the few individuals of unusual ability produced in each generation, we may well feel that the production of a higher degree of variability is desirable. This is particularly true if mankind is going to be faced with other crises in the future as serious as the one which at present confronts us. A variant (30, 36) with considerable originality will be required to solve our problems.

REFERENCES FOR CHAPTER XIII

1. Abel, W., *Zeit. Morph. & Anthrop.*, *36*, 311–329 (1937).
2. Bernstein, F., *Zeit. f. ind. Abst.-u. Verer.*, *37*, 237–270 (1925).
3. Behr-Pinnow, C. v., *Arch. f. Rass. u. Ges.-Biol.*, *27*, 395–412 (1934).
4. Boudreau, F. G., *Trans. N. Y. Acad. Sci.*, *8*, 112–123 (1946).
5. Boudreau, F. G., *Federation Proc.*, *7*, 427–434 (1948).
6. Burch, G. I., and E. Pendell, *Human Breeding and Survival*. Penguin Books, Inc., New York, 1947.
7. Carus, C. D., and C. L. McNichols, *Japan: Its Resources and Industries*. Harper & Bros., New York, 1944.
8. Castle, W. E., *Genetics and Eugenics*. Harvard Univ. Press, Cambridge, 3rd Edition, 1927.
9. Castle, W. E., *Science, 71*, 603–606 (1930).
10. Cook, S. F., *Human Biol.*, *15*, 153–165 (1943).
11. Davenport, C. B., *A. J. P. A.*, *8*, 73–94 (1925).
12. Fischer, E., *Die Rehobother Bastards*. Jena, Fischer, 1913.
13. Fischer, R., *Schweiz. Mschr. Zahnhlkd.*, *36*, 349–424 (1926).
14. Fleming, R. M., *Ann. Eug.*, *9*, 55–81 (1939).
15. Gates, R. R., *Human Genetics*. Macmillan Co., New York, 1946.
15a. Grubb, *Nature, 162*, 933 (1948).
16. Haldane, J. B. S., *New Paths in Genetics*. Harper & Bros., New York and London, 1942.
17. Hauschild, R., *Zeit. Morph. & Anthrop.*, *38*, 67–71 (1939).
18. Herskovits, M. J., *Am. Nat.*, *61*, 68–81 (1927).
19. Hitler, A., *Mein Kampf*. Reynal & Hitchcock, New York, 1940.
20. Hogben, L., *Genetic Principles in Medicine and Social Science*. Williams & Norgate, Ltd., London, 1931.
21. Hu, P. C., *Eugen. Rev.*, *30*, 109–116 (1938).
22. Krogman, W. M., *Eugen. News*, *21*, 139–146 (1936).
23. Lebzelter, V., *Zeit. Morph. & Anthrop.*, *34*, 213–231 (1934).
24. Little, K. L., *J. Roy. Anthrop. Inst.*, *73*, 57–73 (1943).
25. Ludwig, W., and C. Boost, *Zeit. f. menschliche Vererbungs-u. Konstitut.*, *24*, 577–619 (1940).
26. Malthus, T. R., *Essay on the Principle of Population*. London, 1798.
27. Martin, R., *Lehrbuch der Anthropologie*. Gustav Fischer, Jena, 1928.
28. Muller, H. J., *Am. Nat.*, *70*, 409–442 (1936).
28a. Muller, H. J., *J. Heredity*, *38*, 259–270 (1947).
29. Notestein, F. W., *Milbank Mem. Fund, Quart.*, *22*, #4, 424–444 (1944).
30. Padgett, L., *Astounding Science Fiction*, *39*, #2, 74–92 (1947).
31. Race, R. R., *Brit. Med. Bull.*, *2*, 165 (1944).
32. Race, R. R., *Nature, 153*, 771–772 (1944).
33. Salaman, R. N., *Jour. Genet.*, *1*, 273–292 (1911).

34. Smyth, H. D., *Atomic Energy for Military Purposes*. Princeton Univ. Press, Princeton, 1945.
35. Snyder, L. H., *The Principles of Heredity*. D. C. Heath & Co., Boston, 1946.
36. Stapledon, W. O., *Last and First Men*. Jonathan Cape and Harrison Smith, New York, 1931.
37. Tao, Y. K., *Zeit. Morph. & Anthrop., 33*, 349–408 (1935).
38. Terry, C. S., *The Origin of the Family of Bach Musicians*. Oxford Univ. Press, London, 1929.
39. Toynbee, A. J., *A Study of History*. Abridgement of Vols. I–VI, D. C. Somervell, Oxford Univ. Press, New York and London, 1947.
40. Wallis, W. D., *Am. Anthrop., 40*, 680–697 (1938).
41. Whitney, D. D., *Family Treasures*. Jacques Cattell Press, Lancaster, Pennsylvania, 1942.
42. Wiener, A. S., *Blood Groups and Transfusion*. Charles C Thomas, Springfield, 1943.
43. Wright, S., *U. S. Dept. Agricult. Bull. 1090*, 1121 (1922).

APPENDIX A Statistical Methods

Introduction

No single characteristic has been discovered which is sufficient to identify an individual as belonging to a certain race. This statement holds true whether we define race as we proposed in Chapter IX or whether we accept the older and more conventional definitions of race. The various races or groups of mankind are "polymorphic" in regard to practically every character which can be used for racial classification, and there is no one way in which the members of each race are all alike.

Means

If we make a particular observation on each of a number of individuals and find, as we usually do, that they are not all identical in this respect, we shall find, if the number of individuals is at all great, and especially if we wish to compare them with some other group, that it will not be convenient to enumerate seriatim the various results obtained. Instead, we resort to the device of finding the *mean* of the series, that is, we add up all the observations (using whatever numerical scale we find convenient for the characteristic in question), and divide the sum by the number of individuals included. This gives us a value which does not coincide, perhaps, with the results for any one individual, or any large group of individuals, but does represent the population as a whole. Thus our mean will just be the arithmetical average with which we are familiar from school arithmetic. Other estimates (e.g. *median, mode*), similar to the mean but differing from it somewhat, are also sometimes used in statistics but we shall not consider them here. (The median is not the arithmetical average, but the value which is just half-way from the smallest to the largest. The mode is the value observed most frequently.)

By comparing the means of two populations, we are, somewhat indirectly, comparing the populations themselves. Much use has been made of such comparisons.

Let x symbolize the numerical value of an observation, and n the number of observations. Then

$$m = \frac{\Sigma x}{n}$$

where the symbol m represents the mean, and the Greek letter Σ indicates the addition of all the observed values of x.

Deviations

A survey of a table or especially of a graph of a series of observations on a population which varies in the ordinary way will reveal that there are usually two characteristics which are worthy of note. One is the value of the mean, and the other is the width of the curve, or in other words the extent of the range over which the observed values are found to be distributed. This latter property, if the observations conform to a certain mathematical curve called the Normal Curve of Error, or, more briefly, the normal curve, can be measured by determining a value called the standard deviation, which is usually represented by the Greek letter σ. Two different ways of estimating σ have been proposed, both depending on the average value of the deviations of the various observations from the center of the curve. The simplest way is just to take the average of the deviations from the means. The larger the average deviation, the larger the value of σ, and the flatter the curve. This method of estimating σ had a considerable vogue at one time, and indeed if an infinitely large number of observations were available for each series being examined, one could always get the true value of σ by this method. But in practice we do not have an infinite set of observations for properties we wish to study, and our value of σ will be only an estimate of the σ of the (assumed and hypothetical) infinite set of observations of which our set is but a sample. Fisher calls attention to this difference by representing the true value of the standard deviation by the Greek letter σ, and our estimate of it by the Latin letter s. With a limited population to deal with, it has been found mathematically, although the proof of it is beyond the scope of the present text (37, 44) that the best estimate of σ is obtained if we square the deviations before adding them, and then divide, not by the number of observations, but by the number of *degrees of freedom,* which in this case is one less than the number of observations. Then extracting the square root of this quantity gives us our estimate of σ. In mathematical symbols, we have,

$$\sigma \neq \frac{\Sigma \, |\, (x-m)\, |}{n}$$

where the vertical lines represent the fact that we add the absolute value of $x-m$, or in other words, pay no attention to whether $x-m$ is positive or negative, and

$$\sigma = \sqrt{\frac{\Sigma \, (x-m)^2}{n-1}}$$

Instead of σ, for a long time it was customary to use 0.6745 σ, which was called the probable error (P.E.) because values up to $\pm$ 1 P.E. included just half of the results. The advantages of the P.E. are negligible, however, and modern writers use σ and avoid the continual multiplication by a constant.

Let us consider a typical series of observations (Table 43) of the

TABLE 43

Distribution of 400 Individuals into 9 Skin Color Categories. The Larger Numbers Indicate Darker Pigmentation

Class	Number of Individuals
1	3
2	50
3	106
4	109
5	80
6	42
7	7
8	2
9	1
	400

sort we might get in anthropology. Suppose skin color could be classified into nine numerical grades, and we examined a population which was variable, but on the whole rather intermediate for pigmentation. If we graph the observations, we obtain Figure 48, which approximates fairly well to a typical normal distribution.

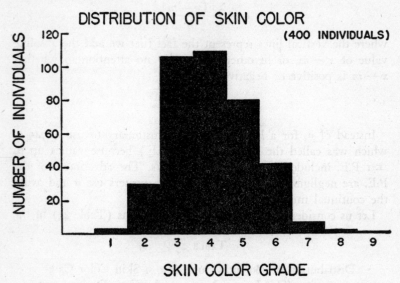

FIGURE 48. *Distribution of various grades of skin color in a population.*

It should be mentioned that our classification of the data into discrete classes of pigmentation has resulted in a simplification which is common in genetic anthropology, but which has to be introduced after the observations are made on metrical characters. If the height of 1583 individuals were measured, to the nearest millimeter, it would probably be found that practically every possible height class (and there might be 50 or more of these) was represented at least once. To obtain the mean it would be necessary to multiply each height by the number of individuals who possessed it, add, and divide by the number of individuals. This would involve a lot of arithmetic, and we should soon get into the habit of collecting the observed heights into groups, say one centimeter in size. So we should collect all the heights from 175.1 to 176.0 into one group, those from 176.1 to 177.0 into another, and so on.

In the present instance we have already performed the grouping, so the calculation of the mean reduces simply to the calculation of a weighted mean (Table 44). It will be noted, however, that the

TABLE 44

Calculation of a Weighted Mean and Its Standard Error
by the Detailed and More Laborious Method

Pigmentation Class Number	Frequency	Product
(x)	(f)	xf
1	3	3
2	50	100
3	106	318
4	109	436
5	80	400
6	42	252
7	7	49
8	2	16
9	1	9
	400	1583

Mean $= 1583/400 = 3.958$

To calculate σ (the standard error or standard deviation), it would be necessary to take the difference between each pigmentation value, square it, multiply by the frequency of that class, and add. Then this sum would be divided by one less than the total number of observations (i.e. 399), and the square root would be extracted. This involves much manipulation of numbers all containing three decimals, which is laborious. The next table (Table 45) shows how to do the calculations in much simpler fashion.

calculation of σ will still offer some difficulties. It is better to choose the value of a central pigmentation group and use this as the working mean. In this way both the true mean and σ can readily be calculated (Table 45).

The first column of Table 45 shows the skin color class, the second the number of individuals found in each class. The third column

TABLE 45

Calculation of Mean and Standard Deviation

Skin Color Class	Number of Individuals (f)	Deviation from Working Mean (d)	d × f	d² × f
1	3	−3	−9	27
2	50	−2	−100	200
3	106	−1	−106	106
			−215	
4	109	0		—
5	80	+1	+80	80
6	42	+2	+84	168
7	7	+3	+21	63
8	2	+4	+8	32
9	1	+5	+5	25
Total	400		+198	701
			−215	
			− 17	

Correction for mean $= \dfrac{(-17)^2}{400} =$ 0.7

Corrected $d^2 f$ 700.3

Mean $= (4-17/400) = 3.958$ Estimated variance $= 700.3/399 =$ 1.755

(Estimated σ ± 1.325)

Sheppard's adjustment for grouping $=$ 0.083

Adjusted variance $=$ 1.672

Adjusted estimate of $\sigma = \pm 1.293$

shows the deviation of each class from the working mean. The fourth column is formed by multiplying each deviation by the frequency of its class, and the fifth column by multiplying each frequency by the square of the deviation. The fifth column is added directly, but in the fourth column the upper portion, representing negative deviations, is added separately and subtracted from the sum of the lower portion (or vice versa). The difference enables us to correct the working mean to the true mean (by dividing the difference by the total number, 400, and adding the quotient algebraically to the working mean).

We then correct the fifth column by subtracting a correction, so as to obtain the true mean. This correction is obtained by taking the result obtained by adding the two parts of the fourth column, squaring, and dividing by the number of observations. The corrected column five, divided by 399 (one less than the number of observations), gives us the estimate of the quantity which Fisher calls the variance. All subsequent calculations are based on it. We obtain the value 2.175. By taking the square root of this quantity we get an estimate of the standard deviation, which proves to be 1.480.

For more precise work we have to allow for the fact that our data were grouped. It has been pointed out by Fisher (21) that the process of grouping may be represented as the addition to any true value of a "grouping error," positive or negative, which takes all values from $-\frac{1}{2}$ to $+\frac{1}{2}$ of the grouping unit with equal frequency. The effect of this on the population, and its average effect on samples, is to add a constant quantity $\frac{1}{12}$ to the number called the "variance") of which we take the square root in order to estimate the standard deviation. Sheppard's method of adjustment for grouping consists simply in subtracting this quantity from the estimate of the variance before the square root is extracted. This changes our first value and consequently the value of the estimated standard deviation.

The mean and the standard deviation together characterize the sample. In general, giving the mean of a series together with the standard deviation as calculated above is equivalent to giving all of the information contained in the series of observations, since the mean and the standard deviation are the only two variables determining the description of a normal distribution curve.

Non-Normal Distributions

If the curve is not a normal curve, other factors may be considered. In actual practice, it has not usually proved possible to do much more than examine the arithmetical series to see if there is evidence of a bimodal distribution, as shown in Figure 49, from which we may suspect that we are dealing with two different populations and with two different means. If the curves overlap, however, as shown here, it may be difficult to estimate the standard deviation of either series, although, if we wish to run a certain risk, we can reconstruct what we think the two curves would look like if separate (as shown by the dotted lines) and then estimate means and deviations.

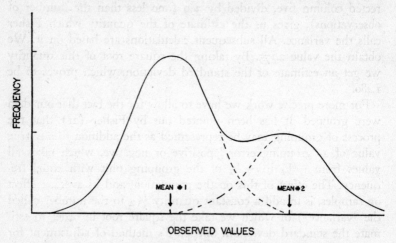

FIGURE 49. *Bimodal curve, resulting from the combination of two normal curves (see Fig. 50).*

Although we have used the term "normal curve" in the above discussion, we have on the whole restricted ourselves to what could be found out about an actual set of data, without making any assumptions as to the mathematical laws which such data may conform to. Nevertheless, we cannot attempt an exposition of statistical methods without giving the reader at least a glimpse of the theoretical foundations of the methods which are so often useful in dealing with anthropological data. So a bare minimum of theory seems required at this point.

Probability

The basis of all the more elaborate statistical methods is the concept of probability. But there has been considerable disagreement, even among those most expert in the subject, as to how probability ought to be defined, and it would not be wise to enter into that dispute here. We are going to be practical, not philosophical. Let us simply say that if we have a coin, symmetrically made, and toss this coin into the air and allow it to fall to the floor, either the side of the coin which usually bears a head, or the obverse side which is called tails, will be visible when the coin comes to rest. (We ignore the very remote chance that the coin might come to rest on its edge.) Since the coin is symmetrical, we say that the probability that the throw will result in heads is ½, or 50 per cent, and likewise the probability that the throw will result in tails is ½. Which will *actually* happen we cannot predict, for a probability is different from a certainty. A probability simply makes a statement about the chances that a thing *may* happen but does not assert that it necessarily must happen. However, if we toss the coin repeatedly, say several thousand times, probability enables us to assert that it is very unlikely that the coin (assuming it really is perfectly symmetrical) will fall heads every time, or tails every time. Probability even allows us to assert that it is very unlikely that out of a thousand throws the number of heads will differ very much from 500, and the same for the number of tails. In throwing dice, the probability of getting any one number (with honest dice) is 1 out of 6, and a veteran player would become *very* suspicious if, after a thousand throws, he found the number 6 was turning up about two thirds of the time. In fact, we may be quite certain that it would not require anything like a thousand such throws to convince a professional gambler that there was something wrong with the dice. Probability in this sense is pretty well understood by most people, and all we need to go into here is the arithmetical principles involved in applying it to the study of samples, large or small, which may represent a portion of the population we are investigating, or may actually be the whole population.

Let us revert to our hypothetical example of throwing a coin, and let us symbolize the chance of throwing heads by the letter h and the chance of throwing tails by the letter t. Since we assume that one or the other must happen, and since in the language of probability certainty is represented by the figure *one,* we know that, even if h and t differ somewhat, $h + t = 1$. If we toss the coin two

times in succession the chance that we shall obtain heads the first
time is represented by the probability h and, if conditions remain
the same, the chance that we shall obtain heads the second time is
also represented by the probability h. The probability of two independent events occurring simultaneously or in succession is equal
to the product of the respective probabilities. So the probability that
we shall throw heads twice in succession is represented by

$$h \times h = h^2$$

The probability, similarly, that we shall throw tails twice in succession is equal to t^2. The probability that we shall throw heads and
then tails is equal to $h \times t$ and the probability that we shall throw
tails and then heads is equal to $t \times h$, which amounts to the same
thing, so the probability of throwing heads and tails in the two
tries is equal to

$$2ht$$

Therefore we shall obtain:

Chances of two heads........................... h^2
Chances of one head and one tail............ $2ht$
Chances of two tails........................... t^2

The reader who remembers his algebra will recognize these as
the successive terms of the binomial expansion of $(h + t)^2$, and it
is easy to show that when more tries are involved, the chances of
the various outcomes are calculated similarly from the expression
$(h + t)^n$, where $n =$ number of trials. The observations obtained
in observing an actual group can be compared with this hypothetical
prediction which is made on the basis of pure chance.

Normal Curve of Error

If n is at all large, the computations become laborious, for the
number of terms in the expansion becomes larger and larger. Fortu-
nately, this need not distress us too much since we are very seldom
interested in the actual probability of various individual outcomes,
such as heads, followed by tails, followed by heads, and so forth;
but merely wish to know if a given observed result is likely or

unlikely on the basis of pure chance. This enables us to make use of a short cut. When *n* is large, the curve obtained by plotting, against the probability of each possible outcome, the number of times this outcome is to be expected, is the curve shown in Figure 50, which is known as the normal curve of error, or probability curve,

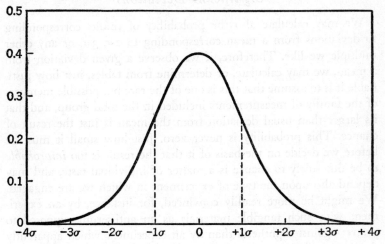

FIGURE 50. *Normal frequency curve, or standard curve of error.*

which has a known formula. (To be exact, we get this curve if *n* is infinite and $h = t$. However, even if *n* is of the order of 20–50, and *h* is not exactly equal to *t,* the resulting curve comes very close to the one shown here.) We know that this curve has a certain simple function, called the standard deviation, and which is represented by the Greek letter σ (sigma), which has this property: if we lay off distances equal to σ on each side of the center of the probability curve — which will correspond to the mean of our measurements on the population we have examined — these lines will include between them about two thirds (67.45 per cent) of the area under the curve, or in other words, the probability of a result represented by a point outside these lines is only about one third.

We have already seen (p. 370) that the value of σ is a measure of the range of variation in observations which obey the normal curve. Thus we can begin to see a tie-in between facts we observe, and predictions we make on the basis of probability.

Significant Deviations

We may calculate also the probability of results corresponding to deviations from a mean corresponding to 2σ, 3σ, or any other multiple we like. Therefore, if we observe a given deviation from a mean, we may calculate, or determine from tables, just how justifiable it is to assume that this is one of the rare but possible members of the family of measurements included in the total group, and that its larger than usual deviation from the mean is just the result of chance. This probability is never zero. Just how small it must be before we decide on the basis of it that the result is too *improbable* to be due solely to chance is a matter of individual taste, and may depend also upon the type of experiment in which we are engaged. We might be more readily convinced, for instance, by an experiment with such tangible materials as an anti-serum supposed to protect against diphtheria than by an experiment which apparently demonstrated the existence of telepathy or clairvoyance. If we do not believe that the observed departure from expectation is due to chance, we decide that the measurement in question really lies outside the range of the remainder of the measurements which we have been examining, and is due to something other than chance.

In biological work in general it has proved satisfactory to consider a deviation as being "significant" if it lies as much as 2σ from the center of the curve, because such an observation would be made by chance only about once in 20 times (5 per cent of the cases). Something which occurs in 5 per cent of the cases examined is not outside the realm of probability, it is true, and if we wish to be quite certain that the observations in question should be considered significantly different from the mean of our other observations, we should have to take a higher multiple of σ as our guide. But this procedure will have the disadvantage that the higher the multiple of σ, and the more improbable the observation must be for us to consider it significantly different, the less are the chances that we can differentiate, by our sampling methods, two groups which are actually different.

We should not progress further without trying to make clear to the reader the sense in which we are using the word "significant." It is true that it is a technical term, standing for an idea common in experimental science, but not in daily life, but, as Fisher points out (24), there is no need for anyone to fail to understand it, since it can be made plain in very simple terms. Fisher says, let us suppose that we have measurements of the statures of 100 Englishmen and 100 Frenchmen. It may be that the first group are, on the average, an inch taller than the second, although the two sets of heights overlap widely. Of course, if the two groups have been chosen from their respective populations in such a way as *not* to be random samples of the populations they represent, then it is clear that an examination of these samples will not enable us to draw adequate conclusions about those populations, but if we know, or assume, that our samples are satisfactory as to the manner in which they have been obtained, the further question then arises as to whether the magnitude of the observed difference between them might not have occurred *by chance* in two samples taken from populations of exactly the *same average* height. If the probability of this is considerable, that is, if this would have occurred in 50 or even 10 per cent of such samplings, the difference between our samples is usually said to be insignificant. If the probability of accident is too small, such as 1 in 1000 or even 1 in 100 or 1 in 20 trials, it is usually termed "significant," and is regarded as providing substantial evidence of a difference in average stature between the two populations sampled. We must notice that the test can never lead us to assert that the two populations are identical in stature. In the first example, we are only allowed to say that the data provided from our samples are not sufficient to justify the assertion that they are different. In the second case, where we call the difference significant, we are able to be somewhat more positive, for we can state that: either our sampling has been exceptionally unfortunate, or the populations really do differ more or less in the way indicated by the available data. The chances of our being deceived in the last conclusion may be very small, and what is more important, they may be calculated with accuracy without our having to rely on personal judgment.

It may not be immediately clear to some people how it is possible to calculate how often a certain average would be recorded in, say, 1000 trials, if as a matter of fact we have never made a thousand such trials, and have only one small sample on which to base our opinion. Fisher (24) points out that the simplest way of understanding quite rigorously, yet without the use of mathematics, what the calculation of the test of significance amounts to is to consider what would happen if our 200 actual measurements of Englishmen and Frenchmen were written on cards and then without regard to nationality were divided at random into two new groups of 100 each. This division into two groups could be done in a very large number of ways, but though the number is enormous, it is a finite and calculable number. Let us suppose that for each of these ways of division the difference between the two average statures of the two artificially established groups was calculated. Sometimes the difference in average stature will be less than one inch, and sometimes greater. If it is very seldom greater than an inch, for instance in only 100 of the many ways in which the subdivision into two artificial populations can possibly be made, the statistician will have been right in saying that the original two samples differed significantly. For if in fact the two populations were homogeneous, and the two samples also not significantly different, there would be nothing to distinguish the particular subdivision in which the Frenchmen are separated from the Englishmen from any of the other possible subdivisions of 100 results versus another 100 results. Actually, as Fisher points out, the statistician does not have to carry out this simple but in practice very tedious process, but makes other calculations, more practicable, but based on exactly the same principle.

The test of significance does no more, and attempts to do no more, than to answer the straightforward question: could these samples have been drawn at random from the same population? — and calculate a probability. If the probability is very small the answer given is *no*. If it is not so small as to reach the level of significance required, the answer is, "Yes, they could." Fisher points out that the answer is *never,* "Yes, they must have been."

If we want a measure of the significance of a given deviation from chance expectation, we may calculate it for the coin-tossing experiment, where the probabilities h and t are known, as

$$\sigma = \sqrt{nht}$$

where n is the number of trials. If we tossed a coin 100 times, and knew it was absolutely unbiased, we should find $\sigma = \sqrt{100 \cdot \frac{1}{2} \cdot \frac{1}{2}} = 5$. Therefore, if we were presented with a set of results in which 65 heads had been obtained, and only 35 tails, we should say that since the 65 observed heads differed from the predicted number (50) by 15 (this number is called the deviation, or D), and therefore $\dfrac{D}{\sigma} = \dfrac{15}{5} = 3$, it looked as if something other than chance had been operating.

In most scientific work the absolute values of h and t, or whatever corresponds to them, are not known, but must be estimated experimentally. In such cases we are forced to be satisfied with an *estimate* of σ. We have already shown (p. 374) how such an estimate is obtained in the case of a simple distribution.

Unless the characteristic which we are measuring or testing for is actually determined solely by chance, we cannot expect that its distribution in a population will follow the normal frequency curve, which is derived from the idea of pure chance. In a population where a lethal gene is operating, we shall find that in the offspring the distribution will not be that of a normal curve, since the individuals receiving a double dose of the lethal gene die before reaching the adult stage and thus will not be represented. (There are many other kinds of deviation from normality which can affect a population.) The kind of curve obtained can also be affected by the procedures of observation and the methods we use to record the characteristic in question. If we ask a group of subjects to compare a group of weights, by lifting them, with a standard weight, we can express the errors they make as so many ounces or grams in each case. These errors could be plotted against the number of times they were observed. But we could also plot the *logarithms* of the weights, and obtain quite a different curve. The latter turns out to be more nearly a normal curve (34).

Frequencies

In reasoning about populations of various sizes, to make our observations comparable, we must take the frequency with which a character is observed in each population.

Suppose we are examining a large number of individuals and observing them for the presence or absence of some certain feature. If the first two subjects we examine differ in such a way that one displays the characteristic, whereas the other does not, from these observations we should be led to calculate an incidence of the character of 50 per cent. But is this result characteristic of the rest of the population? Obviously we have very little reason to believe that it is, since our estimate is based on a sample of only two individuals. Even if we make observations on ten individuals, our estimate of the frequency of the characteristic will still be subject to possible error, and only if we study the entire population, which is often an impossible task, will we know the actual frequency of expression of the characteristic in this particular group.

It seems logical therefore that there should be a standard deviation attached to any estimates of the *frequency* of a characteristic in a population. This will obviously depend on the size of the sample selected. It can readily be derived from the formula for σ we have already given, and if we change our symbols, so that $h = p$, $t = 1 - p$, and $n = V$, we find that it can be proved (34, 41, 42) that

$$\sigma = \sqrt{\frac{p\,(1 - p)}{V}}$$

where σ stands for our estimate of the standard deviation of the frequency p, p for the observed frequency of the characteristic, V for the total number of individuals examined and the square root sign $\sqrt{}$ has the usual significance. It is not difficult to compile a table from which standard deviations of frequencies or, if we prefer, of per cents (since a per cent is just a frequency multiplied by 100) of any observed characteristic may be obtained. We offer such a table in Table 46. We may use this to test roughly if an observed difference in percentages is significant. More accurate eval-

TABLE 46

Standard Deviations (σ) of Observed Per Cents (43)

Size of Sample (V)	Observed Per Cent				
	10 or 90	20 or 80	30 or 70	40 or 60	50
100	3.00	4.00	4.58	4.90	5.00
150	2.45	3.27	3.74	4.00	4.08
200	2.12	2.83	3.24	3.46	3.54
250	1.90	2.53	2.90	3.10	3.16
300	1.73	2.31	2.65	2.83	2.89
400	1.50	2.00	2.29	2.45	2.50
500	1.34	1.79	2.05	2.19	2.24
750	1.10	1.46	1.67	1.79	1.83
1000	0.95	1.27	1.45	1.55	1.58
1500	0.78	1.03	1.18	1.27	1.29
2000	0.67	0.89	1.03	1.10	1.12
3000	0.55	0.73	0.84	0.89	0.91
5000	0.42	0.57	0.65	0.69	0.71
10,000	0.30	0.40	0.46	0.49	0.50
20,000	0.21	0.28	0.32	0.35	0.35

Use of Table. Suppose we have two samples of a population, each of 100 individuals. In one the per cent of group O has been found to be 40 per cent, in the other 50 per cent. May we assume a real serological difference in the two samples? From the table, σ for 40 per cent and 100 individuals = 4.90; for 50 per cent and 100 individuals we find 5.00 We obtain $\sigma_D = \sqrt{\sigma_1{}^2 + \sigma_2{}^2}$. We find $\sigma_D = 6.85$. The difference, 10, between the two observations, divided by $\sigma_D = 1.46$. Since this is less than the ratio 2.00, which is arbitrarily taken as the boundary between significance and non-significance, the observations cannot be said to differ significantly. If the samples had been twice as large, we should obtain a ratio D/σ_D of about 2.2, which is by agreement significant, but not strikingly so.

uation of the significance of a difference between two series may be had by other methods, such as the χ^2 test.

Of course no amount of statistical calculation can be counted on always to protect us from false conclusions due to erroneous determinations. Calculations may even at times create a false picture of certainty which is not justified. If an investigator, using an unsatisfactory blood grouping anti-A serum, should find a percentage of group O of 70, while a more careful worker found for another sample of the same population a percentage of O of 40, the difference between the two series would appear mathematically significant even though the samples might not be very large. And although the data obtained by the first worker might even be compatible with the conditions of genetic equilibrium, suggesting an anthropological difference between the two samples, the real cause of the discrepancy would have been faulty technique.

Chi Square

There is another statistical estimate which proves useful in anthropological work. This is the statistic known as χ^2 (21). The χ^2 test was specifically designed to test whether an observed distribu-

TABLE 47

Hypothetical Results of Tests for "Taste-Blindness"
on Populations A and B

Population	Tasters	Non-tasters
A	150	50
B	75	25

tion of individuals into different categories could be due solely to chance. In other words, it enables us to test if a difference between two populations is merely a matter of sampling error, or reflects a real difference in the composition of the populations. For example, suppose we merely classify individuals into "tasters" and "non-tasters" (p. 278). If for two populations, A and B, we find the results shown in Table 47, it is clear without further tests that the data do not indicate any difference in respect to taste gene frequencies, for the numbers are exactly proportional.

Suppose, however, we test two populations C and D, and obtain results which are not so easily analyzed (Table 48). The proportion of "tasters" is different in the two populations, but is it "significant"? We can answer this question by computing χ^2.

TABLE 48

Hypothetical Results of Tests for "Taste-Blindness"
on Populations C and D

Population	Tasters	Non-tasters
C	75	25
D	60	40

The value of χ^2 is obtained by dividing (in each class) the square of the difference between the number observed and the number expected, by the number expected, and adding all these quotients. The "expected" numbers are calculated from the assumption that the observed difference is simply due to chance, and the two samples are both representatives of the same population. Consequently we compute the expected values from the observed proportions found in the sum of the two populations C and D. The details are shown in Tables 49 and 50.

In general, the larger the value of χ^2 the more unlikely it is that the observed distribution could be due solely to chance. To find what the probabilities are that chance alone is responsible, we must look up our value of χ^2 in a table such as that given by Fisher (21), and note that for our present case, in which there is one "degree of freedom," the probability of getting a χ^2 as large as 5.12 is less than 0.05 and not much more than 0.02. Since it is generally agreed that a probability of less than 0.05 is significant (p. 380), it follows that we shall incline to the belief that the incidence of tasters in populations C and D is actually somewhat different.

The number of "degrees of freedom" in a 2×2 table such as the above is always equal to one. For larger tables the degrees of freedom can be calculated by ascertaining how many of the "cells" of the table could be filled in arbitrarily and still leave enough of them empty so that, by filling the remainder in properly, the original marginal totals would remain the same. (There are 4 cells in a

TABLE 49

Preliminary Calculations for χ^2

Population	T	t	Total
C	75	25	100
D	60	40	100
C + D	135	65	200

Expected value of T for population $C = \dfrac{135}{200} \times 100 = 67.5$

Expected value of $t = \dfrac{65}{200} \times 100 = 32.5$

Expected value of T for $D = \dfrac{135}{200} \times 100 = 67.5$,

for $t = \dfrac{65}{200} \times 100 = 32.5$

TABLE 50

Calculation of χ^2

Population	T		t	
	observed	expected	observed	expected
C	75	67.5	25	32.5
D	60	67.5	40	32.5

Taking the differences between observed and expected values for C(T), C(t), D(T), and D(t) in succession and dividing each by the expected value, we have:

$$\frac{(7.5)^2}{67.5} + \frac{(7.5)^2}{32.5} + \frac{(7.5)^2}{67.5} + \frac{(7.5)^2}{32.5} = 5.12$$

2 × 2 table, 6 in a 3 × 2 table, etc.) It is clear that in a 2 × 2 table like the present one, only one cell can be filled in arbitrarily. In filling in the remaining cells we may make use of any values we please, positive or negative, and thus obtain the original marginal totals.

If the numbers involved are small, so that the number expected in any class is less than 10, a "correction for continuity" should be applied to the simple calculations just outlined, for greatest accuracy (27). This is particularly desirable if the results appear to be just barely significant (probability slightly less than 0.05). A method of making this correction is given by Fisher and Yates (27).

Application of the χ^2 test to biological experiments, even to some of the results which have been published as showing real differences between small samples, or the advantage in medical practice of some certain mode of treatment, sometimes gives surprising results. For instance, if out of one group of 73 individuals examined, only 28 possessed the epicanthic eye fold, whereas out of another group of 13 it was found that 9 possessed this characteristic, it is probable that some workers would postulate a greater Mongoloid influence on the second group. Actually, however, accurate application of the χ^2 test shows that the results are below our usual level of significance (27).

Another example of the use of the χ^2 test in anthropology is its application to a test of genetic expectation. For instance, in crosses involving two Mendelian characters, by breeding the first hybrid generation we should expect to obtain four classes in the ratio of 9 : 3 : 3 : 1. Good observations on such families in man are not available, but the principle can be illustrated by an example from a plant experiment. Fisher analyzed some observations on *Primula* to see if they agreed with this hypothesis. The plants were first classified as having flat leaves or crimped leaves. Then these categories were classified according to the character of the "eye." The observed numbers of individuals and the expected numbers based on the Mendelian formula are shown in Table 51. From these χ^2 is calculated to be 10.870, and, when we consult the tables, remembering that here the number of degrees of freedom is 3, we see that the chance of exceeding this value of χ^2 is between 0.01 and 0.02,

TABLE 51

Observations (de Winton and Bateson) on Segregation of Two Characters in *Primula*

| | FLAT LEAVES | | CRIMPED LEAVES | | |
	Normal Eye	Primrose Queen Eye	Normal Eye	Primrose Queen Eye	Total
Observed (B)	328	122	77	33	560
Expected (E)	315	105	105	35	560
d²/E	0.537	2.752	7.467	0.114	10.870

The symbol B stands for the observed number in each class, E for the "expected" number calculated from the assumption that the classes ought to show frequencies in the ratio $9 : 3 : 3 : 1$ (p. 37). This symbol $d = B - E$. The sum of the four different values of d^2/E is equal to χ^2.

so that if we take the usual limit of 0.05 as significant we shall say that in this case the deviations from expectation are definitely significant.

The χ^2 test can be used to test whether, in a collection of random observations made on brothers and sisters, the character being studied behaves genetically as a unit. This test can thus be of great value in the identification of characters determined by individual genes. We have seen (Ch. XI) that uncertainty about the mode of inheritance, and the absence of any information as to the frequencies of the genes acting, is one of the defects of the anthropological characters formerly used to determine racial differences. By use of the χ^2 test, Cotterman (12) seemed to show that the taste reaction to PTC behaved genetically as a unit. However, some unexplained exceptions (tasting children resulting from non-tasting $\times$ non-tasting matings) have since been reported, and the χ^2 test fails to work when applied to these results. Either these exceptions represent errors, or the inability to taste PTC is not inherited as a simple recessive.

The χ^2 method can be applied to test whether differences in numbers of individuals belonging to various blood groups in different populations are significant. For instance, in the Egyptian town of Assiut, Boyd and Boyd (8) found the following distribution of M, MN, and N individuals among the Copts (Christians) and Muslims respectively: Copts, M = 105, MN = 223, N = 84; Muslims, M = 30, MN = 63, N = 13. Is there any reason to suppose that the incidence of the three phenotypes is different in these two different religious groups? Calculation (Table 52) shows that

TABLE 52

M, N Blood Types in Assiut

	M	MN	N	Totals
Copts	105 (107.4)	223 (227.5)	84 (77.2)	412
Muslims	30 (27.6)	63 (58.5)	13 (19.8)	106
Totals	135	286	97	518

Figures in parentheses are the value to be expected if the two populations do not differ in M, N frequencies.

$$\chi^2 = \frac{2.4^2}{107.4} + \frac{4.5^2}{227.5} + \frac{6.8^2}{77.2} + \frac{2.4^2}{27.6} + \frac{4.5^2}{58.5} + \frac{6.8^2}{19.8} = 4.433$$

for this case χ^2 = about 4.43, and examination of Fisher's table shows that for one degree of freedom such a value of χ^2 has a probability of about 0.03. In other words, the observed difference could arise only in about 3 per cent of the trials in samples drawn purely by chance from the same population, and the observed difference is significant.

Another example of the use of the χ^2 method will be found in Chapter XII where the test was used to determine whether or not the observed blood group distribution in certain American Indian tribes could reasonably be ascribed to the results of mixture with Europeans. In this case, the procedure was to calculate the results of varying degrees of mixture with a European stock which had blood group frequencies similar to those at present found in the white population in North America, and compare these with the observed distributions. Certain ones of these hypothetical mixed populations would of course give better agreement (that is, smaller values of χ^2) than would others. In most cases, χ^2, as thus computed, passed through a minimum, and if this *minimum* was found to be larger than could reasonably be attributed to chance, then it was concluded that it was unreasonable to attribute the frequencies observed in these Indians to any possible race mixture.

Correlation Coefficient

Still another statistical technique which we must discuss is the determination of the correlation coefficient. Fisher states that no quantity is more characteristic than this of biometrical work. Certainly extensive use of the correlation coefficient has been made in physical anthropology. In determining the correlation coefficient we are merely trying to answer the question whether or not two observed measurements or quantities tend to go together more often than would be expected on the basis of pure chance. The simplest way of getting a preliminary idea of this is to make a graph, plotting one variable as the abscissa and the other as the ordinate and let each individual combination of the two measurements be represented by a dot, which gives us a so-called "scatter diagram" as shown in Figure 51. From the shape of this diagram it is very often evident to the eye, even without calculation, that the two quantities are correlated. Complete absence of correlation would generally give a more or less circular pattern, if we plot both our measurements on linear scales. The existence of correlation is shown by the presence of an elliptical pattern, and the greater the eccentricity of the ellipse, the greater is the correlation.

One of the earliest and most striking successful applications of the method of correlation was in the biometrical study of inheritance. This was at a time when nothing was known of the mechanism of inheritance as we have outlined it in Chapter II, but by the method of correlation it was possible to demonstrate the existence of inheritance in human families, that is, to show that qualities present in the parents tended to be present in the children more often than would be expected on the basis of chance. In future anthropological work,

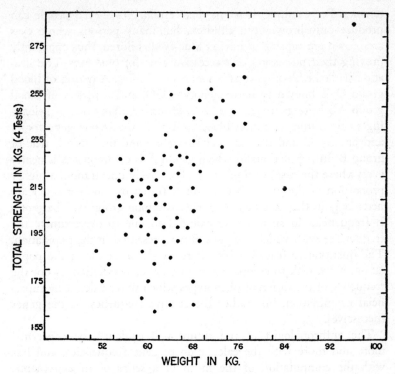

FIGURE 51. *Scatter diagram, strength vs. weight (after Jones).*

the method of correlation will probably be less and less used, since we shall be dealing more and more with characters inherited in a known manner, and in such cases χ^2 can be used. Those working with genetic traits will seldom find it necessary to compute correlation coefficients. Therefore methods of calculating such coefficients are not presented here.

Gene Frequencies

When we observe the color of the skin, hair or eyes of a group of people, or even when we determine their blood groups, in most individuals this only tells us their superficial or phenotypic characteristics. For example, it seems that certain brown-eyed people can produce only brown-eyed children, but many persons whose eyes are brown are capable of having blue-eyed children, thus apparently proving their possession of a recessive gene for blue eyes. The situation with the blood groups is somewhat similar. A person of blood group O is known to be of genotype OO, and a person of blood group AB belongs to genotype AB. However, many people belonging to the rather common blood group A possess one gene for A and one for O and thus are heterozygous; and the same is true of group B. In populations in which group A is common (as is nearly everywhere the case) and group B is relatively uncommon, a higher proportion of the group B individuals (often over 90 per cent) are heterozygous than is true of the more common group A. The *group* B frequencies in such a case would lead one to overestimate the frequencies with which the *gene B* is represented in the population. The quantitative feature which is really characteristic of the population, if we seek to compare it with another population, is not the frequency of the different phenotypes which we can detect by superficial examination, but rather the relative frequency of the genes themselves.

The anthropologist of the future will evidently be concerned more and more with the calculation of gene frequencies, and less with the computation of the mean of a series of measurements. Let us turn, then, to the problem of estimating gene frequencies and methods of testing the significance of differences which are found in such frequencies.

When we speak of the number of genes in a population, we really mean the number of genes which have *gone into producing the population we are studying*. A *single gene* coming from a single reproductive cell is all that is needed to give one individual the property of having genes of this sort in his body cells, and of being able to transmit the gene to his offspring. In a population all the individuals of which are homozygous for a certain gene, say *X*, it is obvious that each individual's character in respect to the specific factor we are considering is a result of the reaction of two genes for *X*. If *X* is a dominant gene, of course a single gene for *X* would have been sufficient to produce the same characteristic. A population of *n* homozygous individuals for the gene *X* would be the result of the action of $2n$ genes for X. A population of n individuals all heterozygous would be the result of the action of n genes for X. For convenience, we take the gene frequency of X as equal to 1.00 for a population all of whose members are homozygous for X. This means we shall count only half of the genes in each homozygous individual's make-up, so the gene frequency of X in a population of n individuals all homozygous for X would be $\frac{2n}{2} = n$. In this simple case we calculate the gene frequency simply by dividing by two the actual number of genes we know to have produced the population. This of course gives a number equal to the population number n itself.

A slightly more complicated case is found in the M, N gene series, where we find just three genotypes, *MM, MN,* and *NN.* All three are recognizable directly by serological tests. The individual of phenotype *MN* obviously has one gene for M and one for N. The individual of phenotype *MM* has two genes for M and the *NN* has two genes for N, so we may enumerate the gene frequency in the population by a simple process of counting. It will prove most convenient to have our computed gene frequencies add up exactly to 1.000, so we shall have to allow for the fact that the adult individual possesses two genes at each homologous chromosome locus, and thus obtain the following formulas:

$$m = \overline{MM} + \frac{\overline{MN}}{2} \qquad [1]$$

$$n = \overline{NN} + \frac{\overline{MN}}{2} \qquad [2]$$

The gene frequency for M, which we represent by small $m,$ is given by [1] and the gene frequency for N by [2]. Fisher (21) has pointed out that in some cases more than one way exists to estimate a quantity from observation and some ways are preferable to others because they give what he calls the maximum likelihood values. It happens in this case that this simple method of estimating the M and N gene frequencies satisfies Fisher's criteria.

The reliability with which we can compute the gene frequencies from a given sample will of course depend on the population being tested, for the frequencies observed may vary, depending on the size of the sample. Figure 52, taken from a paper by Moureau (38), shows how the blood type frequencies computed from samples of various sizes fluctuate, while the samples are still small, from the

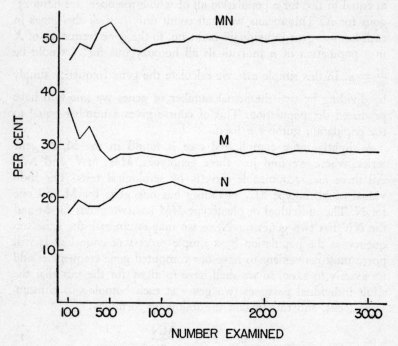

FIGURE 52. *Random fluctuations in blood group frequencies, showing influence of sample size (after Moureau).*

obviously more reliable value estimated from a population of 3000 individuals.

From the principle of random mating (p. 410) we know that in a population in genetic equilibrium the frequencies of the three blood types M, MN and N will be given by the successive terms of the binomial expansion of $(m + n)^2$, where $m + n = 1$. Thus we obtain

$$\overline{M} = m^2$$
$$\overline{MN} = 2mn$$
$$\overline{N} = n^2$$

where the bar ($^-$) over the letter shows that the symbol represents the frequency of the type in the population. If the population is really in genetic equilibrium (and we have made no errors in our determinations), it follows that $m = \sqrt{M}$, $n = \sqrt{N}$, and $\sqrt{M} + \sqrt{N} = 1.000$ exactly. Now of course it may happen that, due to accidents in our sampling of the population, the value $\sqrt{M}$ does not give exactly the right result for m, or $\sqrt{N}$ for n. In such a case we may find that the sum of $\sqrt{M}$ and $\sqrt{N}$ does not equal 1.000. Designate the difference between the sum $(\sqrt{M} + \sqrt{N})$ and 1.000 as D. Then it has been shown by Wiener (49, 50) that this quantity D has a standard deviation, σ_D, which is very simply calculated by the formula

$$\sigma_D = \frac{0.5}{\sqrt{V}}$$

where V represents the number of individuals examined.

We may use σ_D to test whether our observed D is so great as to suggest that we have made serious errors in our determinations, or the population is not in genetic equilibrium, or both. Just as a matter of chance, $\dfrac{D}{\sigma}$ should not exceed the value 2.00 more than about once in 20 times. When series of M, N tests done by reliable workers are tested in this way, we find that the statistical expectation is confirmed (50).

The standard deviation of our estimations of the M and N gene frequencies by simple counting (p. 395) has been shown by Wiener (50) and Stevens (47) to be equal to:

$$\sigma_m = \sqrt{\frac{MN}{2V}}$$

where V is the number of persons examined. The standard deviation is the same for both gene frequencies. It will be noted that, as is usual in statistics, it falls off as the square root of the number of individuals tested.

From the principle of random mating we deduce for the *O, A, B* series of genes that the frequencies of the various phenotypes will be given by the binomial expansion of $(p+q+r)^2$, where $p+q+r = 1.000$. This gives us

$$\bar{A} = p^2 + 2pr$$
$$\bar{B} = q^2 + 2qr$$
$$\overline{AB} = 2pq$$
$$\bar{O} = r^2$$

where the letters have the usual significance.

Solving these equations for p, q, and r, we are enabled to estimate these gene frequencies from the observed blood group frequencies (51).

We have $r = \sqrt{O}$. Substituting in the first equation, we get

$$p^2 + 2p\sqrt{O} = A$$

Solving this quadratic equation, we obtain

$$p = \sqrt{O + A} - \sqrt{O},$$

similarly,

$$q = \sqrt{O + B} - \sqrt{O}$$

These seem to be the best *simple* formulas to use for computing these gene frequencies, for the method allows extension to cases in which we have more than three allelomorphs.

For instance, if we wish to consider the sub-groups of A and AB, and let p_1 represent the frequency of the gene for A_1, and p_2 that for A_2, we can easily show that

$$p_1 = \sqrt{O + A_1 + A_2} - \sqrt{O + A_2}$$
$$p_2 = \sqrt{O + A_2} - \sqrt{O}$$

Bernstein (2, 3) was able to show, for the simple case of three allelomorphs, that

$$r = \sqrt{O}$$
$$p = 1 - \sqrt{O + B}$$
$$q = 1 - \sqrt{O + A}$$

These formulas have been much used, and are historically earlier than those just given, but they offer no advantage, the labor of computation is the same, and either computation can be done by a nomogram (6, 7, 30). If we represent the difference of the sum of our gene estimates from unity by D, as before, the value of D obtained in either way will have the same value, but will differ in sign (7).

Bernstein (3) showed how to compute the standard deviation of D in this case. Let

$$D = 1 - (p + q + r)$$

The standard deviation of this difference is given by the expression:

$$\sigma_D = \sqrt{\frac{pq}{2V}/(1 - p)(1 - q)}$$

By dividing the observed difference by its standard deviation one may estimate whether or not the deviation could be due to chance. This computation can also be performed with the aid of a nomogram (6, 7).

The computation of Rh gene frequencies, if we assume with Wiener that they are inherited by a series of multiple alleles, is much the same as that in the A_1, A_2, B, O system. Wiener and Sonn have offered fairly simple formulas (51a) and Fisher (25, 26) has shown how to obtain the best statistical estimates.

The above estimates of p, q, and r are not the best possible, and usually do not satisfy the relation $p + q + r = 1$ exactly (see Table 55). Bernstein (2, 3) devised a method of estimation which gave values which came closer to adding up to unity, and which at the same time gave as good a statistical fit as was desired. His revised formulas were

$$p = \left(1 - \sqrt{\overline{O + B}}\right)\left(1 + \frac{D}{2}\right)$$

$$q = \left(1 - \sqrt{\overline{O + A}}\right)\left(1 + \frac{D}{2}\right)$$

$$r = \left(\sqrt{O} + \frac{D}{2}\right)\left(1 + \frac{D}{2}\right)$$

Stevens (47) later showed how the values of p, q, and r giving the best statistical estimate could be derived, to any desired degree of approximation, from Fisher's method of "maximum likelihood." If the gene frequencies of different populations are to be compared, or if one wishes to do computation of degrees of race mixture (p. 418), it is preferable to get the best statistical estimates of p, q, and r, either by Bernstein's adjustments, or by Stevens's method. The latter is somewhat more difficult, but has the advantage that the standard deviations (p. 370) of the gene frequencies can be estimated simultaneously (see App. IV–3).

Alleles vs. Independent Factors

Now it will be of interest to take up the statistical considerations by which Bernstein (2) proved that the two factor hypothesis of von Dungern and Hirszfeld (13) was incorrect, and that his own triple allele theory fitted the statistical facts in addition to the fact that it predicted more correctly the outcome of $O \times AB$ matings (p. 410).

From the principle of random mating, again (p. 218) we find if the blood groups, as von Dungern and Hirszfeld supposed, are inherited as a series of two independent pairs of factors A and a and

TABLE 53

Frequencies of the Four Blood Groups

(Theory of von Dungern and Hirszfeld)

Groups	Genotypes	Frequencies	
$\bar{O}$	aabb	$\bar{p}^2\bar{q}^2$	
$\bar{A}$	AAbb Aabb	$\left.\begin{array}{c} p^2\bar{q}^2 \\ 2p\bar{p}\cdot\bar{q}^2 \end{array}\right\}$	$= q^2(1 - p^2)$
$\bar{B}$	aaBB aaBb	$\left.\begin{array}{c} \bar{p}^2q^2 \\ \bar{p}^2\cdot 2q\bar{q} \end{array}\right\}$	$= \bar{p}^2(1 - \bar{q}^2)$
$\overline{AB}$	AABB AaBB AABb AaBb	$\left.\begin{array}{c} p^2q^2 \\ 2p\bar{p}q^2 \\ p^2\cdot 2q\bar{q} \\ 2p\bar{p}\cdot 2q\bar{q} \end{array}\right\}$	$= (1 - \bar{p}^2)(1 - \bar{q}^2)$

B and b, that the frequencies of the four blood groups would be represented by the following formulas (Table 53), where $p =$ the frequency of the gene $A,$ and $\bar{p}$ the frequency of the gene $a,$ q the frequency of B and $\bar{q}$ that of b:

From the gene frequencies in Table 53, it follows that

$$\overline{O} \times \overline{AB} = \overline{A} \times \overline{B}$$

Bernstein examined this relation for various populations, and found it did not generally hold. Table 54, based on selected data known

TABLE 54

Statistical Test of Theory of von Dungern and Hirszfeld

(Data from (7))

| Population | Number of People | Frequencies of Groups | | | | $\overline{O} \times \overline{AB}$ | $\overline{A} \times \overline{B}$ |
		O	A	B	AB		
English	422	0.479	0.424	0.083	0.014	0.0067	0.0352
Danish	406	0.396	0.436	0.125	0.043	0.0170	0.0545
Finns	972	0.340	0.424	0.171	0.065	0.0221	0.0725
Germans	39,174	0.365	0.425	0.145	0.065	0.0237	0.0616
Russians	489	0.319	0.344	0.249	0.088	0.0280	0.0856
Welsh	192	0.479	0.328	0.162	0.031	0.0148	0.0531
Bantu	500	0.632	0.164	0.174	0.030	0.0189	0.0285
Japanese	29,799	0.301	0.384	0.219	0.097	0.0291	0.0841
Syrians	306	0.392	0.386	0.173	0.049	0.0192	0.0667
'Iraqis	386	0.337	0.314	0.282	0.067	0.0225	0.0885
Bedouin	208	0.433	0.221	0.303	0.043	0.0186	0.0669
Chinese	1,000	0.307	0.251	0.342	0.100	0.0307	0.0858
"Hindus"	694	0.329	0.190	0.396	0.085	0.0279	0.0752
Egyptians	502	0.273	0.384	0.255	0.088	0.0240	0.0979

to be reliable, shows that the relationship fails to hold for various populations in different parts of the world.

At the same time Bernstein pointed out that a statistical test of his theory, making use of the ratio $\dfrac{D}{\sigma}$, did hold as well as could be expected, and Table 55, based on the same data as the previous

TABLE 55

Statistical Test of Bernstein's Theory of Blood Group Inheritance

Population	p	q	r	$p+q+r$	D	σ	D/σ
English	0.250	0.050	0.692	0.992	0.008	0.0046	1.7
Danish	0.282	0.088	0.629	0.999	0.001	0.0068	0.1
Finns	0.285	0.126	0.583	0.994	0.006	0.0054	1.1
Germans	0.285	0.110	0.604	0.999	0.001	0.00079	1.3
Russians	0.246	0.186	0.565	0.997	0.003	0.0087	0.3
Welsh	0.199	0.102	0.692	0.993	0.007	0.0086	0.8
Bantu	0.102	0.108	0.796	1.006	0.006	0.0037	1.6
Japanese	0.279	0.172	0.549	1.000	0.000	0.0012	<0.1
Syrians	0.248	0.118	0.626	0.992	0.008	0.0085	0.9
Iraqis	0.213	0.193	0.581	0.987	0.013	0.0092	1.4
Bedouin	0.142	0.191	0.658	0.991	0.009	0.0097	0.9
Chinese	0.193	0.253	0.554	1.000	0.000	0.0064	<0.1
"Hindus"	0.150	0.280	0.574	1.004	0.004	0.0070	0.6
Egyptians	0.273	0.190	0.523	0.986	0.014	0.0094	1.5

The gene frequencies p, q, and r were calculated according to the original (unadjusted) Bernstein formulas (see above), and the difference between their sum and unity is compared with the Standard Deviation of that difference. Since D/σ in no case exceeds the value 2.00, it is seen that all the series of data in this table conform to the Bernstein theory.

table, shows the conformity of the Bernstein theory to the observations.

Linkage

It was pointed out in the chapter on genetics that the fact that only a finite (24 pairs in man) number of chromosomes carry the entire number of genes which the species possesses results in the phenomenon which we call linkage; that is, factors which occur together in the parent tend to occur together in the offspring. This results in deviations from the expected (on the basis of independent assortment) Mendelian ratios in the offspring.

In the lower organisms, it is not difficult to determine linkage between two characteristics, since a crucial experiment can generally be arranged where both factors are present and the deviation from the expected independent assortment ratios in the offspring can readily be ascertained. The "crossing-over" value (p. 66) can also be estimated from a number of such experiments.

In man we have a different situation, since we cannot set up crucial breeding experiments to determine linkage or absence of linkage, but must depend on observations of the results of matings made outside of our control.

Sex linkage provides the simplest case. Because of the fact that sex in man is determined by the X, Y pair of chromosomes, it has been possible to determine the linkage of any gene which occurs on the X chromosome with any other gene determining a character occurring on this chromosome. Madlener (36) discovered in 1928 a family in which hemophilia and color blindness were both present in three males. Further information about this family is given by Bell and Haldane (1).

It is not nearly so easy to detect linkage between characteristics on the other chromosomes, or autosomal linkage as it is called. Such linkage has been claimed a number of times, but examination has generally shown that it rested on faulty calculations. In 1926 Snyder (45) showed that various claims of linkage of certain diseases and the blood groups were not sound statistically. At the same time he determined the probable independence of eye color, the blood groups, and recessive polydactyly, also of telangiectasis and the blood groups.

Methods of detecting linkage in man have, however, been continually improved in a statistical sense. In 1931 Bernstein (4) pointed out that linkage could be detected and estimated from data involving parents and children only. It thus proved to be unnecessary, although it would be highly desirable, to follow two characters through a series of generations in man, a process which is time consuming and often extremely difficult. Bernstein, by use of his method, confirmed the opinion of Landsteiner and Levine that the A, B blood groups were probably independent in inheritance of the M, N blood types. In 1932 Wiener (48) pointed out that the families which we are testing for autosomal linkage can be divided into three classes: linked, cross-overs, and indeterminate. The last class provides no information about linkage, and is discarded on analysis. The frequencies of the other two classes can then be compared with the expectation for various assumed linkage intensities or, if we like to phrase it so, for linkage with various degrees of crossing-over, since of course two genes on the same chromosome which exhibit no crossing-over will exhibit 100 per cent linkage intensity. In 1934 Hogben (33) improved these methods.

If dominance is complete the following three classes of matings allow us to estimate the proportion of phenotypes which depend on crossing-over values:

[1] $CcDd \times ccdd$
[2] $CcDd \times Ccdd$ or $CcDd \times ccDd$
[3] $CcDd \times CcDd$

Bernstein showed that linkage could be determined from matings [1] and [2] when Cc was distinguishable from CC and Dd from DD. However, in man the heterozygotes are often indistinguishable from one or the other of the homozygotes, or else the character of the homozygote is unknown because of its rare occurrence. Hogben derived a more general expression and drew up tables for testing gene linkage. He called attention to the fact that, since possessors of rare dominant genes can be assumed without serious error to be all heterozygous, Bernstein's method can be used to assign a cross-over value regardless either of inbreeding or of homogamy (mate selection). This would not be true of a rare recessive.

In 1934 Haldane (29) extended these methods for detecting autosomal linkage and included the case of three allelomorphs, developing a number of new formulae for linkage of various types of autosomal genes.

In a later paper Fisher (22) pointed out that Haldane's technic, using the Bernstein method, scored all types of families adequately except one. He gave an alternative u statistic for scoring backcross families which is applicable to all cases and enables families of different size to be combined.

Snyder, Burks (9, 10, 11) and Penrose (39, 40) evidently realized independently that information about linkage could be derived from information on a single generation only. This was based on the rather elementary consideration that if linkage is occurring certain types of pairs of sibs will be commoner than others in some families, and an analysis of different families will enable us to detect this fact, if enough children from families possessing both characteristics are examined. However, this method has the disadvantage of including a large number of families (or, more precisely, of sib pairs) whose characteristics provide absolutely no information as to linkage, which results in a tendency for the valuable information obtained from the few pairs which are really significant to be obscured by the uninformative pairs. Fisher points out (23) that the value of the data from large families is much enhanced by scoring the families individually instead of classifying all of the sib pairs in a fourfold table as first proposed by Penrose. Later on, Finney (14, 15, 16, 18, 19, 20) took up the problem (17) and showed how even partial information regarding a character in the parents could add to the information provided by sibs alone about linkage. He also noted that adequate information concerning a few families, parents and children, was of greater value than a relatively vast amount of information concerning sibs only. The methods used by these workers in testing for autosomal linkage involve statistical principles analogous to those which we have used above. They are rather complicated, however, so that it seems inadvisable to present them here, and any reader with a taste for pedigrees and a hope for turning up a case of autosomal linkage should examine the original papers.

Problems of linkage should not be approached without an adequate grounding in this sometimes difficult subject, however, for mistakes have been made even by some of the best workers in this and related fields. Thus Hogben (31) published a formula giving the standard deviation of the expected number of recessives as calculated from data on small families. However, Haldane (28) showed that it contained, as an implicit assumption, one of the facts which it was desired to ascertain. Hogben in a later paper (32) showed that the formula could be derived independently and correctly without making use of this assumption. Also Finney (14), who has done some of the best work in the field, deduced from the data of Zieve, Wiener, and Fries (52) that there was linkage between the A, B, O blood groups and allergy. Bernstein and others (5), however, found this claim actually to be unjustified. It is therefore best to proceed with caution in analyzing data for possible evidence of autosomal linkage in man.

The most extensive linkage study to date, involving examinations for 171 possible linkage relations in man, was reported by Kloepfer (35); some evidence for linkage between certain characters presumably determined or influenced by autosomal genes was claimed. Thus there seemed to be some evidence that genes affecting finger length and eye color were linked. But the author was very cautious about attempting the construction of even a rudimentary map of human chromosomes. Nevertheless, the sort of results reported show that careful study of adequate family material, especially if more than one generation can be included, would enable such chromosome maps to be begun.

Snyder, Russell, and Graham (46) have apparently detected autosomal linkage between the gene causing sickle-cell anemia and the M, N genes. Although the numbers they report are small, the results seem to be statistically significant.

REFERENCES FOR APPENDIX A

1. Bell, J., and J. B. S. Haldane, *Proc. Roy. Soc.*, B, *123*, 119 (1937).
2. Bernstein, F., *Zeit. f. ind. Abst.-u. Verer.*, *37*, 237–270 (1925).
3. Bernstein, F., *Zeit. f. ind. Abst.-u. Verer.*, *54*, 400–426 (1930).
4. Bernstein, F., *Zeit. f. ind. Abst.-u. Verer.*, *57*, 113–138 (1931).
5. Bernstein, F., H. L. Borison, and S. Finkel, *J. Imm.*, *46*, 245–248 (1943).
6. Boyd, W. C., *Ann. Eug.*, *8*, 337–342 (1938).
7. Boyd, W. C., *Tabulae Biologicae*, *17*, 113–240 (1939).
8. Boyd, W. C., and L. G. Boyd, *A. J. P. A.*, *23*, 49–70 (1937).
9. Burks, B. S., *Yearbook Carnegie Inst.*, *36*, 312–319 (1937).
10. Burks, B. S., *Proc. Nat. Acad. Sci.*, *24*, 512–519 (1938).
11. Burks, B. S., and R. S. Tolman, *J. Gen. Psych.*, *40*, #1, 3–15 (1932).
12. Cotterman, C. W., *Ohio J. Sci.*, *37*, 127–140 (1937).
13. von Dungern, E., and L. Hirszfeld, *Zeit. Imm.*, *6*, 284–292 (1910).
14. Finney, D. J., *Ann. Eug.*, *10*, 171–214 (1940).
15. Finney, D. J., *Ann. Eug.*, *11*, 10–30 (1941).

16. Finney, D. J., *Ann. Eug., 11*, 115–135 (1941).

17. Finney, D. J., *Jour. Hered., 33*, 157–160 (1942).

18. Finney, D. J., *Ann. Eug., 11*, 224–232 (1942).

19. Finney, D. J., *Ann. Eug., 11*, 233–244 (1942).

20. Finney, D. J., *Ann. Eug., 12*, 31–43 (1943).

21. Fisher, R. A., *Statistical Methods for Research Workers*. Oliver and Boyd, Edinburgh, 1932.

22. Fisher, R. A., *Ann. Eug., 6*, 187–201 (1935).

23. Fisher, R. A., *Ann. Eug., 6*, 339–351 (1935).

24. Fisher, R. A., *J. Roy. Anthrop. Inst., 66*, 57–63 (1936).

25. Fisher, R. A., *Ann. Eug., 13*, 150–155 (1946).

26. Fisher, R. A., *Ann. Eug., 13*, 223–224 (1947).

27. Fisher, R. A., and F. Yates, *Statistical Tables*. Oliver & Boyd, Ltd., London, 1943.

28. Haldane, J. B. S., *J. Genetics, 25*, No. 2, 251–255 (1932).

29. Haldane, J. B. S., *Ann. Eug., 6*, 26–65 (1934).

30. Hirszfeld, L., *Konstitutionsserologie und Blutgruppenforschung*. Julius Springer, Berlin, 1928.

31. Hogben, L., *J. Genetics, 25*, 97–112 (1931).

32. Hogben, L., *J. Genetics, 26*, 75–79 (1932).

33. Hogben, L., *Proc. Roy. Soc., 114*, 340–363 (1934).

34. Kelley, T. L., *Fundamentals of Statistics*. Harvard Univ. Press, Cambridge, 1947.

35. Kloepfer, H. W., *Ann. Eug., 13*, 35–71 (1946).

36. Madlener, M., *Arch. f. Rass. u. Ges.-Biol., 20*, 390–394 (1928).

37. Mather, K., *Statistical Analysis in Biology*. Interscience Publishers, Inc., New York, 1947.

38. Moureau, P., *Rev. belge des Sci. méd., 7*, 177–233; 540–588; 589–629 (1935).

39. Penrose, L. S., *Ann. Eug., 6*, 133–138 (1935).

40. Penrose, L. S., *Ann. Eug., 13*, 25–29 (1946).

41. Rietz, H. L., *Mathematical Statistics*. Open Court Publishing Co., Chicago, 1927.

42. Romovsky, V., *Biometrika, 15*, 410–412 (1923).

43. Schiff, F., and W. C. Boyd, *Blood Grouping Technic*. Interscience Publishers, New York, 1942.

44. Snedecor, G. W., *Statistical Methods*. Collegiate Press, Inc., Ames, Iowa, 1938.

45. Snyder, L. H., *Z. f. Imm., 49*, 464–480 (1927).

45a. Snyder, L. H., *Hereditas*, in press (1949).

46. Snyder, L. H., H. Russell, and E. B. Graham, *Science, 106*, 347–348 (1947).

47. Stevens, W. L., *Ann. Eug., 8*, 362–375 (1938).

48. Wiener, A. S., *Genetics, 17*, 335–350 (1932).

49. Wiener, A. S., *Human Biol., 7*, 222–239 (1935).

50. Wiener, A. S., *Blood Groups and Transfusion*. Charles C Thomas, Springfield, 1943.

51. Wiener, A. S., M. Lederer, and S. H. Polayes, *J. Imm.*, *16*, 469–482 (1929).
51a. Wiener, A. S., and E. B. Sonn, *Ann. N. Y. Acad. Sci.*, *46*, 969–992 (1946).
52. Zieve, I., A. S. Wiener, and J. H. Fries, *Ann. Eug.*, *7*, 141–162; 163–178 (1936).

Reference numbers in the following appendices refer to the bibliographies of the respective chapters.

Appendix IV-1

LET us suppose that a fraction q of the germ cells produced in a given population contained the gene Y, and the remainder of the sex cells, or the fraction $1 - q$, carried the alternative gene y. If mating occurs at random, the frequencies of homozygous YY and yy and heterozygous Yy individuals in the next generation will be produced as shown in Table 56.

TABLE 56

Frequencies with Random Mating

Genotype	Frequency
YY	$q \times q = q^2$
yy	$(1 - q)(1 - q) = (1 - q)^2$
Yy	$q(1 - q) + q(1 - q) = 2q(1 - q)$

In other words, we shall have the genotype YY equal in frequency to q^2, Yy equal to $q(1 - q) + (1 - q) = 2q(1 - q)$, and yy equal to $(1 - q)^2$.

Again, if these three types of individuals are equally viable and fertile, each of them will produce a proportional share of the sex cells of the next generation. The frequency with which we shall find sex cells carrying the gene Y will be $q^2 + \dfrac{2q(1 - q)}{2} = q^2 + q(1 - q) = q$. The frequency of sex cells carrying y will be $(1 - q)^2 + q(1 - q) = 1 - 2q + q^2 + q - q^2 = 1 - q$. These are just the frequencies we started with. In other words, mere reproduction will not change the gene frequencies from one generation to another, and if the gene Y causes dark eyes and the gene y causes blue eyes, the percentage of blue eyes at the end of any number of generations (assuming always that there has been no action of selective or other evolutionary forces) is going to be the same as it was originally. Weinberg (26) even extended the demonstration to the case of multiple allelomorphs, although no actual examples of multiple allelomorphs were known to him at the time he wrote his paper.

There may be some readers who, retaining a certain distrust of reasoning based on gene frequencies, would prefer to see a more direct demonstration that one generation of random mating gives a population which is in equilibrium, or in other words, will not change in its genetic composition unless evolutionary forces come into play. Such a demonstration can be given, and nothing more than simple algebra is required, plus an elementary knowledge of genetics. Let us assume a population possessing two genes, one dominant over the other. Then three types of individuals will exist: dominants, heterozygotes, and recessives. Let us assume that we start with a population not in equilibrium, so that the recessives, heterozygotes and dominants are in the ratio a : b : c, where the only condition on a, b, and c is that they must add up to *one,* since by hypothesis the three types account for the whole of the population.

If mating occurs at random, that is, the genetic types do not influence the choice of partners for the production of offspring, matings will occur in the frequencies $R \times R$, $H \times H$, $D \times D$, $2R \times H$, $2R \times D$, and $2H \times D$. This can be obtained by writing out the possible matings, or by observing that they are the various terms of

TABLE 57a

Frequencies of Different Types of Offspring Resulting from Various Matings

Mating	Offspring		
	R'	H'	D'
R × R	1	0	0
H × H	¼	½	¼
D × D	0	0	0
R × H or H × R	½	½	0
R × D or D × R	0	1	0
H × D or D × H	0	½	½

the expansion of the expression $(R + H + D)^2$. In terms of frequencies, we have $a^2 + b^2 + c^2 + 2ab + 2ac + 2bc$. From these frequencies, and an elementary knowledge of genetics (Table 57a), we can compute the frequencies of offspring of the various types.

If we want to see if random mating has given us equilibrium, we must first see what are the frequencies of the three types in the first generation resulting from random mating, then see if these frequencies change following another generation of random mating. From Table 57a we can see fairly easily that the frequencies of the various types in the first generation are going to be those set forth in Table 57b.

TABLE 57b

Frequencies of Offspring from Various Types of Matings

Mating	Offspring		
	R	H	D
R × R	a^2	o	o
H × H	$\dfrac{b^2}{4}$	$\dfrac{b^2}{2}$	$\dfrac{b^2}{4}$
D × D	o	o	c^2
R × H or H × R	ab	ab	o
R × D or D × R	o	$2ac$	o
H × D or D × H	o	bc	bc

If we add the various columns in Table 57b, we find that the three types, recessive (R′), heterozygote (H′), and dominant (D′), are found in the first generation of random mating in the proportions

$$\left(a^2 + \frac{b^2}{4} + ab\right) : \left(\frac{b^2}{2} + ab + 2ac + bc\right) : \left(\frac{b^2}{4} + c^2 + bc\right).$$

The next step is to calculate from these frequencies the frequencies of R, H, and D which will emerge after one more generation of random mating. From Table 57a we notice that we may calculate the new frequency of R, which we may call R″, by adding up the expressions

$$\left(a^2 + \frac{b^2}{4} + ab\right)^2 + \frac{1}{4}\left(\frac{b^2}{2} + ab + 2ac + bc\right)$$
$$+ \left(a^2 + \frac{b^2}{4} + ab\right)\left(\frac{b^2}{2} + ab + 2ac + bc\right).$$

If we do this, and simplify the resulting equation, we find that

$$R'' = a^2 + \frac{b^2}{4} + ab$$

or, in other words,

$$R'' = R'.$$

We find similarly that $H'' = H'$ and $D'' = D'$, which completes our demonstration that a single generation of random mating produces genetic equilibrium, and that the composition of the population does not thereafter change, unless acted on by evolutionary forces.

The reader should be told that the demonstration outlined above, although correct in principle, and very simple in outline, involves some rather arduous algebra, and that few persons succeed in carrying it through the first time without making some simple but annoying errors. A demonstration which is better mathematically consists in starting with a population which is known, from its gene frequencies, to be in equilibrium, and showing that the frequencies are not changed by a generation of random mating. Such a proof is to be found, for example, in Hogben's "An Introduction to Mathematical Genetics."

It should also be remarked that in such proofs we assume the population to be very large, as otherwise random fluctuations might alter our predicted probabilities, and that we assume the gene frequencies in the males to be the same as those in the females. It is obvious, for example, that a mating of 5,000,000 recessive females with 5,000,000 dominant males could produce only heterozygotes, so that genetic equilibrium would not be attained in such a case in one generation of what would usually be termed random mating. In actual populations we do find that the frequencies of autosomal genes are for all practical purposes the same in the two sexes.

One further mathematical conclusion results from the above equations. If our population had already been in genetic equilibrium when we started, we should have found that the frequency of recessives in the parent generation would be the same as that in the first generation where we assumed random mating. In other words,

$$a - a^2 + \frac{b^2}{4} + ab.$$

If in this expression we substitute for b the value $1 - a - c$, we obtain

$$b^2 = 4ac$$
or
$$b = 2\sqrt{ac}$$

which shows that the condition for equilibrium is that the frequency of the heterozygotes be equal to twice the square root of the product of the frequencies of the dominants and the recessives.

The distribution of sex-linked genes in a system of random mating obeys a different law. A sex-linked gene is carried only by the female (X) chromosome, so no male heterozygote can exist. The only heterozygotes are females. If $(a + b) = 1$, a population is in equilibrium when the proportions are as follows:

Females			Males	
R	H	D	R	D
$\dfrac{a^2}{2}$	ab	$\dfrac{b^2}{2}$	$\dfrac{a}{2}$	$\dfrac{b}{2}$

As before, a and b are the gene frequencies of the recessive and dominant allelomorphs for the population as a whole. That a population with this constitution is in equilibrium is seen as follows: a dominant female has two chromosomes carrying the dominant sex-linked gene; a dominant male has only one, plus a "blank" male chromosome which we represent by Y. The various matings occur in the proportions:

Mating	Relative frequency
RY × RR	a^3
RY × RD	$2a^2b$
RY × DD	ab^2
DY × RR	a^2b
DY × RD	$2ab^2$
DY × DD	b^3

APPENDIX IV-I

These relative frequencies are obtained from Table 58 by multiplying all values by 4 to simplify the numbers.

TABLE 58

Random Mating, Sex Linkage

	Females		
	R $\frac{a^2}{2}$	H ab	D $\frac{b^2}{2}$
R $\frac{a}{2}$	$\frac{a^3}{4}$	$\frac{a^2b}{2}$	$\frac{ab^2}{4}$
Males			
D $\frac{b}{2}$	$\frac{a^2b}{4}$	$\frac{ab^2}{2}$	$\frac{b^3}{4}$

The frequencies of the resulting offspring will be

Mating	RR	RD	DD	RY	DY
RY × RR	$\frac{a^3}{2}$	—	—	$\frac{a^3}{2}$	—
RY × RD	$\frac{a^2b}{2}$	$\frac{a^2b}{2}$	—	$\frac{a^2b}{2}$	$\frac{a^2b}{2}$
RY × DD	—	$\frac{ab^2}{2}$	—	—	$\frac{ab^2}{2}$
DY × RR	—	$\frac{a^2b}{2}$	—	$\frac{a^2b}{2}$	—
DY × RD	—	$\frac{ab^2}{2}$	$\frac{ab^2}{2}$	$\frac{ab^2}{2}$	$\frac{ab^2}{2}$
DY × DD	—	—	$\frac{b^3}{2}$	—	$\frac{b^3}{2}$

By adding the columns, we get

$$RR = \frac{a^3 + a^2b}{2} = \frac{a^2}{2}(a + b) = \frac{a^2}{2} \text{ etc.}$$

Thus we have as before,

	Type	Relative frequency
	RR	$\frac{a^2}{2}$
Females	RD	ab
	DD	$\frac{b^2}{2}$
	RY	$\frac{a}{2}$
Males	DY	$\frac{b}{2}$

However, this condition of equilibrium is not attained in a single generation as with autosomal gene substitutions. If the pre-existing equilibrium is displaced, the new one is approached gradually, and the proportions in ensuing generations oscillate about their new equilibrium values.

Appendix IV-2

IN order to determine the gene frequencies of a new population resulting from the mixture of two others with different gene frequencies, it is only necessary to take the average of the gene frequencies of the two parent populations, weighted according to the numbers of individuals which are involved in making up the cross (13) (ignoring possible complications produced in such cases as the one where one group consists mostly of males, the other mostly of females, and polygamy is practiced). Let us suppose, for instance, that 325 North American Indians all belonging to blood group O, that is, possessing only the gene for O and no genes for A or B, are mixed genetically with a hypothetical population of 150 white English possessing the genes A, B, and O in the proportions $p = 0.281$, $q = 0.059$, $r = 0.660$. The initial population we will start with will be $325 + 150 = 475$, and the method of computing the gene frequencies which would result is shown in Tables 59 and 60. From these gene frequencies we can calculate the blood group frequencies in the new mixed population from the usual formulas

$$O = r^2$$
$$A = p^2 \times 2pr$$
$$B = q^2 \times 2qr$$
$$AB = 2pq$$

TABLE 59

Calculation of Weighted Gene Frequencies

	p	q	r
Indians	$\dfrac{325}{475} \times 0$	$\dfrac{325}{475} \times 0$	$\dfrac{325}{475} \times 1.00$
"Whites"	$\dfrac{150}{475} \times 0.281$	$\dfrac{150}{475} \times 0.059$	$\dfrac{150}{475} \times 0.660$

TABLE 60

Weighted Gene Frequencies and Frequencies in New Population

	p	q	r	Total
Indians	0	0	0.6842	—
"Whites"	0.08874	0.01863	0.2084	—
Total	.08874	.01863	0.8926	0.9999

Therefore we obtain:

$$O = (.8926)^2 = 0.7966$$
$$A = (.08874)^2 \times 2(.08874)(.8926) = .1663$$
$$B = (.01863)^2 \times 2(.01863)(.8926) = .0336$$
$$AB = 2(.08874)(.01863) = .0033$$

or, in other words, expressed in per cents, the new frequencies are:

$$O = 79.9$$
$$A = 16.6$$
$$B = 3.4$$
$$AB = 0.3$$

From the above proof (App. IV-1) that genetic equilibrium is attained in one generation of random mating, it is apparent that if the offspring of this hypothetical race mixture mated at random (nonassortively) from now on, the above blood group frequencies would not alter, in the absence of selection (p. 140) or isolate effects (p. 154).

Appendix IV-3

IF two populations interbreed, the resulting hybrids are generally intermediate in character. The final result will depend on the numbers of the parental populations, and the mode of inheritance of the features we choose to examine.

If the characteristics we are interested in are determined by a known number of genes acting in a known manner, we can make quantitative predictions about the hybrid population, just as a chemist could predict the percentage of Cl in a mixture of 5 parts of NaCl and 5 parts of KCl. Bernstein (2c) showed how such calculations could be made for the O, A, B blood groups and also mentioned that the calculations could be reversed in dealing with problems of mixture. The reverse of the process is exactly analogous to the calculations of "indirect analysis" in quantitative chemical analysis (see for example Fales and Kenny 13b) and involves no new principle. Examples of such calculations have been published by Wiener (26a), Boyd (3), Ottensooser (24a), and da Silva (25a).

Laughlin (23a) recently examined the M, N blood types in the Aleutian Islands. He found for one probably mixed population a gene frequency of $n = 0.171$. It was of interest to determine, if possible, how much white mixture this population had received during the days of Russian rule. Assuming that the original Aleut population had a value of $n = 0.087$ (the value found by Fabricius-Hansen [13a] for the Eskimo of Angmassalik), and assuming for the Russian element the value of $n = 0.417$ (the value found by Boyd and Boyd [4] for the Russians of Kharkov) it is possible to calculate very simply the amount of Russian "blood" in the present Aleutians. Let $n_R =$ the N frequency of the Russians, $n_A =$ the N frequency of the Aleuts, and $n_E =$ the N frequency of the Eskimos who are assumed to be similar to the original Aleuts. Let us assume that the hybrid population was made up of x Russians and y Eskimos. Then

$$\frac{xn_R + yn_E}{x + y} = n_A$$

$$xn_R + yn_E = xn_A + yn_A$$

$$(n_R - n_A)x = (n_A - n_E)y$$

$$\frac{y}{x} = \frac{n_R - n_A}{n_A - n_E}$$

But $\dfrac{x}{x + y} \cdot 100$ = per cent Russian mixture. Let $\dfrac{y + x}{x} = g$

Then $\dfrac{100}{g}$ = per cent Russian mixture

Now $\dfrac{y}{x} + 1 = \dfrac{y + x}{x} = g = \dfrac{n_R - n_A + n_A - n_E}{n_A - n_E}$

Therefore, the per cent of Russian mixture $= \dfrac{n_A - n_E}{n_R - n_E} \cdot 100$

Substituting the above values for n, we obtain

$$0.084 \div 0.330 \times 100 = 24.45 \text{ per cent Russian mixture.}$$

Laughlin (23a) concludes that this value is consistent with other observations on the Aleuts.

A similar calculation can be applied to the value of the frequency of the blood group A gene found for a group of Navaho school children by Allen and Korber (1a), and the results of Boyd and Boyd (7) for a group which was probably purer. Allen and Korber found $p = 0.148$, Boyd and Boyd found $p = 0.120$. If we assume the higher value of p in the first group is entirely due to mixture with white Americans, and that the white group had a value of $p = 0.281$ (3), we obtain

$$\frac{0.148 - 0.120}{0.281 - 0.120} \times 100 = \frac{0.028}{0.161} \times 100 = 17.4 \text{ per cent}$$

white mixture.

In the case of the M, N blood types, no problem of estimation of the gene frequencies arises, for they are given directly by the relations $m = \overline{M} + \overline{MN}/2$, $n = \overline{N} + \overline{MN}/2$. But in the case of the O, A, B blood groups, since the heterozygotes cannot all be recognized directly, the exact gene frequencies p, q, and r cannot be determined, but instead estimates must be made, based on the observed phenotypic frequencies (see p. 399). Two simple ways of estimating p, q, and r have been proposed. They are described in Appendix A. When the populations tested are small, and not in genetic equilibrium, the two methods may yield results which differ rather widely. An example of this is to be found in the paper by da Silva (25a), who tested whites, Negroes, and mulattoes in Brazil, and attempted to estimate from the resulting blood group frequencies the proportion of white and Negro "blood" in the mulattoes. Using the frequencies of the gene A (p), he estimated, when he employed the Bernstein formulas, that the mulattoes were 52.7 per cent Negro. Using the Wiener formulas, the result would be 32.8 per cent Negro. Clearly these values differ more than is desirable, and the question arises, which is more nearly correct? Da Silva apparently assumed that the most nearly correct value would be arrived at by averaging the two sets of gene frequencies for each population, and then carrying out the calculation of the degree of mixture. He thus obtained the value of 44.3 per cent Negro mixture.

The procedure used by da Silva would not usually give the best estimate of the proportion of Negro to white in the ancestry of the mulatto population, because neither the Bernstein nor the Wiener formulas give the best estimate of the gene frequencies from the data employed, nor does an average of the two. Stevens (25b) has shown how the best statistical estimates can be arrived at, for any given set of data, by Fisher's method of "maximum likelihood." It is clear that the best notion of the degree of mixture will be obtained if we base our calculations on the best estimates which we can make from the data.

If we apply Stevens's methods to the data of da Silva, we obtain the estimates shown in Table 61. From them, using the values of p, we can calculate that the mulattoes represent 50.8 per cent Negro. This is obviously the best value we can estimate from p, but it is also obvious, from the size of the standard errors of the values, that it cannot be too precise, since the samples are small, and some of them, at least, do not seem to represent populations in genetic equilibrium. It is interesting to note, however, that da Silva's estimates

TABLE 61

Blood Group Gene Frequencies Calculated by Various Methods
(from da Silva's data)

	Gene Frequency	Bernstein (2a)	Wiener (26b)	Average	Stevens (25b)	Bernstein (2b)
	p	.133	.108	.121	.131 ± .018	.131
Negroes	q	.147	.122	.135	.145 ± .018	.145
	r	.745	.745	.745	.724 ± .024	.723
	p	.202	.186	.194	.202 ± .025	.200
Mulattoes	q	.112	.096	.104	.111 ± .019	.111
	r	.702	.702	.702	.687 ± .029	.688
	p	.279	.224	.252	.274 ± .025	.271
Whites	q	.125	.070	.098	.119 ± .016	.122
	r	.651	.651	.651	.607 ± .027	.606

of the degree of mixture, based on the Bernstein formulas, are
closer to the best estimate than his results obtained from the values
of p obtained by averaging the results of the two formulas. His
first estimate is 1.9 points too high, but his second (average) result
is 6.5 point too low. Thus the Bernstein formulas gave the better
results in the present instance. In other cases it would be expected
that the Wiener formulas would be preferable. But in all cases it
would seem best to base calculations of mixture on the maximum
likelihood estimate of the gene frequencies.

Estimation of gene frequencies by the method of Stevens is not
very difficult, and has the advantages that the frequencies obtained
add up exactly to 1.0000, and that the standard deviations can
easily be calculated. However, Bernstein (2b) proposed a method
which is simpler mathematically, and which, as Stevens (25b)
points out, gives values also satisfying exactly the maximum likelihood equations (App. A).

It is well worth while to adjust the crude gene frequencies as
calculated by the original Bernstein or Wiener methods, for both
methods employ the inefficient estimate $r = \sqrt{O}$. In the case of the
"white" group examined by da Silva, the use of this inefficient

estimate instead of the efficient estimate is equivalent to rejecting 22 of the 196 observations.

The method of Stevens can, however, be applied whenever desired to the blood group frequencies found in tables (e.g. 4a), and will give the best possible statistical estimates.

Finally, it may be stated that it might well be doubted if da Silva's mulattoes are really the result of mixture of the Negro and white populations he examined. The value of p, it is true, is compatible with the assumption that the mulattoes represent a cross of the other two groups in about equal numbers, but the values of q (frequency of gene B) are not, for we find the mulattoes to have a value of q (0.111 ± .019) lower than that for Negroes (0.145 ± .018) or the whites (0.119 ± .016), a result impossible from mixture alone. On the other hand, if we examine data on American Negroes, for example, from New York City, we find p higher than in West Africa, and q lower, in about the amounts expected from roughly 40 per cent white mixture. In any precise calculations we should make use of information furnished by both p and q, but such calculations would not be worth while unless we knew rather precisely the genetic composition of each population entering into the mixture.

In making the best estimate of gene frequencies for more complicated cases, such as the Rh blood types, the method of maximum likelihood may be employed, and Fisher (13c, 13d) has given an example of its use in such calculations. The calculations are somewhat more complicated, as matrices of the sixth or eighth order are employed, but the principle is the same.

A simple method of estimating the Rh gene frequencies has been offered by Wiener and Sonn (26c), making use of certain simplifying assumptions. This method does not give the maximum likelihood solutions, however.

Appendix V-1

WRIGHT (88) shows how one may represent the effect on gene frequencies of recurrent mutation in simple mathematical terms. Let q be the frequency of a given gene Y, and $(1 - q)$ the frequency of all its alleles lumped together. Let the alleles, collectively, mutate to Y at the rate b per generation. The gene Y may be supposed to mutate to one of its alleles sometimes, since mutation is observed to be reversible in many cases (57, 73). Let us represent the rate of reverse mutation as c. The net mutation pressure may be written

$$\Delta q = b(1 - q) - cq$$

At a certain point we shall have equilibrium, then the two opposing mutation rates balance each other.

$$\Delta q = 0 \text{ at } \overline{q} = \frac{b}{b + c}$$

Appendix V-2

THE treatment presented here is a combination of some of those referred to. Let q represent the frequency of the "unfavorable" (or abnormal) gene, k the "selection coefficient," * and μ the mutation rate per chromosome per generation (assuming the mutation appears only on one or the other of a certain pair of chromosomes). If N represents the effective size of the population (see Appendix V-7), the number of new cases per generation is approximately 2N, while the number eliminated is $2(k)q^2N$. At equilibrium, these will be equal, so that

$$2(k)q^2N = 2\mu N, \text{ or } kq^2 = \mu$$

Therefore, $q = \sqrt{\dfrac{\mu}{k}}$ or, if we wish to discuss the mutation frequency, we can write $\mu = kq^2$.

Wright points out that q may be fairly high. Thus if $\mu = 0.000,01$ and $k = 0.01$, then $q = \sqrt{0.0001} = 0.032$.

---

* If on the average there are retained only 999 gametes carrying a gene, while 1000 gametes carrying its allele are retained, the value of the selection coefficient, k, $= 0.0001$.

Appendix V-3

FROM our simple assumption that z and Z are reproduced in each generation in the ratio $\frac{z}{Z} = (1 - k)$, we note that the probability that z survives in the next generation is just $\frac{1 - k}{c}$, where c is a constant depending on population size, mode of reproduction, etc. Similarly, the probability of survival of Z is $\frac{1}{c}$. From the frequencies we have assumed for the alleles, we compute that the probability that a gene will survive and be Z is $\frac{q}{c}$, and the probability that it will be z is $\frac{(1 - q)(1 - k)}{c}$.

The sum of these two probabilities must equal 1.000, since by hypothesis we have assumed only the two alleles z and Z at the locus in question. Therefore the probability that a surviving gene in the next $(n + 1)$ generation will be Z is the first probability divided by the sum of the two, or

$$\frac{\dfrac{q}{c}}{\dfrac{(1 - q)(1 - k)}{c} + \dfrac{q}{c}}$$

It is easily seen that the constant c cancels out. Performing the rest of the algebra, we obtain for the new frequency of Z, which we may call Z_{n+1}, the value

$$\frac{q}{1 - k(1 - q)}$$

To get the difference in gene frequency caused in this one generation by the selective process, we subtract the value for the nth generation, with which we started, from the value for the $(n + 1)$st generation, and represent the difference, as usual by the symbol Δ.

We obtain

$$\Delta q = \frac{q}{(1 - k)(1 - q)} - q = \frac{kq(1 - q)}{(1 - k)(1 - q)}$$

Since the selective coefficient k is quite small in actual situations, the whole expression $k(1 - q)$ can be neglected in comparison with unity, and thus the entire denominator, to a sufficiently good approximation, can be considered unity. Therefore we get the approximation

$$\Delta q = kq(1 - q)*$$

Under actual conditions, of course, selection affects the individuals possessing the genes, and not the genes directly, so we should examine the results of mathematical work on problems somewhat more closely analogous to those which real populations present.

In 1924 Professor J. B. S. Haldane began the task of elaborating a mathematical theory of natural selection (30, 31, 32, 33, 34, 35, 36). He began with the simple assumption that as a result of selection, only a certain fraction of the individuals possessing a characteristic against which natural selection is acting would survive to breed and produce offspring. Of course many of the "favored" type might also fail to survive and produce offspring, but the numbers of the "unfavorable" type would still be smaller in proportion, since we must suppose that accidents, and other destructive agencies unrelated to natural selection, would by and large affect all types equally. Haldane said: let us suppose that a generation of

---

* For the benefit of those familiar with the methods of the calculus, we may note that this expression can be integrated, by methods which are used below, if we replace the finite difference Δq by the infinitesimal $\dfrac{dq}{dn}$ which it would approach as a limit, where n represents time measured in generations. The result is

$$kn = \log_e \frac{q(1 - q_0)}{q_0 (1 - q)}$$

where q_0 is the frequency of Z when $n = 0$.

zygotes (fertilized eggs) immediately after fertilization consists of two phenotypes X and Y, and that the ratio is $vX:1Y$ or $X/Y = v$. If the proportion in the next generation which form fertile unions is $vX:(1 - k)Y$, we shall describe k as the coefficient of selection (in favor of X over Y) (see above).

It is not too hard to follow Haldane's further reasoning, if we are willing to take for granted a simple application of the calculus which he makes. The only calculus involved is really rather simple, and the result can be looked up in any handbook. Haldane's originality consisted largely in reducing the (actually rather complex) problem to a simplified formulation amenable to really simple mathematical treatment.

Let us first consider the case of a population composed of dominants, heterozygotes, and recessives. The dominants and the heterozygotes are the group which have allele Z, and the recessives are the group $zz = Y$. If we let the ratio of the numbers of genes Z_n/z_n, where z is the recessive gene, equal v_n, the three types will exist in the ratio

$$v_n{}^2 2ZZ : 2v_n Zz : zz$$

If only $(1 - k)$ of the recessives survive to breed, the survivors are then in the ratio of

$$v_n{}^2 ZZ : 2v_n Zz : (1 - k)zz$$

Haldane (30) then proceeds to show that random mating among these three types in the new proportions will give the same result we obtain if we calculate the new ratio v_{n+1} directly from the ratio Z/z among the gametes of the population as a whole. The easiest way to see this is to consider some very simple case, such as an aquatic organism which sheds its gametes directly into the water. If each zygote produced N gametes which conjugate, the numbers of gametes of type Z and z will clearly be

$$N(v_n{}^2 + v_n)Z, \text{ and } N(v_n + (1 - k))z,$$

so that in the $(n + 1)$st generation

$$\frac{Z_{n+1}}{z_{n+1}} = v_{n+1} = \frac{v_n(1 + v_n)}{1 + v_n - k}$$

Hence,

$$\Delta v_n = v_{n+1} - v_n = \frac{k v_n}{1 + v_n - k}$$

If the rate of selection is low, we can neglect k in comparison with $1 + v_n$. Also, since the change in v each time will be small, we make the transition from changes in v by steps to the continuous change which is more amenable to the methods of the differential calculus (in other words, replace Δv by dv_n/dn). We thus get a simple and well-behaved equation which will give results not too far from the truth, if our assumptions have been reasonable.*

We then write $dv_n/dn = k v_n/(1 + v_n)$ approximately.

Integrating, we obtain

$$\int_{v_0}^{v_n} \frac{1 + v}{v} \, dv = \int_0^n k \, dn$$

or $kn = v_n - v_0 + \log_e \dfrac{v_n}{v_0}$. Table 15 (p. 146) is calculated from this equation.

---

* It is not necessary to neglect k in the denominator of the equation just above in order to obtain an equation which can be integrated, but it is perhaps a good idea, since neglecting it introduces a change which is in the opposite direction from the error we commit when we take the step of replacing v by dv_n/dn.

Appendix V-4

LET the selection rate for homozygotes and heterozygotes be different. In other words, if the frequencies of the three genotypes, assuming that only two genes Z and z are involved (the treatment for more complex cases is similar), in the nth generation are in the ratio

$$v_n{}^2 ZZ : 2v_n Zz : zz$$

in the $(n+1)$st generation they will be in the ratio

$$v_n{}^2 ZZ : 2v_n(1-h)Zz : (1-k)zz$$

where k is the selective disadvantage of the homozygous recessive as compared to the homozygous dominant, and h is the selective disadvantage of the heterozygote as compared with the dominant. The selective factors h and k are assumed to be constants; their values will serve as a measure of the disadvantage under which individuals of these types must labor under the conditions of their environment.

Since v_{n+1} is the ratio of the frequency of the gene Z to the frequency of gene z, in the $(n+1)$st generation,

$$v_{n+1} = \frac{v_n{}^2 + v_n(1-h)}{(1-k) + v_n(1-h)}$$

and

$$\Delta v_n = v_{n+1} - v_n = \frac{hv_n{}^2 + (k-h)v_n}{(1-k) + v_n(1-h)}$$

This difference equation determines v_n as a function of n. If there is no selection against the heterozygotes (Zz), $h = 0$, and the above equation reduces to the one derived earlier. The above equation can also be integrated, but the integral is rather complicated and it is probable that any readers who would be capable of using it would also be capable of deriving it, so it is not presented here.

Appendix V-5

WIENER's procedure is mathematically very easy, and will be presented practically in his notation because of its simplicity. It is essentially the same as that of Koller (47). He assumes that we are dealing with a population of constant size, containing Z genes for Rh and z genes for rh (the Rh negative gene). The initial distribution would be as follows:

$$Rh_n = \frac{Z}{Z + z}, \quad rh_n = \frac{z}{Z + z}$$

If the number of fetuses and newborn that die from erythroblastosis during one generation is C, then the distribution of the genes in the second generation would be

$$Rh_{n+1} = \frac{Z - C}{Z + z - 2C}, \quad rh_{n+1} = \frac{z - C}{Z + z - 2C}$$

Therefore, if at the outset the number of Rh genes (all together) equaled the number of Rh negative (rh) genes, the relative proportions would remain the same, for then we should have $Z = z$ and the two fractions above would be equal.

Appendix V-6

Spontaneous Decay of Variability

THE idea of the spontaneous decay of variability, or loss of genetic factors with time, was apparently first stated by Brooks in 1899 (6). The genetic implications were clarified by Hagedoorn and Hagedoorn in 1921 (29) and the idea was later developed largely independently by Fisher (22), Dubinin (17), Romaschoff (67), Dubinin and Romaschoff (18), and particularly Wright (89). Dubinin and Romaschoff (18) conducted an experiment to serve as a model of what would happen to a small population. They used a bowl containing 100 marbles, each marble having a different number, to illustrate the results of the process of reproduction as applied to such a population. Twenty-five marbles were taken out at random and discarded. Another set of twenty-five marbles was taken out, and in place of those removed, for each number of the second set of marbles removed, two new marbles bearing the same number as the originals for which they were substituted were returned to the bowl so that the original number of marbles (100) was restored. This operation corresponded to one generation of breeding and resulted in the elimination of 25 "alleles," but consequently doubled the frequency of 25 others, chosen at random. As this operation was repeated again and again, Dubinin and Romaschoff observed a progressive decay in the variability of the "population," for they found that fewer and fewer different numbers remained in the bowl, although the numbers which were left had come to be represented by many marbles each. Eventually, all the marbles came to have the same number, and the population had become homogeneous, or, in the language of Wright (87), a certain gene had become "fixed." In ten separate experiments of this sort, Dubinin and Romaschoff observed the attainment of a complete "homozygosis" after repetition of the imitation breeding process, sometimes after only 108 and sometimes after as many as 464 "generations." The victorious allele each time had a different number, showing that the process of fixation was purely random, as expected. According to Wright (86), the way in which these experiments were carried out would imitate pretty closely the behavior of a population with an effective population number, N, of about 50. It is implicit in the assumptions of such an experiment, of course, that no new mutations are taking place.

The rapidity of the effect is demonstrated by Wright's calculation that in a population of N breeding individuals, $N/2$ genes either reach fixation or are lost in every generation.

Let us start with a non-mutating population in which gene frequencies vary all the way from 0 per cent to 100 per cent with different gene loci, and for the sake of simplicity let us consider a number of gene loci which can be occupied by two alternative alleles. Then $N/4$ of these genes will reach "fixation" and $N/4$ will be lost in every generation and therefore $N/2$ of the gene loci become homozygous in all individuals each generation. Wright's formula for describing this process is approximately $L_T = L_0 e^{-T/2N}$, where L_0 and L_T are the numbers of unfixed genes (i.e., not of frequency 100 or 0 per cent) in the initial and the T generation respectively; N is the effective population number, and e is the base of natural logarithms.

Dubinin and Romaschoff furnished an illustration of the importance of differences in population numbers by making their experiments with marbles in two ways. In some experiments they used bowls which contained 100 marbles. It required many more repetitions of their process or "generations" to obtain a complete uniformity of the population in the former series of experiments than in the latter. With 100 marbles the number of "generations" varies from 108 to 464 generations and with ten marbles from only 14 to 51 "generations." Again we should remember that the numbers of marbles used corresponded more nearly to 2N than to N for an actual population.

If we have a population which has genes distributed according to the Hardy-Pearson-Weinberg law (i.e., in equilibrium), and each allele has a frequency of 50 per cent, then if N = 100, half of these genes will be fixed in 137 generations, another half in another 137 generations, etc. In mathematical terms, we write $\frac{L_T}{L_0} = 0.50 = e^{-T/200}$, and solve for T, finding T = 137. The smaller the effective population size, the greater the random variation of gene frequency and the less effective selection pressure becomes.

Appendix V-7

Effective Population Size

THE number N which we have been using is not, as said above, the number of the total population, but the "effective population" number. What we have said about it already will give the reader a sufficiently good idea. The best way to define it seems to be in mathematical terms (87, 88). Suppose that we have a certain number of parents, N_o, who produce different numbers of young (who belong to the new generation). If the population is static, each parent produces on the average 2 gametes which result in surviving offspring. Let the number of gametes which an individual contributes to the next generation be k, and let the variance in this number among different individuals be σ_k^2. Then $N = \dfrac{4N_o - 2}{2 + \sigma_k^2}$. This is a very hypothetical and unlikely case, in which the effective size of the population is twice as great as the apparent size. If, as would often be the case in nature (and is usually true even of human populations), most of the offspring came from a small percentage of the mature individuals of the parental generation, the effective size would be much less than the apparent size.

Many populations, as already indicated, vary tremendously in numbers from generation to generation. Suppose the breeding population of a certain variety in an isolated region increases tenfold in each of six succeeding generations ($N_6 = 10^6 \times N_o$) but then falls to its original number (N_o), the *effective* size of the population (N) for this period turns out to be 6.3 N_o.

Appendix XIII-1

WHEN a character is determined by a single dominant gene, we note that matings in which the character does not appear in either parent always result in children also without the character, and that matings between parents both of whom have the character may produce some children who have the character, and some who have not.

If the gene is truly dominant, and exhibits complete penetrance (p. 77), one will find, if large enough numbers of families are studied, that the second type of mating can be subdivided into two classes: those in which all the children are like their parents, and those in which 75 per cent of them are like their parents, but 25 per cent lack the character in question. The first of these classes will consist mostly of matings where one or both of the parents is homozygous (p. 34), plus a few cases where one or both are heterozygous (p. 40), but by chance produced no recessive type children; the second class will include the (usually more numerous) cases where both parents are heterozygous for the gene in question.

Matings between parents, one of whom has the character and one of whom does not, will again fall into two classes; the first including those families in which only positive children (i.e., those with the characteristic) will be found, and the second, and usually more numerous, including the families where approximately 50 per cent of the children display the characteristic. These correspond to matings of a homozygous positive individual to an individual not showing the character, and of a heterozygote to an individual not showing it.

Hypothetical Example

We may illustrate these facts by taking an imaginary gene C as a typical dominant, and the gene c as a recessive (Table 62). (The reader should not, however, conclude from this illustration that all, or even the majority, of genes exhibit clear-cut dominant-recessive relationships — p. 42.)

Table 62

Results of Various Possible Matings (see text)

$cc \times cc$	$CC \times CC$
cc	CC
(100 per cent)	(100 per cent)

$cc \times CC$
Cc
(100 per cent)

$cc \times Cc$		$Cc \times CC$	
cc	Cc	Cc	CC
(50 per cent),	(50 per cent)	(50 per cent),	(50 per cent)

$Cc \times Cc$
cc Cc CC
(25 per cent),   (50 per cent),   (25 per cent)

To show that a character is recessive, it is necessary, but not sufficient, to demonstrate that it always appears in the children of parents both of whom have the characteristic (p. 33). It will, however, appear also in the children of some parents who do not exhibit the character.

It is apparent that the frequency with which the character appears in children of parents who do not openly show it is not independent of the frequency of affected individuals in the population. In fact, we can calculate the expected frequency and compare it with the observed, and test any discrepancy statistically (App. A). A little thought will show that three types of individuals are possible, CC, Cc, and cc, and that if we represent the gene frequency of C by p and that of c by r (where $p + r = 1$) we shall find the frequencies of the three classes are given by the binomial expansion of $(p + r)^2$ so that $CC = p^2$, $Cc = 2pr$, $cc = r^2$. So, from the frequency of affected individuals in the population, we can calculate $r = \sqrt{\bar{c}\bar{c}}$, $p = 1 - r$. (The bar over the $\bar{c}\bar{c}$ signifies that we are dealing with frequencies, not per cents.) Snyder (35) gives more details of such computations.

If we represent the homozygous recessive (cc) by R, the heterozygote (Cc) by H, and the homozygous dominant (CC) by D, we may tabulate the matings as follows (20): (Table 63). We then can

Table 63

Proportion of Recessives from Different Types of Mating (20)

Types of mating	Proportions of recessive offspring
R × R	1
R × H	½
H × H	¼
R × D or H × D or D × D	0

calculate, assuming random mating, that the matings between the three classes will occur in the proportions given by $(D + H + R)^2 = D^2 + H^2 + R^2 + 2DH + 2DR + 2HR$.

The frequencies of the matings which contribute recessives (see Table 63) in terms of the gene frequencies are:

$$H \times H = 4r^2(1 - r)^2$$
$$H \times D = 4r(1 - r)^3$$
$$D \times D = (1 - r)^4$$

Since we want the *relative* proportions, we can divide each of these expressions by the common factor $(1 - r)^2$, and obtain

Mating	*Frequency*
H × H	$4r^2$
H × D	$4r(1 - r)$
D × D	$(1 - r)^2$

If we add the right-hand column, we obtain, making the usual algebraic simplifications, $(1 + r)^2$. Therefore the ratio of matings of the H × H type to the total is

$$4r^2 \div (1 + r)^2 = \frac{4r^2}{(1 + r)^2}$$

From Table 63 we see that 1/4 of the offspring of such matings will be of the recessive type (*cc*). None of the offspring of the D × H or D × D matings can show the recessive character *c*. Therefore the proportion of recessives from matings of types showing the dominant characteristic is

$$\frac{4r^2}{(1 + r)^2} \div 4 = \frac{r^2}{(1 + r)^2} \quad \text{or} \quad \left(\frac{r}{1 + r}\right)^2$$

If the observed frequency checks with this value (using for r the value we calculate from the presumptive recessive class), our conclusion that we have identified a recessive gene is strengthened.

Since only two genes are involved, and one is completely recessive, the population is divided on this basis into two classes, and the ratio between them can be anything, depending on the value of the gene frequency r of the recessive.

If neither gene is dominant, but both exert their characteristic effects, as is the case with the M and N blood group genes (Ch. VIII), the population will be divided into three classes, and we shall find, within the limits of the errors of random sampling, that the relationship $\sqrt{M} + \sqrt{N} = 1$ will hold (42). The gene frequencies in such a case are estimated very simply and exactly by the relationships $m = M + \dfrac{MN}{2}$ and $n = N + \dfrac{MN}{2}$, and the sum of these values always has to be one, from the simple way they are computed.

Statistical Methods of Detecting Genes

If a population can be divided neatly into two categories, one possessing a character and the other not possessing it, studies on family material, if properly analyzed, will enable us to decide if the characteristic we are recording is determined by a single gene, and therefore inherited in the simplest possible manner. Eight methods of analysis have been proposed by various workers. They are: 1) the "direct" or "a priori" method of Bernstein, 2) the "sib method" of Weinberg, 3) the method of "empty sib series" of Lenz, 4) the "sib method" of Fisher and Mather, 5) the "proband method" of Fisher, 6) the "percentage affected" method of Macklin, 7) the direct estimation of segregation ratios of Haldane, and 8) the "Hogben method." The mathematics required for such calculations is too advanced to be treated here; it will be found summarized by Ludwig and Boost (25), who demonstrate that mathematically these eight methods reduce to four — namely, the methods of Haldane, Bernstein, Lenz, and Weinberg. The Bernstein and Lenz methods differ mainly in a constant factor, and are the preferred procedures. The Weinberg method yields less information from a given set of data, while the Haldane method, although good in regard to the information it extracts from the data, is very laborious to calculate. Examples of the various calculations are to be found in (25). The method of "maximum likelihood," as used by Hogben, seems to be the best statistical method of detecting rare recessive genes.

Multiple Pairs vs. Allelomorphs

When the inheritance of a character is complicated, it is not always easy to decide whether its heredity is due to several gene pairs acting independently or to the action of a series of allelomorphic genes, all capable of occupying the same chromosome locus, but present in any individual only two at a time (p. 242). Either may make a considerable number of genotypes and phenotypes possible.

Sometimes mathematical calculations enable us to reach a decision in this matter. Considering two characters X and Y, and representing the frequency of individuals having the gene X by $X+$ and the frequency of those not having X as $X-$, and so on, it is, as has been pointed out by Bernstein (2) and Wiener (42) a necessary, but not necessarily a sufficient condition that genes be independent, that

$$(X-Y-) \times (X+Y+) = (X+Y-) \times (X-Y+)$$

For if the genes are not independent, but allelomorphic, that is, if either can occupy the same locus in a chromosome, then the left side of the equation $[(X-Y-) \times (X+Y+)]$ could be greater than the right. Also, the frequency of the $X+Y+$ type cannot exceed 50 per cent. Also, $\sqrt{X-} + \sqrt{Y-}$ must be greater than or equal to 1. If the expression $[(X-Y-) \times (X+Y+)]$ (the left hand side of the above equation) is greater than the right hand side, but the frequency $X+Y+$ is greater than 50 per cent, then the characters X and Y are probably complex characters determined by a single gene, each of which however produces more than one effect. Examples of this in human inheritance are found in the Rh series of genes, for example, when the Rh_1 (*CDe* in Fisher's nomenclature) gene causes the production in the red blood cells of the individual of two distinct antigens, rh' (C) and Rh_o (D).

Characters of the latter sort evidently belong in the class of what Darwin called correlated characters. By this term we may denote characteristics which are actually caused by the same gene or genes and also characters which are caused by genes which lie close together on the chromosome, and are thus closely linked. Fisher (32) apparently considers that the Rh characters are actually of the second sort with linkage virtually complete.

To summarize, we are able to recognize a dominant gene most readily, and a recessive gene having a common dominant allele somewhat less readily. Multiple alleles are recognized less readily, but statistical studies on populations may disprove or, alternatively, support a theory of the action of a certain number of alleles if the effect of each gene is clearly recognizable. When considerable numbers of genes with similar or ill-defined effects are involved, analysis, at least of human populations, becomes nearly impossible.

Examination of Human Pedigrees

In particular families the ratio of different hereditary types in individuals may differ widely from that which would be found in large populations. Suppose, for instance, that we have two parents who are both known to be heterozygous for a recessive character (say $Cc \times Cc$). Let us suppose that the first child is a recessive (cc). Such matings produce, on the average, $\frac{1}{4}$ pure recessive (cc) and $\frac{3}{4}$ dominant ($2\ Cc$ and $1CC$). It does not therefore follow that the next three children in this family will be dominants (CC or Cc). The chances each time are 1 in 4 that a child can be a recessive type (cc), and the chance of the two parents in question producing four children of type cc is $\frac{1}{4} \times \frac{1}{4} \times \frac{1}{4} \times \frac{1}{4} = \frac{1}{256}$, which is by no means so low a probability that we can say it will never happen, although it is true that it is not too likely. So we *might* actually find each successive child of a family of four produced by the mating $Cc \times Cc$ coming up as pure recessives (cc).

Conversely, suppose two parents have produced several children all type CC. Does it follow that one or both of the parents must be pure dominant (CC)? No, for such a family could be produced by two *Cc* parents, just by chance failure of any *cc* child to appear. However, if we know that *C* is completely dominant over *c,* we may state that even one type *C* (*CC* or *Cc*) child in a family proves that the parents are not *both cc.* For two such parents could produce only *cc* children. If we are not sure about dominance, however, we cannot make such a statement.

From this it will appear that the conclusions we can draw from the inspection of a single family will be rather limited, even with genes which have clear-cut effects, 100 per cent penetrance, and uniform expressivity. If penetrance is incomplete and expressivity variable, the situation is still worse and analysis will be difficult.

If a trait is rare, it may be dangerous to combine studies on more than one family in order to enlarge the mass of data we wish to study, for the trait may be inherited in different ways in different families. If the trait is common, there will be enough matings of unrelated individuals, some of whom exhibit the trait, to test this point.

Another difficulty with human pedigrees is that the investigator may not be able to examine all of the family himself, or that some key members may already be dead. In such a case he may have to rely on statements made from memory by relatives. Such statements, even from scholarly people, can be very unreliable. For example, one lady known to me, who has published a number of good scientific papers, stated on several occasions that one of her brothers had webbed toes. On actually checking this with the brother (and his mother) it turned out that this was not so, and never had been. How the error arose is hard to explain, but there it was.

The influence of sex, as well as possible sex linkage, must also be considered. Thus white females seldom become bald, as the male sex hormone seems to be required, as a rule, for the gene (or genes) for baldness to manifest itself (or themselves) (p. 288). Yet the condition would not be called sex-linked, but rather sex-influenced, or sex-limited. In fact the absence of the expression of a trait in one sex is by no means proof that it is sex-linked in inheritance. Nor is its presence in both sexes proof that it is not sex-linked. Red-green color blindness is believed to be inherited by a gene on the X chromosome, and is thus sex-linked, but color-blind women are sometimes found.

INDEX

Index

Index of subjects and authors (names of authors in small caps).

A

A and B, antiquity of, 231, 335
    distribution similar in different peoples, 264, 265
    in animals, 333, 334
    tables of distribution, 223 ff., 269
A and B blood factors, 212 ff.
A and B subgroups, absence in certain populations, 237
    possible selection for, 345
    tables of distribution, 238, 239, 269
Abyssinians, blood groups in, 224
Adaptation, 147, 148
Adaptive characters, 19, 150, 170
African (Negroid) race, 268, 269
Ainu, blood groups in, 234, 274
Albinism, 289
Alleles (allelomorphs), 47, 53, 439
Alleles vs. independent factors, 400, 439
ALLEN, 174
ALLEN and KORBER, 120, 419
Allergy, inheritance of, 286
    racial differences in, 287
Allopatric, defined, 199
Alpines, skull characters of, 305
ALVORD, 315
American Indian race, 268
American Indians, and mutations, 330
    blood groups of, 223, 234, 238, 332
    color blindness in, 289
    I.Q. of, 104, 105
    secreting gene in, 284
    tasting ability for PTC, 280
AMMON, 299
Ancestors, fossil, 21, 22, 324, 325
    gene contribution from remote, 56

Anthropoids, blood groups of, 334, 343, 345
    taste reactions of, 281
Anthropometry, limitations of, 24, 27
Arabs (Bedouin), blood groups in, 225, 234, 235, 238
Arabs ('Iraqis), blood groups in 225, 235, 244
    eye color in, 312
Armenians, blood groups in, 224, 235, 238
"Aryans," 6, 184
ASDELL, 71
Asiatic Indians, blood groups in, 225, 238, 244
Asiatic (Mongoloid) race, 268
Australia, 151, 162, 168, 206, 346
    absence of B in, 168, 227
    blood groups in, 168, 223, 234, 238, 245, 265, 267, 268, 274
    M and N in, 234
Australoid race, 268, 269
Axalotl, 27

B

B gene, 217, 223, 227, 229, 230
    absence in certain populations, 169, 223
Baldness, 287, 288
Bantu, 191
Barriers, geographical, 163 ff., 169, 170
    modes of penetrating, 169
    overcoming, 167, 169
Basques, blood groups in, 118, 152, 223, 239, 244
    eye color in, 312
    Rh in, 244, 268

BAUR, FISCHER and LENZ, 64, 291, 304
BEADLE, 61, 74
BEAN, 308
Bedouin, blood groups in, 225, 234, 235, 238
Belgians, blood groups in, 224, 235
BELL, 70, 126
BELL and HALDANE, 403
BENEDICT, 28
"Berbers," blood groups in, 224
BERGMAN, 174
Bering Strait, 168
BERNSTEIN, 216, 284, 398, 400, 403, 418, 421, 438
"Biochemical Index," 263
BIRDSELL and BOYD, 342
Birth rate in various populations, 361
Blackfeet Indians, blood groups in, 223
BLAIR, 181
BLAKESLEE, 279
"Blending" inheritance, 39, 41, 44
"Blood" in inheritance, 39
Blood groups, 66, 67 ff., 77, 83, 210, 211 ff., 223 ff., 234 ff., 244, 245
    and archaeology, 247, 248, 335
    antiquity of, 330, 335
    genes for, 216, 217, 232, 237, 240, 241, 242
    in anthropological classification, 69, 83, 221, 264, 268 ff.
    inheritance of, 67, 68, 214, 217, 219
    permanence of, 217
Blood transfusion, 219
Bloods Indians, blood groups in, 223
Blue Andalusians, 41, 42
BLUMENBACH, xiii
BOAS, 13, 44, 88, 197
Bogobos, blood groups in, 225
Bones, 18, 21 ff.
BOYD, 126, 250, 286, 418, 419
Brachycephaly, 152, 298, 300, 302
    increase of, 88, 89, 152, 302, 304
Breeding population, 157
BRIDGES, 75
BROOKS, 431
BRUES, 286
BRYCE, 186
Bulgarians, blood groups in, 224
BURCH and PENDELL, 362
Buriats, blood groups in, 225

BURKES, 284, 404
BURTON, 5
Bushmen, 191

C

C (Rh gene), 241, 242, 243
CANDELA, 116, 117, 249, 314
CASTLE, 82, 364
Caucasians, 118
    blood groups in, 224, 235
    eye color in, 312
    mid-digital hair in, 285
Caucasoids, skull characters of, 305
CDE nomenclature (Rh system), 241, 242, 243
Cephalic index, changes in, 88, 89, 152, 302, 304
Chakkas, 10
CHAMBERLAIN, 8
CHARLES and GOODWIN, 202
Chemical effects on gene expression, 93
CHETVERIKOV, 44
Chi square, 386 ff.
    computation of, 388
CHIEN LUNG, 9
CHILDE, 326
Chimpanzees, taste reactions of, 143
Chinese, blood groups in, 225, 235, 245, 268
    color blindness in, 289
Chromosome maps, 74, 75
Chromosomes, defined, 45
    crossing over of, 71
Chukchi, color blindness in, 289
Climate, and evolution, 173, 177 ff.
    influence on human pigmentation, 176 ff.
Clines, 170, 204, 258
Cobalt, role of in nutrition, 182, 183
"Coefficient of racial likeness," 24
Color blindness, in different races, 289
    inheritance of, 69, 70, 71, 289
COOK, R. C., 157
COOK, S. F., 364
COON, 190, 306
Correlated characters, 440
Correlation coefficient, 392
CORRENS, 31
COTT, 154

COTTERMAN, 390
Cranial index, changes in, 152
Craniometry, 25, 304
Cross breeding, 32, 36, 37, 389
Crossing over, 71, 72, 73, 74
  defined, 66
Cultural anthropology, 3
Cultural traits, 5

D

D (Rh gene), 241, 242, 243
DAHLBERG, 188, 207
Danes, blood groups in, 224, 235
  secreting gene in, 284
DANFORTH, 284
DART, 191
DARWIN, 41, 44, 140, 142, 158, 163
DAVENPORT, 41, 308, 309, 365, 366
DENIKER, 299
Deviations, significance of, 380, 381
Diabetes mellitus, 87, 320
DIXON, 190, 194, 318
DOBZHANSKY, xvi, 13, 38, 72, 87, 94, 110,
  155, 165, 193, 198, 262, 325, 327
DOBZHANSKY and EPLING, 24, 202, 204
Dolichocephaly, 152, 298, 300, 302
Dominance, 32, 42, 49, 51, 53
  defined, 32
  degree of, 42, 43, 52
  origin of, 49 ff.
Dominants, 33, 35
Drosophila, 53, 56, 85, 87, 91, 148, 149,
  205, 206
DUBININ and ROMASCHOFF, 158, 431
DUDLEY and ALLEN, 157
DUNGERN, VON, and HIRSZFELD, 216, 218
Dwarf forms, 33, 180

E

E (Rh gene), 236, 241, 242, 243
Early European race, 268, 336
Early man, blood groups of, 268, 336,
  338
EAST and JONES, xvi, 122, 192
EDWARDS and DUNTLEY, 308, 309
Effective population size, 434
Egyptians, blood groups in, 224, 225,
  234, 238

color blindness in, 289
eye color in, 312
mid-digital hair in, 285
taste for PTC in, 280
ELSDON-DEW, 222
ELTON, 156
England, inbreeding in, 126
  blood groups in, 224, 234, 238, 244
Environment, 77, 79 ff., 86, 88, 89
  effects of on gene expression, 83, 86,
    91, 93
  and heredity, 94, 96
Epicanthic fold, 314
  inheritance of, 314, 319
EPLING, 241
Erythroblastosis fetalis, 240
Eskimo, 144, 179
  blood groups in, 223, 234, 238, 265
  color blindness in, 289
Estonians, blood groups in, 224, 235
ETCHEVERRY, 152
Eugenics, 358
European (Caucasoid) race, 268, 269
Evolution, defined, 131
  mechanisms of, 131 ff., 158
"Expressivity," 77, 315, 351
Eye, inherited abnormalities of, 211,
  292
Eye color, 285 ff., 311, 312
  inheritance of, 311, 313, 319
  sex difference in, 311, 312
  table of distribution of, 312

F

Facial features, 210
Family studies, 101
Fauism, 287
Filipinos, blood groups in, 225, 234, 238,
  245
FINNEY, 405
Finns, blood groups in, 224, 235, 239
  secreting gene in, 284
FISHER, xvi, 25, 44, 50, 51, 65, 138, 241,
  344, 370, 375, 389, 395, 399, 404,
  431, 438
FISHER, FORD and HUXLEY, 143, 281
FISHER and MATHER, 438
FISHER and YATES, 389
Flathead Indians, blood groups in, 223

FLEURE, 176, 177, 178, 179, 206
FORD, 52, 148
Fossil remains, scarcity of, 324
FOX, 278
French, blood groups in, 224, 235, 244
Frequencies, 226, 384
   vs. per cents, 226
FÜRST, 300

G

G blood factor, 236
GALTON, 44
GARTH, 104
GATES, 10, 191, 207, 289, 291, 314
Gene, defined, 40
   spread of a, 116, 117, 138
   survival of an individual, 138, 158, 424, 425 ff.
Gene equilibrium, 109, 396 ff., 409 ff., 417, 432
Gene frequencies, 108, 131, 393 ff.
   calculation of, 395 ff., 416, 421
   changes in, 131 ff., 141, 145 ff., 204, 423 ff.
   in random mating, 409
Gene mutations, 135 ff.
   defined, 133, 136
Gene symbols, 59, 60
Genealogy, 56, 59
Genes, 26, 33 ff., 75, 216
   effect of environment on expression, 83 ff., 93 ff.
   equivalence of, 253
   fixation of, 132, 146, 154, 158, 336
   general effect of, 62, 65
   introduction of new, 116
   mechanism of action of, 60, 61
   methods of discovering, 350 ff., 435 ff.
   methods of identifying, 435 ff.
   multiple effects of, 62, 357
   nomenclature of, 59, 60
   number of, 55, 56, 58
   producing identical effects, 63
   separation of, 72, 73, 118
   size of, 55, 56
   stability of, 48, 82
   statistical methods of detecting, 438

Genetic drift (Isolation, Sewall Wright effect, Random genetic drift), 115, 132, 139, 154, 165, 233, 337
Genetic equilibrium, 78, 108 ff., 119, 412
Genetics, 30 ff., 435
Genophagy, 153, 304
   defined, 109
Genotype, defined, 43
Geographical barriers, 162 ff., 166
Geographical influences, 162 ff., 180
Geography, in relation to race, 269, 271, 273
GEPPERT and KOHLER, 143
GERHARDT, 301
Germans, blood groups in, 224, 235, 238
   secreting factor in, 284
GLASS, xvi, 40, 46, 61, 96, 200
GLOGER, 174
GOBINEAU, 7, 9
GODIN, 304
Goiter, 85
GOLDEN, 333
GOULD, 325
GOWAN and GAY, 56
GRAYDON, 233
Greeks, blood groups in, 224
Greenland, M and N in, 234
GRUBB, 356
GULICK, 56, 57
GÜNTHER, 299
GUTHE, 88

H

H blood factor, 240
HAGEDOORN and HAGEDOORN, 431
Hair color, 318
Hair form, 307
   inheritance of, 308, 318
HALDANE, 51, 52, 70, 137, 142, 145, 147, 191, 336, 364, 404, 426
HAMILTON, 288
Hand clasp, 16, 17
Handedness, 18
HARDY, 109, 432
HARRIS, 287
HARRISON, 148
HASEBROEK, 148
Hawaii, physique of immigrants in, 89
Headform, 298 ff.

Hemophilia, 70, 135, 137
HERDER, 186
Heredity, and environment, 82 ff., 94
Heterosis, 125
Heterozygote, defined, 36, 40
    selective advantage of, 281
HIRSCH, 88
HIRSZFELD, 221
HITLER, 4
HOGBEN, xvi, 23, 78, 83, 96, 128, 147,
    201, 279, 281, 344, 359, 404
HOLZINGER, 99
Homo faber, 22
Homo osseus, 22
Homo sapiens, 22
    time and place of origin of, 325
Homozygote, defined, 34, 40
HOOTON, 19, 188
Hornlessness, 71
Hottentot, 39
HOVANITZ, 181
HOWELLS, 23, 190, 306, 327
Hr factor, 241, 242
HRDLIČKA, 6, 23
Hungarians, blood groups in, 224, 235
HUXLEY, 51, 52, 56, 150, 158, 164, 170
HUXLEY and HADDON, 189
Hybrid vigor, 124, 125
Hypothetical worlds, 253 ff.

I

Iceland, blood groups in, 224
Ideal types, 197
Immigration pressure, 115
Inapparent adaptation, 153
Inbreeding, 120 ff.
    in actual populations, 126 ff.
Independent assortment, 35 ff.
India, blood groups in, 225, 238
Indians, American, 268
    color blindness in, 289
Indonesians, blood groups in, 223, 235,
    238, 245
Inheritance, independent assortment in,
    35 ff.
    particulate nature of, 32, 39
"Intelligence," 104
Intergradations, inheritance of, 54
Iodine deficiency, 85

I.Q., in mixed races, 104
'Iraq, blood groups in 225, 235, 238, 244
Irish, blood groups in, 224, 235, 239
Island populations, aberrant characteris-
    tics of, 158, 162
Isogenes, 226, 228, 229, 231
Isolation (see Genetic Drift), 115, 132,
    139, 154, 162 ff., 233, 337
Italians, blood groups in, 224, 235

J

Japanese, blood groups in, 224, 231, 235,
    245
    color blindness in, 289
    physical changes in immigrants, 89
    secreting gene in, 284
Java man, 325
Javanese, blood groups in, 225
JENKS, 23

K

KABAT, 219
KAUFMAN, 76
KEERS, 308
KEITH, 6, 11, 13
Kirgiz, blood groups in, 225
KLINEBERG, 13
KLOEPFER, 71, 406
KLUCKHOHN, 190
KOLLER, 430
KROEBER, 105, 289
KROGMAN, 306, 366
Kwakiutl Indians, blood groups in, 223

L

LAHOVARY, 264, 265, 266
LANDSTEINER, 59, 212, 240, 277, 334,
    343
LAPOUGE, DE, 299
Lapps, blood groups in, 224
    color blindness in, 289
LARSEN and GODFREY, 314
LAUGHLIN, 109, 418
LENZ, 438
Lethal genes, 40
LEVINE, 59

Lewis blood antigen, 356
Linkage, defined, 66
    detection of, 66 ff., 402 ff.
    in man, 68, 71, 403 ff.
    sex, 68
LINTON, 29
LIPSCHÜTZ, 331
LUDWIG and BOOST, 438
LUSIADA, 294
LYDE, 177

M

M and N blood types, 127, 232
M and N genes, 232 ff.
M and N, tables of distribution of, 233,
    234, 235, 268
MACKLIN, 438
Madagascans, blood groups in, 224
MADLENER, 403
MALTHUS, 367
MARETT, 78, 94
Marsupials, 150
MARTIN, 353, 354
MATHER, 314, 438
Maximum likelihood, 400, 420, 421
MAYR, 88, 133, 172, 198
Mean, computation of, 371 ff.
    defined, 369
Median, defined, 369
Mediterraneans, skull characters of, 305
Melanesians, blood groups in, 224, 234,
    245
    color blindness in, 289
Melanism, 147, 148
MENDEL, xiv, 30 ff.
Mendelian characters in man, 318, 319,
    320
Mendel's experiments, 30 ff.
Mendel's laws, 32 ff.
Mental abilities, inheritance of, 13, 14
Micronesians, blood groups in, 224
Mid-digital hair, in various populations,
    285
    inheritance of, 284, 285
Migration, in early populations, 336
Minerals of soil, effect of, 181
Minnesota man, 23
Mixture of populations, 111, 132, 416,
    419

Mode, defined, 369
Modifiers, 50
MOHR, 65
Mongolian (epicanthic) eye fold, 314,
    319
Mongolian spot, 313
Mongoloid race, defined, 268, 269
Mongoloids, skull characters of, 305
Mongols, introduction of genes by, 116
MONTAGU, 13, 185
MORANT, 21, 88, 295, 306
MORGAN, 219
MOURANT, 251
MOUREAU, 396
MUELLER, 184
MULLER, 51, 56, 136
Mummified tissue, 247, 333
Mutation, 48, 133, 135 ff., 330, 423
    equilibrium, 139
    pressure, 139
    rates, 137, 423, 424, 425 ff.
Mutations in evolution, 48, 52, 133

N

Nasal index, changes in, 89, 307, 353
Natural selection, 132, 138, 140, 274,
    364, 424 ff.
    effectiveness of, 147
    in man, 142, 144, 150, 364
    time required for, 145, 146
Navaho Indians, 120, 128, 223, 289
Nazi anthropology, 14, 299
Neanderthal man, 325, 327
Negroes, 53, 191, 239, 268
    blood groups in, 239, 244
    color blindness in, 289
    secreting genes in, 284
    skull characters of, 305
Negroid race, 268, 269
NEHRU, 209
New Zealand, soil minerals in, 182
NEWMAN, 100, 102, 103
NIGG, 128
Nomenclature of genes, 37, 38, 59, 62
Nomograms, 399
Non-adaptive characters, 18 ff., 26
Nordics (North Europeans), skull char-
    acters of, 152, 305

Normal curve of error, 371, 373, 379, 383
Noses, inheritance of, 353 ff.

O

Original "pure" races, 119, 190, 192
OTTENBERG, 264
OTTENSOOSER, 418

P

P blood factor, 236
Palmar muscle, absence of, 319
Papuans, 171, 234
PÄTAU, 146
Pathological conditions, inheritance of, 211, 290
PAYNE, 148
PEARL, 49, 326
PEARSON, 109, 432
Pedigrees, examination of, 440
Peking man, 325
Penetrance, 279, 351, 441
    defined, 77
PENROSE, 404
Per cents, vs. frequencies, 226
PERRIER, 313
Phenotype, defined, 43
    vs. genotypes, 108 ff.
Phenylthiocarbamide: see PTC
Phenylthiourea: see PTC
Physical anthropology, 3
Physical traits, 5
    and classification, 15 ff.
Pigmentation, genes for, 144, 200, 277, 285
Pigmentation, of eye, table of distribution, 312
PINCUS and WHITE, 87
Pisum sativum, 31
Plasticity of gene effects, 88 ff.
PLUNKETT, 52
Poles, secreting gene in, 284
Polymorphism, 255, 258
Polynesians, blood groups in, 223, 235, 238, 245
    migrations of, 168
"Polyphyletic" origin of man, 325, 327

Population, limits of, 363
    mixture, 13, 116, 365, 416
Populations, appearance of future, 365
    rate of growth of, 325 ff.
    relative size of, 360, 361, 416
    size of, 325
Primates, blood groups in, 334, 345
    M and N in, 343
Probability, 376 ff.
Probable error (P.E.), 371
Pruner-Bey, 307
PTC, 77, 93, 143, 278 ff.
    and anthropoids, 281
    genes for tasting, 279
    reaction to in different localities, 269, 280
Pueblo Indians, blood groups in, 223
"Pure" races, 119, 190, 192
Pygmies, blood groups of, 225
    stature of, 296

Q

Q blood factor, 236
QUALE, 148

R

RACE, 251
Race, concept of, 184 ff., 204
    defined, 189, 190, 268, 269
    defined by blood groups, 264, 268, 269
    origin of term, 186 ff.
Race mixture (crossing), 12, 13, 53, 116, 191, 367, 416
    computation of frequencies in, 116, 416
    computation of from gene frequencies, 120, 418 ff.
Race prejudice, 10, 360
Races, and geography, 162 ff.
    formation of, 158, 162
    future of, 349 ff., 360
    not originally pure, 190, 192
    of man defined genetically, 201 ff., 268, 269
Racial constellation of characters, 194
Racial differentiation, 162, 175, 180, 194, 198, 268, 269

Racial history of man, 321 ff.
Racial superiority, 7, 10, 273
RAHM, 331
Random genetic drift, 115, 132, 139,
    154, 165, 233, 337
Random mating, 109, 110, 396, 409 ff.,
    414
Random variation, 132
Ratios in Mendelian inheritance, 36, 37
Recessive, defined, 32
Recessives, fixation of, 145 ff.
RETZIUS, xiv, 298, 300
Rh, distribution in different races, 240 ff.,
    244, 268, 269
    inheritance of, 241 ff.
    selection for, 150, 344
Rh factors, 150, 240
RIDDELL, 71, 311
RIPLEY, 299
ROMASCHOFF, 431
RÖSE, 299
RUSSELL, 40
Russians, blood groups in, 224, 235, 238
Rwalla Bedouin, blood groups in, 225,
    234, 235, 238

S

Saltation, 141
SANTIANA, 251
SARGEANT, 197
SARKAR, 222
SCHEIDT, 189
SCHIFF, 283, 284
SCHULTZ, 328
SCHWERZ, 302
SCHWIDETZKY, 152
Secreting factor, table of frequencies in
    various races, 269, 284
    inheritance of, 283
Segregation, Mendelian, 32, 351, 390
Selection, 141, 142, 144, 150, 335, 364
    intensity of, 149
    mathematical theory of, 424, 425 ff.,
    429
Selection coefficient, 141, 142
Selection pressure, 149, 164
Selection rate, 141, 429
Selective advantage, 141, 142, 424

Serological races, 246, 264 ff., 268, 269,
    274
Sewall Wright effect, 115, 132, 139, 154,
    165, 233, 337, 431
Sex influenced genes, 287, 441
Sex limited genes, 441
Sex linkage, 68 ff., 403, 413, 414, 441
SHAPIRO, 89, 113, 306
SHELDON, 317
Shoshone Indians, blood groups in, 223
Siamese, blood groups in, 224, 245
Significance, of deviations, 380 ff.
    test of, 385 ff.
SILVA, DA, 418, 421
SIMMONS, 233, 342
SIMPSON, xvi
Sioux Indians, blood groups in, 223
SISMANIDIS, 148
Skeletal material in classification, 18,
    21 ff., 295 ff.
Skin color, 255, 308 ff.
    adaptive value of, 175 ff.
    inheritance of, 144, 200, 274, 277,
    308 ff., 318
Skull form, inheritance of, 304
Skulls as racial indices, 21, 25, 298 ff.,
    304
Slight advantages, importance of, 154
SNOW, 23
SNYDER, 404
SNYDER, RUSSELL and GRAHAM, 406
Somatotypes, 255, 317
Spanish, blood groups in, 224, 234, 239
Speciation, 164, 199, 202
Species, arising from races, 199
    reality of, 198
SPUHLER, 81
Standard deviation, 371, 378, 385
    computation of, 373, 374
    for A, B system, 399
    for M, N system, 397
    of frequencies, 385
    table of, 385
Standard error (Standard deviation) de-
    fined, 371
STAPLEDON, 368
Statistical methods, 96, 98 ff., 369 ff.
Statistical studies on twins, 98 ff.
Stature, 295 ff., 319
STEGGERDA, 91

STERN, 322
STEVENS, 397, 399, 422
STEWART, 24
STRANDSKOV, 59
STURTEVANT, 72
STURTEVANT and BEADLE, 74
Subgroups, inheritance of, 236, 237
Swedes, blood groups in, 224, 235, 239
Switzerland, goiter in, 85
Sympatric, defined, 199
Syndactyly, 315
Syrians, blood groups in, 224, 234, 238
Syrians, inbreeding in, 126
    mid-digital hair in, 285

T

Tasting gene (*see* PTC), 143, 279
Tatars, blood groups in, 225
Taxonomy, 15, 18
Teeth, hereditary absence of, 318
Temperature effects, 44, 86, 91
Tepexpan man, 249
Tierra del Fuego, 179, 331
Toba Indians, blood groups in, 223
TOCHER, 286
TOYNBEE, 14, 22
TSCHERMAK, VON, 31
Turks, blood groups in, 224
Twins, 33, 98 ff., 100
    and crime, 100

U

Ukrainians, blood groups in, 224, 235, 238
Unit characters, in inheritance, 32, 33, 39 ff.
Universal donor, 220
Ute Indians, blood groups in, 253

V

Variability, loss of in small populations, 115, 132, 154, 159, 165, 233, 337, 431
VRIES, DE, 31

W

WADDINGTON, 74
WALLIS, 25
WEIDENREICH, 94, 153, 299, 302, 327
WEINBERG, 109, 410, 432, 438
WELLS, 87
Welsh, blood groups in, 224, 235
    eye color in, 312
    taste for PTC in, 280
WHITE, 71
WIENER, 151, 240, 242, 268, 334, 343, 344, 397, 418, 430
WIENER and SONN, 399
WIENER, ZIEVE and FRIES, 286
WRIGHT, 48, 51, 123, 128, 138, 145, 154, 158, 337, 366, 423, 431

X

X blood factor, 236

Y

YOUNG, 246

Z

Zulus, 10
Zygodactyly, 315